Scott, Foresman

Earth Science

Authors

Jay M. Pasachoff
Director, Hopkins Observatory
Williams College
Williamstown, Massachusetts

Naomi Pasachoff
Research Associate
Williams College
Williamstown, Massachusetts

Timothy M. Cooney
Science Chairperson
Malcolm Price Laboratory School
University of Northern Iowa
Cedar Falls, Iowa

Scott Foresman and Company
Editorial Offices: Glenview, Illinois

Regional Offices: Palo Alto, California
Tucker, Georgia • Glenview, Illinois
Oakland, New Jersey • Dallas, Texas

Cover: Sandstone Narrows
in Zion National Park, Utah
Credit: David Muench 1982

Series Consultant

Irwin L. Slesnick
Professor of Biology
Western Washington University
Bellingham, Washington

Program Consultant

John Hockett
Professor of Science Education
Governors State University
Park Forest, Illinois

Reading Consultant

Robert A. Pavlik
Reading Department Chairperson
Cardinal Stritch College
Milwaukee, Wisconsin

Editorial Advisors

Abraham S. Flexer
Educational Consultant
Boulder, Colorado

Karin L. Rhines
Educational Consultant
Bedford Hills, New York

Feature Writer

Frederick A. Rasmussen
Science Education Consultant
Boulder, Colorado

David Newton
Professor of Chemistry and Physics
Salem State College
Salem, Massachusetts

ISBN: 0-673-13724-4

Copyright © 1983, Scott, Foresman and Company, Glenview, Illinois All rights Reserved. Printed in the United States of America.

Reviewers and Contributors

LeVon Balzer
Dean of Arts and Sciences
Seattle Pacific University
Seattle, Washington

Marsha Barber
Earth Science Teacher
Lockport Township High School
Lockport, Illinois

Rose Mary Castro
Science Teacher
L.W. Fox Academic and
Technical High School
San Antonio, Texas

Emily Fast Christensen
Science Teacher
Kirby Junior High School
Hazelwood School District
St. Louis County, Missouri

York Clamann
Science Consultant
Abilene Independent School District
Abilene, Texas

Odie B. Cook
District Science Specialist
Oakland Unified School District
Oakland, California

William Fowler
Science Teacher
Sandburg Junior High School
Elmhurst, Illinois

Obe Hofer
Science Department Representative
Whittier Junior High School
Sioux Falls, South Dakota

Chet Hollister
Earth Science Teacher
Algonquin Middle School
Algonquin, Illinois

Dick Pack
Science Department Chairperson
Toll Junior High School
Glendale, California

Frederick Rasmussen
Science Education Consultant
Boulder, Colorado

Susanne Rego
Science Teacher
Belleville Senior High School
Belleville, New Jersey

Victor Showalter
Director of FUSE Center
Capital University
Columbus, Ohio

Lucy Smith
Coordinator of Science Education
Atlanta Public Schools
Atlanta, Georgia

Katherine Taft
Science Education Services
Highland Park, Illinois
Teacher
American International School,
Austria

Elin Terrazone
Science Teacher
Saint Bedes School
LaCanada, California

William D. Thomas
Science Supervisor
Escambia County Schools
Pensacola, Florida

Dorothy Wallinga
Jenison, Michigan

Les Wallinga
Physical Science Teacher
Calvin Christian Junior High School
Wyoming, Michigan

Lawrence Zambrowski
Science Department Chairperson
Churchill Junior High School
East Brunswick, New Jersey

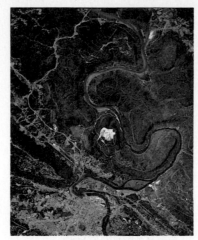

UNIT ONE

Earth and Space *1*

UNIT TWO

The Earth *105*

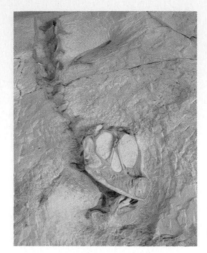

UNIT THREE

The Changing Crust
187

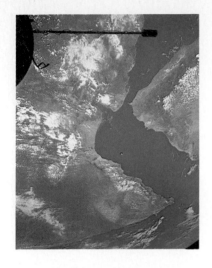

UNIT FOUR

Air and Water *303*

UNIT FIVE

Energy and
Environment *435*

Chapter 24
The Environment *457*

UNIT ONE
EARTH AND SPACE

What do you think is happening in this unusual picture of the Boston skyline? Could it be a photograph used to advertise a science fiction movie? The caption might read "Alien spacecraft beams a blinding ray at Boston and paralyzes the city." Or could this be a picture of the world's largest spotlight in action?

The light beam is not from a spacecraft or a big spotlight. It is a time exposure of the sun setting across Boston Harbor. Instead of taking the picture in one quick shot, the film was exposed for thirty-eight minutes. After sunset, another exposure captured the view of the lighted buildings. Time exposures furnish much of our information about distant stars. This unit investigates the sun, stars, and other parts of the universe.

Chapter 1 Earth Science
Earth science is the study of land, sea, air, and space.

Chapter 2 Studying Our Universe
We have learned most of what we know about the universe from the study of radiation. Light is one kind of radiation.

Chapter 3 Survey of the Stars
Our sun is an average star. Stars go through stages of life then die, much as people do.

Chapter 4 Galaxies, Quasars, and the Universe
Galaxies are the building blocks of the universe.

Chapter 5 The Solar System
All the planets of our solar system, their moons, asteroids, and comets obey the same laws as they orbit the sun.

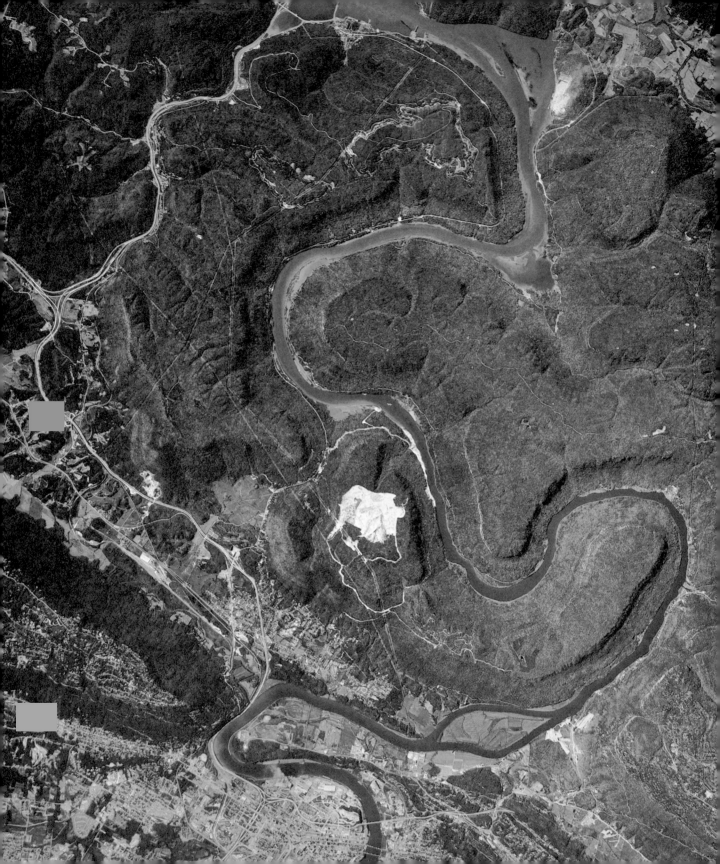

Chapter 1
Earth Science

Pictures taken at high altitudes are one of scientists' most valuable new tools. The photograph on the left was taken about 18 kilometers above Chattanooga, Tennessee. Experts can read these maps as easily as you read a comic strip. You can see the city, the Tennessee River, and mountains, but what is the white section in the middle of the picture? If you guessed snow, a parking lot, or a golf course, you are wrong. It is a lake that is reflecting sunlight.

This chapter begins with an explanation of what earth science is. You will find out about several exciting areas of current research in earth and space science. You will learn some steps scientists use to solve research problems. The chapter ends with information you will need for the earth science activities in this book.

Chapter Objectives

1. List four earth and space sciences.
2. Describe five areas of current earth and space science research.
3. Explain how observation, testing, hypothesis, and theory are related to solving science problems.
4. Define volume, mass, and density and identify an SI label for each.
5. List the LABORATORY CAUTIONS.

1–1
Earth Science

Earth science is like a big patchwork quilt. The many parts of earth science are stitched with invisible threads to form a large pattern. Each part is necessary to develop the design. Think about the questions below as you read:

a. What is earth science?
b. Why is earth science important in our lives?

Earth Science—Land, Water, Air, and Space

Earth science combines several fields of science to study earth and the space that surrounds it. The geologist deals with the surface and interior of the earth. The oceanographer (ō′shə nog′rə fər) studies the oceans, which cover about 3/4 of the earth. The meteorologist (mē′tē ə rol′ə jist) is interested in air conditions and how they affect the weather. Space scientists, such as the astronomer, view the universe from the earth and from space. Space scientists can now look at the earth from space as well.

The picture taken in Oregon illustrates how closely land, water, air, and space are related. What happens to one affects all.

The coast of Oregon

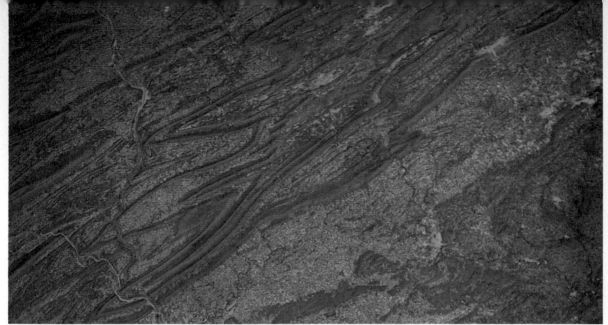

The Appalachian Mountains near Harrisburg, Pennsylvania

Why Earth Science Is Important

We have used what we know about the earth to improve our living conditions. Exploration of the land, for example, tells us where to build our homes and cities. Geologists who work in the field have located essential minerals, oil, and sources of fresh water. We use these materials every day.

Knowing how the air and oceans influence weather helps people to predict floods and storms. Weather predictions can even save lives. In the United States, the terrible destruction by hurricanes and tornadoes is usually limited to property loss.

Pictures of the earth taken from space, like the photo above, also add to our knowledge of the world. For instance, they reveal land structures that cannot be seen by geologists in the field. Exploration of these structures has produced valuable deposits of metals.

We rely more and more on earth science to help us find new resources and to tell us how to use our earth wisely.

Have You Heard?

Fishermen in Alaska use satellite pictures to increase their herring catch. The satellite pictures show where the surface temperature of ocean water is 4°C. Herring gather in water of this temperature.

Review It

1. What topics are studied in earth science?
2. How does earth science affect your life?

1–2
New Developments in Earth Science

Earth scientists have been describing geologic events for many years. During this century, earth science research has produced an explosion of new ideas. With these new ideas, earth scientists can sometimes explain why an event took place as well as describe it. As you read about a few of the many areas of current research, try to answer these questions:

a. Why are scientists studying earthquakes and volcanoes?
b. How do geologists know what is happening in the oceans?
c. How do scientists know that the climate has changed?
d. How do we learn about the planets?

Earthquakes and Volcanoes

Dr. Karen McNally does research at the California Institute of Technology. She works all day, every day, to find what most people would like to avoid—earthquakes.

Dr. McNally, shown in the photograph below, travels back and forth from Cal Tech to areas where there is any unusual activity that might warn of an earthquake. For example, she investigates areas where there is a small but continuous movement of rocks. Dr. McNally and other scientists hope to learn enough about what happens before earthquakes occur to predict major earthquakes.

Scientists are trying to predict the eruptions of volcanoes as well as earthquakes. Hovering in a helicopter over an active volcano, such as Mount St. Helens, is not everyone's idea of fun. Elliot Endo, however, likes his work. Mr. Endo, shown in the photograph on the left below, is a geologist with the United States Geologic Survey. He is one of hundreds of geologists and other scientists who has a bird's-eye view of what is happening at this volcano. Since the volcano erupted in 1980, American geologists have a new natural laboratory near home.

Looking at the Ocean Bottom

One of the most exciting areas of research in earth science is the close-up study of the sea floor under the oceans. Dr. Jeff Karson is a geologist at Woods Hole Oceanographic Institution in Massachusetts. He explores the sea floor in underwater research vessels, which are called **submersibles** (səb mer′sə bəlz). Dr. Karson is shown in the picture with the submersible *Alvin*.

Dr. Karson and many other scientists are making detailed maps of the ocean floor. They use photographs taken on the ocean floor to make these maps. Jeff has explored the earth's largest mountain range, which is located on the ocean floor. This underwater mountain chain runs through the oceans of the world.

Climate—Today, Yesterday, and Tomorrow

Climate is an important field of research. We do not know whether the world climate is cooling off, warming up, or remaining steady. How peoples' activities affect the climate is also unknown. The question is important, because food and water for the world's growing population depend on climate.

The photograph shows Dr. William Donn of Lamont-Doherty Geologic Observatory in New York. He has spent many years studying climates of the past and present. Dr. Donn uses what he knows about ancient and present climates to predict future climates.

He finds clues to climates of the past in the remains of ancient sea life. As the climate changes, the type of life that lives near the water's surface changes. Shells and skeletons of these animals drop to the bottom of the ocean when they die. The evidence of ancient climates is found in layers on the ocean bottom. Research ships from Lamont-Doherty gather samples from the ocean bottom for Dr. Donn and the other scientists to study.

Exploring the Planets

Our knowledge about the planets has also grown tremendously. Each advance in astronomers' tools has brought new discoveries. For example, the invention of the telescope in the 1600s soon led to the discovery that Jupiter had moons.

The **atmosphere** (at′mə sfir), which is the air around the earth, interferes with the astronomer's view of the planets. Fabulous views of distant Jupiter and Saturn came in 1979, 1980, and 1981 when spacecraft carrying cameras flew close by these giant planets.

Candice Hansen is a scientist at the Jet Propulsion Laboratory in California. In the photograph, she is studying and analyzing pictures and information returned to earth from the spacecraft.

Review It

1. How can predicting earthquakes and volcanic eruptions help us?
2. How can we benefit from research in the oceans?
3. Why do we want to know about changes in climate?
4. Why are we now able to learn more about the planets?

1–3
How Problems Are Solved

The way you solve problems probably has a lot in common with the way research scientists solve problems. Some people think scientific research is a mysterious process. But the terms hard work, good judgment, timing, and luck often appear in stories about great scientific discoveries. As you read, keep in mind:

a. What are some steps used to solve problems?
b. How did James Hutton develop his theories?

Problem-Solving Steps

People meet with problems every day. If you are like most people, you begin to solve a problem by thinking about it for a while. After a time, you may come up with a temporary answer. You try out your answer. If it works, you decide the problem is solved.

A scientist starts to solve a research problem the way you do—by thinking about the problem. Usually, however, the answer does not come quickly. Scientists may study research problems from different angles and in different ways. But they approach their research in an orderly fashion that often involves more or less the same steps. You can use these steps to solve science problems too.

The first step often begins when people are puzzled or curious about something. That "something" is often a problem that you want to solve. After observing and thinking about your problem, you may come up with a **hypothesis** (hī poth′ə sis). A hypothesis is a likely explanation of your problem.

Now you can test and observe your hypothesis. You may find that the hypothesis does not always work. You create a new hypothesis that appears to work better. More tests and observations follow.

When you have found a hypothesis that seems to be true in all cases, it becomes a **theory,** which is a complete explanation of the problem. The dividing line between when an idea is a hypothesis and when it becomes a theory is not always clear.

Student laboratory activities usually end with a hypothesis. Theories arise after scientists have tested a hypothesis many, many times or found a hypothesis that explains many facts. A theory that is accepted by everyone and that explains how something takes place may be called a **law.**

Hypothesis, theory, and law are not words you use every day. But you may find the steps useful to complete science laboratory activities.

How Theories Develop

The picture shows James Hutton who was a doctor and a farmer in Scotland in the late 1700s. He was curious about rocks and how they were made. For many years, he observed what was happening to the land around him.

After many careful observations, Hutton came up with a hypothesis. His idea was that rocks are very ancient, and the processes that make and destroy rocks today are the same as those that acted millions of years ago. That idea sounds reasonable if you are familiar with how earth science is taught today. In the 1700s, however, Hutton's hypothesis was revolutionary. Soon, people began to examine Hutton's hypothesis. But his idea could not be tested in a laboratory. Instead, people had to observe rocks from many places. As time passed, scientists gathered a lot of evidence to support Hutton's hypothesis.

Hutton is now called the father of modern geology. His hypothesis is an accepted theory.

Review It

1. Suggest a series of steps that you could follow to solve a science problem.
2. What was James Hutton's theory?

Activity

Making Hypotheses

Purpose

To make up your own hypotheses to explain unknown situations.

Materials

- two beakers containing liquid
- ice cubes
- numbered mystery boxes containing unknown substances

Procedure

Part A

1. Remain in your seat and carefully observe the two beakers that contain liquid and ice.
2. Record on your paper any unusual situation that you notice.
3. Predict and record a hypothesis to explain what you see.

Part B

1. Examine the sealed mystery boxes. Do not open them.
2. Decide what you think is in the boxes. To find out, you may perform any test that will not ruin the boxes or reveal their contents.
3. Make hypotheses that identify the contents of each mystery box. Record them.

Analysis

1. What was the first problem you met in Part A?
2. Can you make a correct hypothesis for Part A by observations alone?
3. List all the tests you used to make your hypotheses in Part B.
4. You found your hypotheses in Part B by indirect observation. This means you were not able to actually see the unknown objects. Do scientists depend on indirect observations? Give an example.
5. How do airlines check the contents of mystery boxes (hand luggage)?
6. How does time influence the change of a hypothesis into a theory?

Issues in Earth Science

Using Our Land Wisely

Suppose there are 100 acres of forest land near your town. A construction company wants to build new houses there. Another company has plans for a shopping center. An oil company hopes to drill for oil and some people want to keep the forest just as it is. What is the best decision? How do *you* think the forest land should be used?

Many communities are faced with problems like this.

People need land for many purposes—homes, factories, office buildings, highways, parking lots, coal mines, farms, dumps, schools, and playgrounds.

But forest land serves many functions too. Forests provide timber, which we use for homes, heat, and paper. Tree roots help hold loose soil in place, which reduces flooding. Like other green plants, trees release oxygen, a gas necessary for life.

Two hundred years ago we did not worry about land use. There was plenty of space for forests, farms, and cities. But times have changed. Today we often have to choose whether to conserve forests, swamps, and meadows, or turn them into airports, golf courses, and strip mines.

The problem gets worse each year. Cities spread into the surrounding country. This wild growth of cities is sometimes called urban sprawl.

Since 1945, urban sprawl has taken over 45 million acres of natural lands. We take another million acres every year.

Laws now control land use. They require that people study the effects of changes they plan. These "impact studies" help us find the best way to use our land.

We are learning how to work with nature, not against it. Highways can be built to follow the shape of hills and valleys. Factories can be required to control the wastes they release. New housing developments can be designed to blend with the land.

There is only a limited amount of land on earth. Our job is to learn to use it wisely.

For Discussion
1. What is meant by the term *urban sprawl?*
2. Why has land use become a problem in this country in recent years?

1—4
SI and Measurements

Many quantities we measure are familiar to us. For example, we use a ruler to measure the length, width, or height of an object. In a laboratory activity, you might also need to find volume, mass, and density. Think about the questions below as you read:

a. What is one SI unit for volume and one for mass?
b. What is density?

Volume and Mass

Scientists and most of the world's people use the International System, called SI, to measure objects. The standard unit to measure length in SI is the **meter.** Prefixes are used with meter to indicate 1/10, 1/100, 1/1000, or 10, 100, 1,000, and so on, times the meter. The same prefixes are used with all units in the SI system. The table lists some commonly used prefixes.

Volume   The amount of space that any object takes up is its **volume.** The box of cereal, for example, has length, width, and height, as shown. The volume of the box is length x width x height. The volume is labeled cubic centimeters (cm³). Correct measurements always have a *number* and a *label*.

Amount	Prefix	Abbreviation	Example
1/1000	Milli-	m-	Millimeter = mm
1/100	Centi-	cm-	Centimeter = cm
1	—	m	Meter = m
1000	Kilo-	k-	Kilometer = km

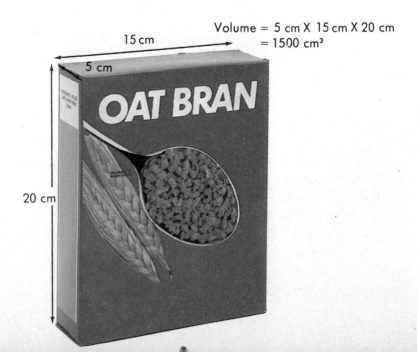

15 cm

5 cm

20 cm

Volume = 5 cm X 15 cm X 20 cm
= 1500 cm³

OAT BRAN

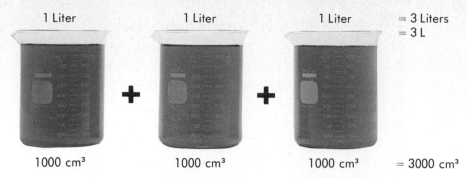

1 Liter   1 Liter   1 Liter   = 3 Liters
                                 = 3 L

1000 cm³   1000 cm³   1000 cm³   = 3000 cm³

The volume of liquid substances is often indicated in **liters** (L) rather than cubic centimeters. One liter is 1,000 cubic centimeters. It is more convenient to ask for three liters than 3,000 cubic centimeters of milk at a grocery store. You will find the term *milliliter* in many laboratory activities. A milliliter is 1/1,000 of a liter.

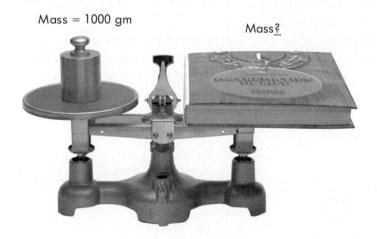

Mass = 1000 gm   Mass?

Mass All things are made up of matter. We measure the amount of matter in a body by giving the body's **mass.** The **kilogram** (kg) is the SI unit for mass. Mass can be measured on a balance like the one in the drawing. To find the unknown mass of the book, you balance it with an object of known mass. The mass of the book in the diagram is one kilogram, which is 1,000 **grams** (g).

Water is such a common substance on earth that it is used as a standard for volume and mass measurements. One milliliter of water has a mass of one gram.

Density—A Descriptive Term

Density tells how much mass is packed into a certain volume. The density is the amount of mass in a body divided by the volume of the body. The silver brick and the butter in the diagram each occupy a volume of 1,000 cubic centimeters. The silver, however, is more dense. It has more mass packed into 1,000 cubic centimeters than the butter has. The density of the silver is the mass divided by the volume.

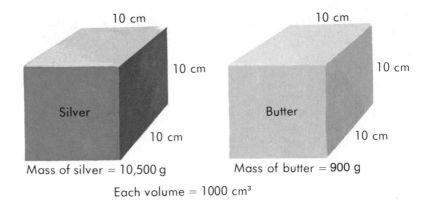

Mass of silver = 10,500 g   Mass of butter = 900 g

Each volume = 1000 cm³

$$\text{Density of silver} = \frac{\text{mass}}{\text{volume}} = \frac{10{,}500 \text{ grams}}{1{,}000 \text{ cm}^3}$$

$$= \frac{10.5 \text{ grams}}{1 \text{ cm}^3} \text{ or}$$

$$= 10.5 \text{ g/cm}^3$$

Solving science problems in earth science sometimes involves measuring. You will be using units such as grams or centimeters throughout this book.

Review It

1. Find the volume of a box that is 5 centimeters high, 25 centimeters long, and 40 centimeters wide.
2. Use milliliters to describe 150 cubic centimeters of water.
3. Calculate the density of salt if 216 grams of salt occupy a volume of 100 cubic centimeters.

Activity

Measuring with SI Units

Purpose
To measure and calculate volume and density using SI units.

Materials
- water
- graduated cylinder or any container marked in milliliters (mL)
- balance
- cm ruler
- block of wood or any rectangular solid
- irregularly-shaped solid

Procedure

Part A
1. Use the balance to find the mass of the block of wood to the nearest whole gram as shown in *a*. Record the mass.
2. Measure and record the height of the block to the nearest .1 cm. Do the same for the width and length of the block.
3. Calculate the volume of the block by multiplying the height x width x length. Show your work. Your answer should be labeled cm³.

4. Find the density of the block. To do this, divide the mass by the volume. Show your work. Your answer should be labeled g/cm³.

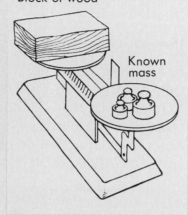

a

Block of wood

Known mass

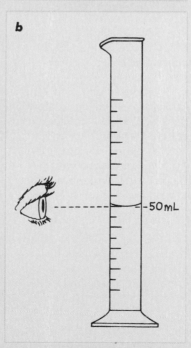

b

—50 mL

Part B
1. Find the mass of the irregularly-shaped object to the nearest whole gram.
2. Fill a graduated cylinder with 100 mL of water. To make certain your measurement is accurate, view the column of water at eye level, as shown in *b*.
3. Carefully lower the irregularly-shaped object into the water. Record how many mL the water level rises. Do this by subtracting the original water level, which was 100 mL, from the new reading. The number that you find is the volume of water that was pushed aside by the object. This also equals the volume of the object. One milliliter is the same as one cubic centimeter (1mL=1cm³).
4. Use the volume and mass to find the density of the object. (See Part A, step 4.)

Analysis
1. When is the Part B method of finding density more useful than the Part A method?
2. Suggest the steps you could use to find the density of your body.
3. Suppose someone offered to sell you a bar of gold at a bargain price. Devise a test to make sure the bar is pure gold.

1–5
Safety Practices in Earth Science Laboratories

What do you do if there is an accident in the laboratory? Or better yet—how can you avoid an accident? Before you start the earth science activities in this book you should read this section carefully. The questions below focus on laboratory safety:

a. What are some ways to avoid accidents in science laboratories?
b. What do you do if there is an accident?

How to Avoid Accidents

Each science has certain types of activities that are potentially dangerous. That means that accidents could happen if you are not careful. The student in the photograph is practicing good safety habits. She is holding the test tube so that any fumes from it do not go near her face. Carefully read the LABORATORY CAUTIONS.

Laboratory Cautions

1. REPORT ACCIDENTS OR HAZARDS TO YOUR TEACHER AT ONCE.
2. Know where all the safety equipment is located and how to use it.
3. Carefully read and follow the directions in each laboratory activity. Do *only* what the procedure section of the activity tells you to do. Do not hurry through the procedure.
4. Be particularly cautious when you are working with Bunsen burners or boiling water. If your clothing or hair catches fire, DO NOT RUN. Smother the fire with a blanket or towels. Run cold water over a minor burn to soothe it.
5. Do not taste any substance used in the laboratory or inhale fumes from chemicals. If chemicals spill or splash on your skin or eyes, immediately wash the affected area with water.
6. Wear safety glasses when you are working with sharp tools, hot materials, or chemicals.
7. Handle glass equipment very carefully. If you break glass, tell your teacher immediately. Dispose of broken glass properly.
8. Put equipment and materials away at the end of the laboratory period as you are instructed. Do not dispose of leftover substances in sinks unless you are told to do this. Wipe up any spilled water.

What to Do If There Is an Accident

If any accident or emergency occurs, TELL YOUR
TEACHER IMMEDIATELY. You should also report any
situation in the room that can lead to trouble. For example,
tell your teacher about any equipment that is not working
properly.

If an accident or emergency happens, do not get excited.
Panic is contagious. When a minor accident is followed by
panic, new problems arise.

Learn the LABORATORY CAUTIONS. If any problem
comes up that is not covered by these rules, use common
sense. For instance, injured people need air. Do not crowd
around someone who is hurt. Wash cuts and scrapes with
soap and water.

Plan ahead. Follow the safety rules and stay calm in
emergencies. That's what safety is all about.

Review It

1. Rewrite the LABORATORY CAUTIONS in your own
   words.
2. What is the first thing to do when there is an accident?

Chapter Summary

- Earth science combines geology, meteorology, and oceanography. Astronomy and space science are closely related to earth science. (1–1)

- Earthquakes, volcanoes, climate, the ocean bottom, and space are only a few of the fields of earth science research. (1–2)

- Scientists identify problems, test and observe the problems, and make hypotheses. Hypotheses that are widely accepted may be called theories. (1–3)

- Scientists use the SI units to measure objects. (1–4)

- Density is the amount of mass in an object divided by the volume of the object. (1–4)

- For safety in laboratory activities, learn and practice the LABORATORY CAUTIONS. (1–5)

Interesting Reading

Ballard, Robert and J. Frederick Grassle. "Return to Oases of the Deep." *National Geographic,* November, 1979, pages 689–708. Tells about an expedition to the ocean bottom.

Canby, Thomas Y. "Can We Predict Quakes?" *National Geographic,* June 1976, pages 830–835. Describes work on earthquake prediction.

Gallant, Roy A. *Earth's Changing Climate.* Four Winds Press, 1979. Examines reasons for climate changes, including cosmic dust storms and sunspots.

Matthews, Samuel W. "What's Happening to Our Climate?" *National Geographic,* November 1976, pages 576–615. Discusses climate change and its importance.

Questions/Problems

1. What fields of earth science could give advice about where to locate a coal mine?

2. How can sea animals that lived 60 million years ago tell us about climate in the future?

3. Compare a theory and a hypothesis.

4. Convert 3, 0.6, and 1.2 meters into centimeters and millimeters.

5. What is the mass in grams of 500 cubic centimeters of water?

6. How many times do you need to refill a 100 milliliter container to get 5,000 cubic centimeters of water?

7. Which matter is more dense—105 grams of silver that occupies 10 cubic centimeters or 8,900 grams of copper in a volume of 1,000 cubic centimeters?

Extra Research

1. Use a *Readers' Guide* to find magazine articles about current earth science research. Look under the headings of oceans, atmosphere, geology, and astronomy. Read one article about each of the four fields and write one paragraph about each.

2. Write to the National Bureau of Standards in Washington, D.C., for information about the use of SI measurements in the United States.

3. Make a poster illustrating one or more of the LABORATORY CAUTIONS.

Chapter Test

A. Vocabulary   Write the numbers 1–10 on a piece of paper.
Match the definition in Column I with the term it defines in Column II.

Column I

1. believed earth processes of the past are the same as those of the present

2. the study of the earth or astronomical objects from space

3. the amount of mass packed into a certain volume

4. an SI unit

5. how much space an object occupies

6. underwater research vessel

7. a trial explanation

8. an explanation that appears to be true

9. one who studies air conditions and weather

10. the quantity of matter a body contains

Column II

a. *Alvin*

b. density

c. Hutton

d. hypothesis

e. mass

f. meteorologist

g. meter

h. space science

i. theory

j. volume

B. Multiple Choice   Write the numbers 1–10 on your paper.
Choose the letter that best completes the statement or answers the questions.

1. Earth science deals with   a) land.   b) air and space.   c) oceans.   d) a, b, and c.

2. Scientists use submersibles to study   a) air.   b) land.   c) oceans.   d) space.

3. The invention of the telescope led to the discovery of   a) Jupiter.   b) the Moon.   c) moons around Jupiter.   d) comets.

4. Many earth scientists are working to predict a) climate changes.   b) earthquakes.   c) volcanic activity.   d) a, b, and c.

5. A theory differs from a hypothesis in that it is   a) more likely to be true.   b) less likely to be true.   c) longer.   d) shorter.

6. A kilometer is   a) 100 meters.   b) 1,000 meters.   c) 10 meters.   d) 10,000 meters.

7. The SI unit for mass is the   a) liter. b) cm³.   c) kilogram.   d) cm².

8. Every measurement consists of   a) mass and volume.   b) mass and weight.   c) a label and number.   d) a linear measure.

9. Units to measure volume are   a) milliliters. b) cubic centimeters.   c) cubic meters.   d) a, b, and c.

10. Density indicates the relationship between a) mass and length.   b) mass and width. c) mass and volume.   d) volume and content.

Chapter 2
Studying Our Universe

The picture at the left is a view alongside a telescope aimed at the sky. Telescopes give us a good look at the stars, glowing gas, and dark dust that are part of the universe.

In this chapter you will learn how and why people study the universe. You will read about telescopes and how they can be used to study the light given off by stars and other objects. You will discover that all objects in the universe give off energy that can be studied from the ground and from space. Finally, you will find out why we had to go beyond the earth's atmosphere to study the universe in new ways.

Chapter Objectives

1. Explain why we study the universe.
2. Explain the purpose of optical telescopes.
3. Define radiation and identify the parts of the spectrum.
4. Explain why it is useful to have telescopes in space.

2–1
Why We Study the Universe

For thousands of years people have looked up into the clear night sky and wondered about what they saw. People have always had a desire to understand the planets and stars. As you read, keep these questions in mind:

a. What is the universe?
b. Why should we study the universe?

The Universe Contains Everything There Is

We are most familiar with the objects in the **universe** that are closest to us: Earth, the other planets, and our star—the sun. But beyond the sun are billions and billions of other stars and many other objects. The picture shows a collection of millions of stars plus gas and dust in between the stars. Millions of objects like these are spread throughout space. All the objects in space make up the universe. The universe is everything that exists.

The Sun Dagger

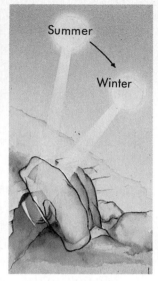

The position of the Sun Dagger changes with the season

Astronomy Is Useful in Our Lives

For thousands of years, people have studied how objects move across the sky. The picture shows a streak of light, called the Anasazi Sun Dagger, on a rock in New Mexico. Seven hundred years ago, the Indians found that sunlight passed a certain spot on a rock only on one day each year. That day was in the middle of summer. They drew a bull's-eye on the spot and used it as part of their calendar.

The Egyptians also made calendars by observing the sky. They used their calendars to predict the yearly flooding of the Nile River to find out when to plant crops.

Ancient sailors learned to navigate oceans by charting the movements of the stars. For example, the North Star —Polaris—showed them where north was located.

The study of astronomy continues to help us on the earth. For instance, observing the sun and stars helped us understand nuclear energy. Nuclear energy produces some of our electricity.

Review It

1. What is in the universe?
2. What are two reasons ancient people studied the stars?

2–2
Light and Telescopes

For many years astronomers learned about the universe by studying only the light that came from the stars. As you read about light and telescopes, keep in mind:

a. What happens when you separate light into its colors?
b. How do telescopes help us see faint objects?

Light Breaks Down into Colors

We cannot go out to touch the stars, but the stars send us energy through space. Stars form the energy deep inside themselves. Some of it comes to us as light—the form of energy we see with our eyes. Telescopes used to study light are **optical telescopes.**

Sunlight seems white, but actually it is made up of many different colors. For example, sunlight can break down, or separate, into a rainbow of colors, such as the rainbow shown in the picture. The light from other stars can also be separated into colors. In many observatories, scientists collect starlight with optical telescopes. Then they break down the light to find out how much of the different colors is in it. From this information, scientists learn what the star is made of and how hot it is.

Optical Telescopes Help Us See Faint Objects

The lenses in your eyes collect light. But most objects in space are too faint for you to see because the openings in your eyes are too small. Optical telescopes use large lenses or mirrors to gather more light. Astronomers use optical telescopes because they collect much more light than your eyes alone can collect.

The first optical telescopes were made in 1609. A Dutch eyeglass-maker put one lens in front of another and discovered that the two together made distant things seem closer. Soon afterwards, the Italian scientist Galileo (gal′ə lā′ō) made his own telescope to study the universe. Though telescopes can magnify, astronomers use telescopes more to collect light than to make things seem closer.

Have You Heard?

Water droplets in the sky bend white sunlight and separate it into its individual colors. This produces a rainbow.

Picture A

Picture B

Picture C

A telescope made with lenses is called a **refracting telescope.** One lens—the objective lens—forms the image. The light of the image is refracted—or bent—toward a single point. This point is called the **focal point.** The second lens—the **eyepiece**—magnifies the image for the eye.

Later in the 1600s, the great English scientist Isaac Newton replaced the objective lens with a curved mirror. He invented the **reflecting telescope,** which uses a large mirror to collect light. The mirror bounces—or reflects—the light toward the focal point. An eyepiece magnifies the image for the eye.

A telescope can gather even more light if it is used as a large camera. When light hits your eye, an image is sent immediately to your brain. Your eye cannot store the light. However, light can be stored on film or on a video camera placed at a telescope's focal point instead of the eyepiece. If the film or camera is exposed to faint starlight for minutes or hours, the light adds up and gives us a better picture. The photographs show the same area of the sky. The length of time the camera was open increases from picture A to picture C. Notice that the number of faint objects you can see is greatest in C. Because of these long exposures, people can make pictures of objects in space that they could not see by looking through a telescope.

Have You Heard?

The largest optical telescopes in the world are reflecting telescopes. The two largest are in the Soviet Union and on Palomar Mountain in California. Three of the world's ten largest telescopes are on a high mountain in Hawaii.

Review It

1. What do you see when you separate sunlight into parts?
2. What is an advantage of using a camera instead of your eye with a telescope?

Activity

Light-Collecting Model

Purpose
To compare the amount of light collected by telescopes of different sizes.

Materials
- cardboard, the size of notebook paper
- compass and pencil
- cm ruler
- 40 straws
- scissors
- sheet of paper

Procedure
1. Use the compass to draw a circle near the edge of the cardboard 1 cm in diameter (0.5 cm radius).
2. Cut this circle out. You will be working with the hole in the sheet of cardboard. The hole represents a telescope lens or mirror.
3. The straws represent rays of light reaching the lens or mirror. Count the number of straws that fit into the hole at the same time. Diagram *a* shows you how they should fit snugly.
4. Copy the table, shown in *b,* onto your paper. Record the results of step 2 on the table.

5. Repeat steps 1 and 2 for circles with diameters of 2 cm, 3 cm, and 4 cm. Record your results on the table.
6. Copy graph *c* on your paper. All horizontal and vertical lines should be 1 cm apart.

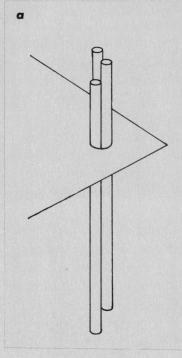

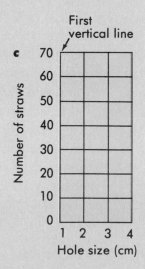

Diameter of hole	Number of straws
1 cm	
2 cm	
3 cm	
4 cm	

7. Transfer the information from your table to your graph. For example, on the first vertical line, put a dot at the point that stands for the number of straws that fit through the 1-cm hole. Do the same for the 2-cm, 3-cm, and 4-cm holes. You should have four dots on your graph.
8. Connect the four dots with straight lines.

Analysis
1. How does the amount of light (number of straws) increase when you double the diameter of the hole?
2. Study your graph carefully. Predict the amount of light (number of straws) that would enter through a lens 8 cm in diameter.

Breakthrough

Spinoffs from Space Research

The National Aeronautics and Space Administration (NASA) is responsible for our space programs. Much of NASA's research has resulted in ideas and products that are very useful on earth. These ideas and products are called "spinoffs."

Because of space technology, we now have such life-savers as smoke alarms and nonflammable furniture. Our everyday lives are made easier with pocket calculators and longer-lasting light bulbs. Crash barriers around telephone poles and new materials for patching roads are also NASA spinoffs.

Sports have benefited greatly from the space programs. A new plastic foam is used in football helmets and shoulder pads. Better gloves and boots for skiers, improved golf clubs, and hang gliders all came from space research.

Perhaps the most beneficial spinoffs have been in the field of medicine. Some hospital patients wear devices like the one in the photograph. This device monitors a patient's heartbeat, leaving him free to move about.

Other medical benefits from space exploration are artificial limbs, better surgical instruments, and an improved pacemaker for heart patients.

Future spinoffs might include a satellite that helps stop crime. Alarms on cars, in homes, or even on people, could communicate with a satellite. Once an alarm is tripped, the signal would go to the satellite and back to a police station. The police would then know the exact location of the crime.

Space research continues to provide us with useful new inventions.

For Discussion
1. What is a spinoff?
2. List five spinoffs of the space programs.

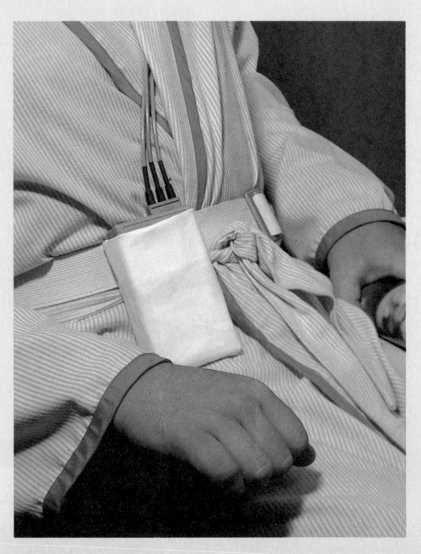

29

2-3
Radiation

The light we see is one form of radiation. Many forms of radiation are important to your daily life. Radiation helps you read this book, brings you radio and television programs, and can even cook your food. It also helps astronomers learn more about the universe. As you read about different forms of radiation, keep in mind:

a. What is radiation?
b. What do we study with radiation beyond the violet?
c. What do we study with radiation beyond the red?

Radiation from Space

Radiation is energy that can travel in waves even through empty space. Light is only one form of radiation. When you separate light energy into all of its colors, shown below, there is energy in each color. If you put a very sensitive thermometer in any color, or even a little beyond the red, there is a rise in temperature. Beyond the red, something invisible makes the temperature rise. Many forms of visible and invisible radiation come to us through space.

The entire **spectrum** includes light and all other kinds of radiation. The radiation spreads out in a particular order, also shown below.

The rainbow of colors that visible light contains is enlarged at the top of the diagram. Suppose the rainbow of colors is squeezed into the small visible light section below. Red is on the right and next to it is infrared radiation. Violet is on the left and next to it is ultraviolet radiation.

Have You Heard?

The spectrum is shown in order of wavelength. Gamma rays have the shortest wavelengths, less than 1/10,000,000,000 m. Radio waves have the longest wavelengths, from 1 mm up to several km and beyond.

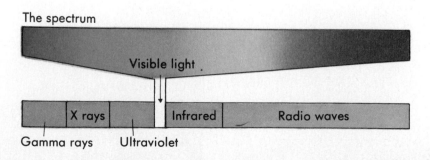

The spectrum

Visible light

Gamma rays   X rays   Ultraviolet   Infrared   Radio waves

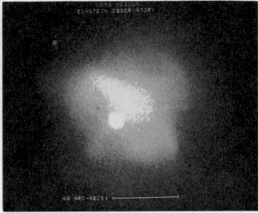

Visible light photograph   X-ray photograph

Beyond the Violet—Ultraviolet, X Rays, and Gamma Rays

All objects give off all kinds of radiation. Different types of stars or other objects can give off more of one type of radiation than another. The object's temperature determines what kinds of radiation are given off.

The **ultraviolet** is the part of the spectrum just beyond the violet. Some special types of ultraviolet radiation come from the outer parts of stars. They show up on film or video cameras that are above the earth's atmosphere. Astronomers study ultraviolet radiation to learn what the outer parts of the stars are like. These outer parts cannot be studied as well in ordinary light.

The hottest stars give off a lot of **X rays** and **gamma rays.** We have special machines on the earth to make X rays. But some stars give off X rays naturally from their hot gases. X rays and gamma rays from stars, like most of the ultraviolet, do not pass through the earth's atmosphere. Therefore, they can be studied only from spacecraft, such as satellites.

The picture shows two views of a star that has exploded. The one at the left shows a view with ordinary light. We see strands of gas left over. The X-ray picture at the right, however, shows that a very hot part of the star remains in the center of the gas. Comparing the visible light and X-ray pictures teaches astronomers what happens when stars explode.

Radio telescopes

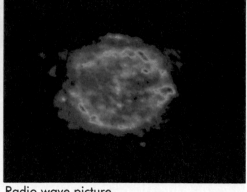

Radio wave picture

Have You Heard?

The set of radio telescopes in New Mexico is called the Very Large Array (VLA). The VLA consists of 27 telescopes forming a large Y. It is the largest radio telescope project ever undertaken.

Beyond the Red—Infrared and Radio Waves

Most objects on the earth, as well as the earth itself, are not hot enough to give off their own light. However, they do give off a kind of radiation that we cannot see. This radiation is **infrared,** which is just beyond the red end of visible light. Many objects in space are as cool as the earth, and we can study them only by their infrared radiation. Since many of these cool objects are stars that are just forming, we can use infrared to tell us about the birth of stars.

Radio waves are beyond the infrared in the spectrum. On earth, we make radio waves to carry radio or television signals from a studio to us. But hot gases make radio waves naturally. **Radio telescopes** collect and focus these waves. The set of radio telescopes above stretches 27 kilometers across New Mexico. To the right above, you can see the picture these telescopes made of an exploded star. You cannot see this star at all in ordinary light, even with the largest optical telescopes.

Radiation is our major link with the universe. Today's astronomers are able to study parts of the spectrum other than light waves. As a result, our understanding of the universe has greatly increased.

Review It

1. Name six kinds of radiation astronomers study.
2. What can astronomers study using ultraviolet radiation?
3. What kind of star does infrared radiation reveal?

Activity

Radio Telescope Model

Purpose
To see how a radio telescope works.

Materials
- small transistor radio
- umbrella
- heavy-duty aluminum foil (enough to line the inside of an umbrella)

Procedure
1. Place the radio on your desk or table. Starting at the far left, turn the dial to find weak stations. Write down the dial numbers of five weak stations.
2. Now, make a model of a radio telescope. Open an umbrella and line the inside of the umbrella with aluminum foil, as in a.
3. Rotate the radio until you get the best reception possible from a weak station.
4. Hold the umbrella behind the radio with the aluminum foil facing the incoming waves, as shown in the lower diagram of a.

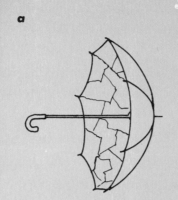

a

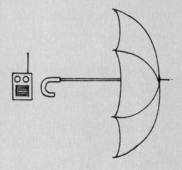

5. Slowly move the umbrella closer to or farther from the radio until you find the position that best improves the strength of the radio waves.
6. Repeat steps 3, 4, and 5 for the other weak stations. Put a check mark next to each station whose radio waves are strengthened by the radio telescope.
7. Besides picking up radio waves, your radio telescope can block unwanted radio waves. Choose any station on the radio. Place your radio telescope model between the radio and the incoming radio waves, as shown in b. Notice what happens.

Analysis
1. Where did the radio waves that your radio received come from?
2. Where do radio waves that are picked up by actual radio telescopes come from?
3. What happened when you put the umbrella between the radio and the transmitting station?
4. What is the function of the aluminum foil in this activity?

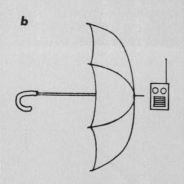

b

2–4
Exploring Space

Before we had satellites in space, scientists had a very limited view of the universe. Keep the following questions in mind as you read how space exploration aids our study of astronomy:

a. How do space studies help astronomy?
b. What will some future space studies be?

Astronomy Moves into Space

The atmosphere that surrounds the earth is constantly moving. This makes the stars appear to twinkle. But it also means we cannot see clear images through an optical telescope. For this reason, most observatories are located on mountain tops where the air is thin and clear. Astronomers could get even clearer pictures of the universe if they had a big enough telescope beyond the earth's atmosphere.

For the last 30 years, astronomers have been making increased use of the satellites that rockets carry into orbit. Gamma rays, X rays, and most ultraviolet rays from objects in outer space can only be studied from above the atmosphere. The satellite below studied X rays from outer space. Other satellites discovered that gas regularly leaves parts of the sun and hits the earth's atmosphere.

Spacecraft have landed on the moon, Mars, and Venus. They have passed close to many of the planets and their moons. They sent back information about their surfaces and atmospheres. Astronomers were not able to make these studies as well from the earth's surface.

Have You Heard?

The harder you throw a ball, the higher and farther it will go. If you could throw a ball 30,000 km/hr it would go into orbit around the earth. At 40,000 km/hr, a ball or rocket could escape the earth's pull. Therefore, 40,000 km/hr is called the escape velocity.

Satellite that studies X rays

Space Telescope

Astronomy's Future in Space

Since 1981, the United States has been launching **space shuttles.** Space shuttles were the first space vehicles that could take off, go into orbit, land, and take off again. Each shuttle can be used many times, while earlier rockets were used only once. The main function of space shuttles is to put satellites, such as those used for communications or for keeping track of what goes on below, into orbit. Another function of the shuttles is to carry people who can perform experiments or bring back satellites that no longer work.

A space shuttle will launch the **Space Telescope,** the first large telescope in space. The Space Telescope, shown in the picture, will "see" seven times more clearly than any telescope on the earth. It will also be able to see fainter objects and study both visible and ultraviolet light. With the Space Telescope, astronomers expect to learn more about the universe. They may even discover planets around distant stars.

Review It

1. Why do astronomers want telescopes above the atmosphere?
2. What are two advantages of the Space Telescope?

Have You Heard?

The European Space Agency (ESA) launches satellites using its Ariane rockets. Most of the western European nations are involved in ESA's space program. ESA launches have been made from tropical rain forests in South America.

Chapter Summary

- The universe is everything that exists. (2–1)

- Stars send energy out into space. The energy we see with our eyes is light. (2–2)

- Scientists can separate light into its colors. The colors contained in light are the same as those displayed in rainbows. Studying the colors tells astronomers what a star is made of and how hot it is. (2–2)

- Astronomers use optical telescopes to collect light from objects in space. Reflecting and refracting telescopes are two types of optical telescopes. (2–2)

- Scientists can now study other kinds of radiation besides light, such as gamma rays, X rays, ultraviolet radiation, infrared radiation, and radio waves. This radiation shows astronomers objects in the universe that they cannot study with light alone. (2–3)

- Satellites and rockets launched into space send back information about the universe that cannot be gathered from studies on the earth. (2–4)

Interesting Reading

Hanbury Brown, R. *Man and the Stars.* Oxford University Press, 1978. Describes the contributions astronomy has made to civilization.

Ross, Frank. *The Space Shuttle.* Lothrop, Lee and Shepard, 1979. Discusses the space shuttle and shows how to make a flying model of the shuttle.

Simon, Seymour. *Look to the Night Sky.* Viking, 1977. Explains how to observe the night sky. Includes information on buying and using telescopes.

Questions/Problems

1. Why would a telescope on the earth be useless for studying ultraviolet waves?

2. The atmosphere interferes with our view of space. Why does the moon often appear hazier near the horizon than high in the sky?

3. A student recently bought a small telescope. She was disappointed because she saw pictures of planets that are much better than what she can see through the telescope. Explain why this might be true.

4. Because of satellites, we know a great deal more about X rays and gamma rays from the stars. Explain why this is true.

5. Why is the space shuttle useful?

Extra Research

1. Make posters that show how light moves through refracting and reflecting telescopes. Use the encyclopedia or an astronomy book for diagrams.

2. Separate the light from a slide projector —or the sun—into its colors. To do this, use a prism, which is a wedge-shaped piece of glass. Draw and color what you see.

3. Write a one-page report on the world's largest, single radio telescope, in Arecibo, Puerto Rico.

Chapter Test

A. Vocabulary   Write the numbers 1–10 on a piece of paper.
Match the definition in Column I with the term it defines in Column II.

Column I

1. radiation that our eyes can see

2. radiation just beyond the violet

3. general term for all energy traveling through space

4. all kinds of radiation in a particular order

5. carries instruments used to study gamma rays and X rays above the atmosphere

6. the radiation farthest beyond the violet

7. radiation given off by newborn stars

8. can be made by observing objects in space

9. telescope used to observe light

10. this telescope will be able to see farthest into the universe

Column II

a. calendars

b. gamma rays

c. infrared

d. light

e. optical telescope

f. radiation

g. satellite

h. Space Telescope

i. spectrum

j. ultraviolet

B. Multiple Choice   Write the numbers 1–10 on your paper.
Choose the letter that best completes the statement or answers the question.

1. Astronomy is and has been studied to help people   a) understand the universe.
b) navigate.   c) keep time.   d) a, b, and c.

2. Starlight   a) is always the same color.
b) can be separated into a rainbow of colors.
c) can be studied only from space.   d) cannot be stored.

3. Stars   a) create energy inside themselves.
b) do not create their own energy.   c) give off more than one kind of radiation.   d) a and c.

4. The *main* purpose of optical telescopes on the earth is to   a) magnify images.   b) collect light from distant objects.   c) collect X rays from distant objects.   d) a, b, and c.

5. Most observatories are on mountain tops because   a) there is less atmosphere to see through.   b) there is less noise.   c) they are as close to the stars as possible.   d) a and b.

6. Energy that travels through space is called
a) spectrum.   b) radium.   c) radiation.
d) reflection.

7. Gamma and X rays   a) are given off by the hottest stars.   b) do not pass through the earth's atmosphere.   c) can be studied only from rockets and satellites.   d) a, b, and c.

8. We study newborn stars *mainly* by their
a) ordinary light.   b) infrared waves.
c) gamma rays.   d) a, b, and c.

9. Radiation that can be observed by optical telescopes on the earth's surface is   a) light.
b) radio waves. c) gamma rays. d) a, b, and c.

10. A reflecting telescope must contain at least
a) two lenses.   b) one mirror.   c) one lens.
d) b and c.

Chapter 3
Survey of the Stars

A solar eclipse like the one at the left is a spectacular sight. The last bit of sun glows so brightly it looks like a brilliant diamond on a ring of light. By the earth's standards, the sun is huge and the moon is small. But the moon is so close to us that it blocks nearly all the sun's light when it moves directly in front of the sun.

The sun is a very special star to us. But it is just an average star among the billions of other stars in the universe. In this chapter, you will learn about our sun, the star closest to us. You will also learn about stages in the life and death of stars and about special kinds of stars. For several years, one of those special kinds of stars has been getting a lot of attention. People have studied it, discussed it, written about it, and even made movies about it. At the close of this chapter, you will read about this unique kind of star—a black hole.

Chapter Objectives

1. Explain how stars form.
2. List the parts of the sun.
3. Explain what makes stars shine.
4. Describe the stages in the life of a star.
5. Define a black hole.

3–1
Discovering the Stars

When you look up at the sky on a clear, dark night, you see more stars than you can easily count. Each star is a glowing ball of hot gas somewhere in space. As you read, answer these questions about stars:

a. How is a star born?
b. How can astronomers tell how far away a star is?

Stars Are Born from Gas and Dust

When you hold a book and then let it go, it falls to earth. The book falls to earth because of the pull of gravity. Gravity pulls any two objects together.

Stars form when the force of gravity pulls together particles of gas and dust in space. The particles begin to move faster in all directions, and the gas becomes hotter. Eventually, energy is produced deep inside the cloud of gas and dust. This energy increases the forces of the particles pushing outward. When the force of gravity pulling the particles together balances the force of the particles pushing outward, a star is born. The picture shows a **nebula** (neb′yə lə) —or cloud of gas and dust. The small dark spots are places where gravity is pulling gas and dust together. The bright spots glowing in the nebula are stars that have already formed.

Lagoon Nebula

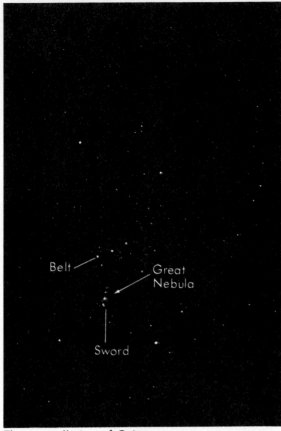

The constellation of Orion

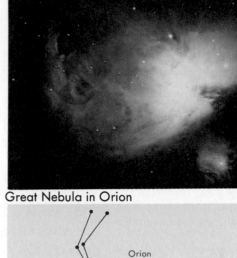

Great Nebula in Orion

Orion the hunter

Scientists have discovered that some very young stars are in a region of the sky we call the **constellation** Orion (ô rī′ən). A constellation is a group of stars named for an object, a person, or an animal. The picture above shows how the stars in a constellation seem to create a picture in the sky. The ancient Greeks imagined that Orion was a hunter with a sword.

The photograph above shows a glowing region in Orion that looks reddish. This glowing cloud of gas is the Great Nebula in Orion. Astronomers using ordinary telescopes can see only a few young stars inside the nebula. But pictures made with radio waves or infrared light show that clouds of dust and gas lie behind the glowing gas. More stars are forming within these clouds. Those stars may shine in hundreds or thousands of years.

Have You Heard?

The stars in a constellation only seem to be close together because they are all in almost the same direction from us. But they are different distances away from us. They are not really near each other in space.

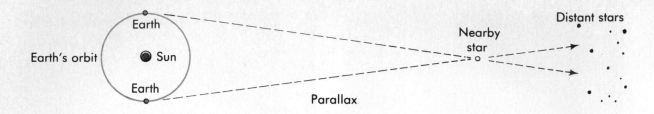

Earth

Earth's orbit

Sun

Earth

Parallax

Nearby
star

Distant stars

Challenge!

Select an object across the room to represent distant stars. With your arm extended, hold up your thumb in front of the distant object. Your thumb represents a nearby star. Look at your thumb and the object with your left eye closed. Do not move your head. Look again with your right eye closed. Now pull your thumb closer to your body and repeat the procedure above, using the same distant object. Analyze your observations.

Distances to the Stars

Light travels 300,000 kilometers in a second, a million times faster than a jet plane. In fact, light can travel seven times the distance around the earth in a single second. Light from the moon reaches us in a little more than a second. The sun is much farther away. Its light takes about 8 minutes to reach the earth.

The stars are much farther away than the sun. The light from stars takes years to reach the earth. The distance light travels in one year is a **light year**—a distance of about 9.5 trillion kilometers. Astronomers measure the great distances of space in light years. Proxima Centauri (prok′sə mə′ sen tor′ē), the star nearest to our sun, is more than 4 light years from the earth. Many stars are millions of light years away.

Astronomers find distances to nearby stars such as Proxima Centauri in the following way. First they observe a star's location in the sky with respect to more distant stars. Then they wait a few months while the earth moves in its orbit around the sun. They observe the star's position again. Notice in the diagram that when the earth has moved, a nearby star appears to shift to a slightly different position with respect to more distant stars. This shift is called **parallax** (par′ə laks). Nearer stars appear to shift farther than more distant stars. Very distant stars have shifts too small to measure.

Review It

1. From what do stars form?
2. What do astronomers measure using parallax?

Activity

Parallax

Purpose

To demonstrate that near objects appear to change their positions more than distant objects when the position of the observer changes.

Materials

- two paper cups
- meter stick
- table or desk
- chalkboard or wall
- chalk

Procedure

1. Put two paper cups about 30 cm apart on the table, as shown in the picture.
2. Make 6 chalk marks 50 cm apart on the wall or chalkboard on the other side of your classroom. Number them 1 through 6, as shown.
3. Place yourself 1 m behind the table like the boy in the picture and with your eyes level with the model.
4. Draw a picture of the paper cups as they appear to you. Include the positions of the chalk marks you made on the wall.
5. Move 1 m to your left. Draw the paper cups as they appear now. Show their position in relation to the chalk marks on the wall.
6. Move to two other positions. Draw what you see.

Analysis

1. Compare your drawings. How do they differ?
2. Which paper cup appeared to move most?
3. What effect does your position have on the apparent position of the things you see?

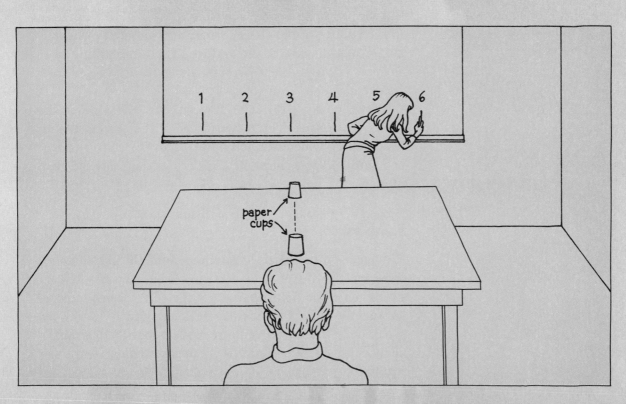

paper cups

3–2
Our Sun

Did you know that the sun can cause static on your radio? The sun can even cause changes in the amount of power on electric lines. As you read, answer these questions about the sun:

a. What are the different parts of the sun?
b. What is the sunspot cycle?
c. What is a solar eclipse?

The Parts of the Sun

The sun can hurt your eyes if you look at it directly. Astronomers use television cameras and special filters to observe, photograph, and record the sun's light. The picture shows what the sun looks like through a filter.

Astronomers have never seen the interior of the sun. But they have calculated that the temperature of the sun's center is 15,000,000°C. The sun is so hot that it has no solid material. It is made up entirely of gases.

The surface of the sun is much cooler than the interior. The surface temperature is about 5,500°C. The dark areas on the picture of the sun's surface are **sunspots,** which are cooler than the rest of the surface. The temperature of the sunspots is about 4,500°C. Most sunspots are bigger than the earth.

Above the sun's surface is a faint layer of gas called the **corona** (kə rō′nə). The temperature of the corona is about 2,000,000°C, which is much hotter than the sun's surface. The corona is less than one billionth as dense as the earth's atmosphere.

Sunspots

A magnet on the earth has a magnetic field that affects some materials near it. In the same way, sunspots have strong magnetic fields that affect the sun's gases. Sunspots are regions of very strong magnetic activity.

Notice in the photograph to the left that the sun has many sunspots. The number of sunspots changes in a fairly regular pattern, called the **sunspot cycle.**

Have You Heard?

The sun is 1,400,000 km across. One million earths would fit inside it. The sun's size and temperature are about average for stars.

The sun

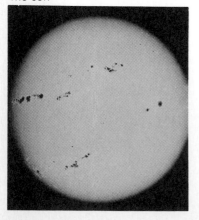

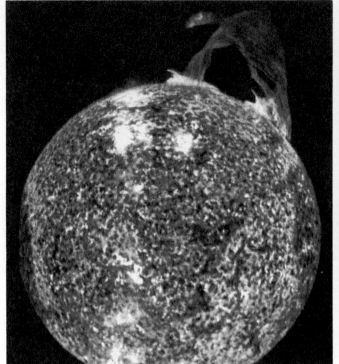

Solar flares erupting from the sun

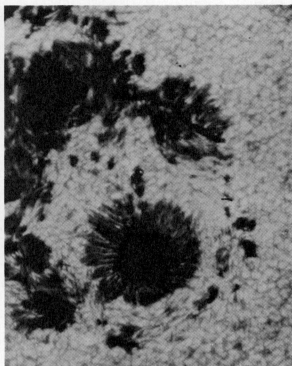

A close-up of sunspots

The highest number of sunspots appears about every 11 years. In between, the sun has fewer sunspots. The highest number of sunspots last occurred in 1979–80. The maximum number of sunspots will occur again about 1990. The photograph to the right above shows a closeup of sunspots.

When the sunspot cycle is at its highest, tremendous explosions—or **solar flares**—erupt from the sun's surface. The photograph to the left above shows a solar flare on the sun's surface. Solar flares shoot particles and radiation out into space. Some of the particles and radiation reach the earth's atmosphere. They can cause static on radios and changes in the amount of power on electric lines. They can also cause colorful **auroras**—or the northern and southern lights. Auroras are glowing rays, bands, or curtains of light that shimmer in the night sky. Most are greenish-white, but sometimes red, yellow, or green auroras are seen. Auroras are more common toward the earth's poles.

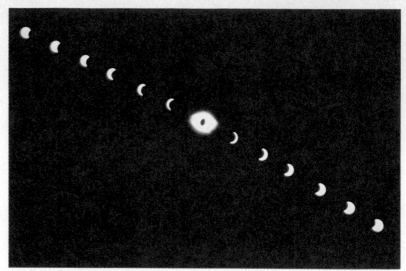

Phases of an eclipse

Eclipses of the Sun

About once every 18 months, the moon comes directly between the earth and the sun. A **total eclipse** of the sun takes place when the moon completely covers the sun. The picture above shows phases of an eclipse. Notice the total eclipse in the center. When the moon hides the bright surface of the sun, it becomes as dark as night in the middle of the day. The darkness of the total eclipse can be as short as a few seconds or as long as almost 8 minutes. Before and after the total part of an eclipse, the moon does not completely block the sun's surface. These partial phases of an eclipse may last for several hours.

The diagram to the left shows how the moon blocks the sun's light from certain parts of the earth. An eclipse is seen from the parts of the earth where the moon's shadow falls. Where the darkest part of the moon's shadow reaches the earth, a total eclipse occurs. In places on the earth where the lighter part of the moon's shadow reaches, only a partial eclipse is seen. Remember, it is always dangerous to look directly at the sun's surface, even if it is partially eclipsed. You cannot see as much of the sun's surface as usual, but the rest is still bright enough to damage your eyes.

A solar eclipse

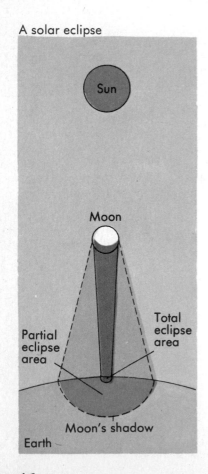

Astronomers travel great distances to observe a total solar eclipse. During a total eclipse, they can study parts of the sun not visible at other times. Notice the photograph below of a total eclipse of the sun. A faint halo of sunlight shows around the edge of the dark moon. This halo is the corona, which is a million times fainter than the surface of the sun. The corona is too faint to be seen from the earth except during a total eclipse. Its shape is different at each eclipse.

Review It

1. What is the hottest part of the sun?
2. How do solar flares affect the earth?
3. Why do astronomers observe total eclipses?

The corona

3–3
Why Stars Shine

Most of the glittering spots you see in the sky at night are stars. They are glowing balls of gas in space. As you read why stars shine, consider these questions:

a. What are stars made of?
b. How do stars get their energy?

Stars Are Glowing Gas

Stars shine because processes deep within them give off energy. The energy escapes into space as radiation. We see some of this radiation as light. To understand how stars produce energy, you must first understand the makeup of stars.

All matter in the universe is made up of particles called atoms that are much too small to see. Atoms are mostly empty space. The center of an atom—the **nucleus**—contains most of the atom's mass. The nucleus may consist of several particles. The **proton** and the **neutron** (nü′tron) are the most common particles in the nucleus. They are about the same size and mass. Another particle in the atom—the **electron**—moves about in the space around the nucleus. Electrons are much smaller and lighter than protons and neutrons.

The diagram shows models of hydrogen (hī′drə jən) and helium (hē′lē əm) nuclei. Notice that a hydrogen nucleus has one proton. A helium nucleus has two protons and two neutrons. Hydrogen and helium are gases found in all stars. About 90 percent of the atoms in a star like the sun are hydrogen. Another 9 percent are helium.

Hydrogen nucleus

Helium nuclei

Fusion

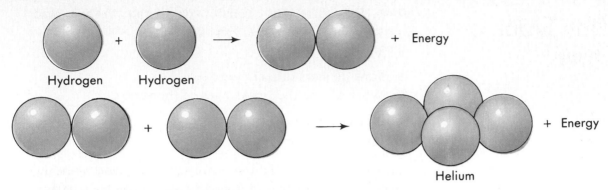

How Stars Get Their Energy

When atoms are heated to higher and higher temperatures, they move about faster and faster. Inside the center of a star, the temperature is so high that the nuclei of atoms move enormously fast. When nuclei moving at high speeds collide, they may join together to form a single, larger nucleus. This combination of two or more nuclei into one is called **fusion** (fyü′zhən). In the center of the sun and many other stars, four hydrogen nuclei combine in several steps to form one helium nucleus. The diagram shows one way the fusion of hydrogen nuclei forms a helium nucleus in our sun.

The helium nucleus formed by fusion contains slightly less mass than the four original hydrogen nuclei. The difference in mass appears as energy. Albert Einstein explained that a small amount of matter can change into a lot of energy. Nuclear fusion within stars changes small amounts of mass into large amounts of energy. This energy makes the stars hot and makes them shine. Scientists believe the sun has enough energy to shine for another 5 billion years.

Have You Heard?

Atoms are so small that 25,000,000 could fit on the head of a pin. If you could stretch an atom until it was 1 kilometer across, the nucleus would be only the size of a pea.

Challenge!

Find out what the symbols in Einstein's equation $E=mc^2$ represent. How does this equation enable scientists to determine how much energy will be produced when mass changes into energy?

Review It

1. What is the source of the energy produced in fusion?
2. Name two particles in the nucleus of an atom.
3. What is the most abundant gas in the sun?

3–4
Life Cycles of Stars

Living things go through stages of birth, life, and death. Stars, too, have stages in their lives. Different kinds of stars have different kinds of life cycles. As you read, answer these questions:

a. How do stars differ?
b. What will be the final stages of the sun?

Differences Among Stars

Some stars are so bright you can see them even when the moon is out. Others can barely be seen even on a dark, clear night. Still others are so faint they can be seen only through a telescope. The brightness a star has when you look at it is its apparent brightness.

Some stars are much farther from the earth than others. Just as a distant street light appears fainter than one near you, distant stars appear fainter than nearby stars of the same absolute brightness—or the brightness a star would have if it were a standard distance away.

Not all stars are the same color. Some look reddish, others appear bluish. The color of a star depends on the temperature of its surface. When a steel bar is heated, it first becomes red hot. At higher temperatures, it glows white hot. In the same way, the coolest stars look reddish. The hottest stars glow blue-white.

Stars also differ in mass. The most massive stars have as much as fifty times more mass than the sun. They are the hottest stars and look blue-white. The more mass a star has, the more rapidly fusion takes place inside it. Very massive stars use up their hydrogen rapidly. They have shorter lifetimes than stars like the sun, even though they began with more mass. Most stars have much less mass than the sun. Fusion takes place slowly in these stars. They live longer than stars like the sun.

The mass of a star determines how the star will live and die. Stars with different masses pass through most of the same stages of life. But they remain in the stages for different lengths of time. In addition, their ends may be different.

The graph below shows one way astronomers group stars. The stars are placed on the graph from left to right by their temperatures. The hottest stars are at the left. Stars are placed on the graph from top to bottom by their absolute brightness. Brighter stars are at the top.

When placed on the graph in this way, most stars are in a group that slants across the graph from the upper left to the lower right. This group is the **main sequence.** Stars on the main sequence are called **dwarfs.** Stars spend the greatest part of their lifetimes as dwarfs. Notice that our sun is almost in the middle of the graph, among the dwarf stars. The brightness of other stars on the graph can be compared to our sun's brightness, which has been set at one.

The surface temperatures of dwarfs range from 60,000°C to 2,400°C. The sun's temperature is about 5,500°C. It is a yellow dwarf. Stars hotter than the sun are bluer. The coolest dwarf stars are reddish.

The stars in the lower left part of the graph are **white dwarfs.** They are dimmer than other stars of the same color. A white dwarf has as much mass as the sun, but is only about as big as the earth. **Giants** are brighter than other kinds of stars of the same color and temperature. They get their name because, to be brighter than other stars of the same color, they must be bigger. They are in the upper right corner of the graph. Supergiants are even brighter than giants.

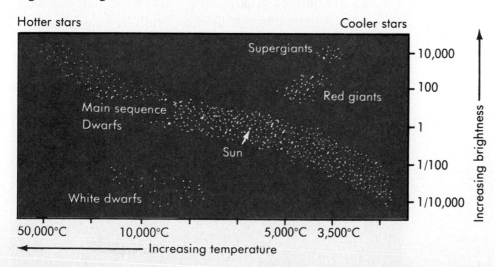

How Stars End Their Lives

Gravity inside all stars pulls the stars' matter inward. The energy formed by fusion inside stars heats the particles, which push outward. Their push balances the inward pull of gravity. But when a star has changed all the hydrogen in its core into helium, the energy of fusion no longer balances gravity. The star collapses inward. The way in which a star then ends its life depends on the mass of the star.

Astronomers believe that in about 5 billion years the sun will have used up all its hydrogen. When fusion stops, there will be no energy to push the particles outward. But gravity will continue to pull matter inward and the sun will begin to collapse toward its center. Then helium nuclei will begin to fuse into more complex nuclei, such as carbon. The energy produced by this fusion will expand the surface of the sun. Our sun will become a red giant.

Eventually, the outer layers of the giant may escape into space. The Ring Nebula, shown below, is glowing gas blown from a dying giant star. The star once had about the same mass as the sun. The nebula now has only about one-fifth as much mass as the sun.

Next, the part of the giant that did not escape into space will collapse until its electrons cannot be pushed together any more. Then it will be a small, faint white dwarf. After still more billions of years, all the energy will be gone and the sun will become a dark, cold **black dwarf.** The sun will follow the same pattern of life and death as other dwarf stars of about the same mass or less.

Ring Nebula

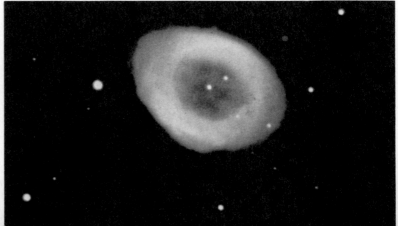

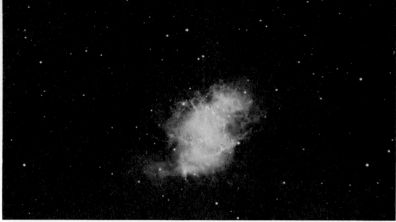

Crab Nebula

Neutron star

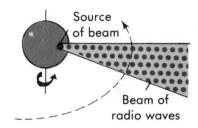

Source of beam

Beam of radio waves

Lighthouse

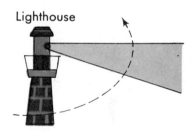

Stars that are more massive than the sun continue to swell after they become giants. They become supergiants. Then they explode. In seconds, the star's outer layers are blown away as glowing gas. This brilliant explosion is called a **supernova** (sü′pər nō′və). The Crab Nebula, shown above, is a remnant of a supernova explosion.

The center of the star may remain after a supernova explosion. It has so much mass that its gravity pushes the electrons that are present into their nuclei. The star collapses until its nuclei cannot be pushed together any more. Astronomers call it a **neutron star.**

Neutron stars rotate very fast. Many of them give off beams of radio waves, as shown in the diagram. As a star rotates, the beam of radio waves appears to pulse on as it sweeps past the earth. Astronomers call these stars **pulsars.** This apparent pulsing works somewhat as a lighthouse beacon does. A beacon also appears to flash on as it rotates. Only three pulsars have been found that give off beams of visible light. One of the pulsars that gives off visible light is in the Crab Nebula.

Some other neutron stars give off X rays. But X rays cannot pass through the earth's atmosphere. Astronomers study them with telescopes on satellites outside the earth's atmosphere.

Have You Heard?

Neutron stars are very small. They may be only 20 kilometers across, a distance you could bicycle in about an hour. But their mass is greater than the mass of the sun. A single teaspoonful of a neutron star would weigh a billion tons!

Review It

1. How does the temperature of a star affect its color?
2. What will happen when the sun uses up its hydrogen?

Activity

Graphing Stars

Purpose
To show that graphing the brightness and temperature of stars produces a pattern.

Materials
• sheet of plain white paper
• cm ruler
• set of colored pencils

Procedure
1. Use the ruler to draw a graph like the sample in *a*. The bottom line is 14 cm long. Vertical lines are 7 cm long and 2 cm apart. Horizontal lines are 1 cm apart.
2. Label the brightness and temperature sides of your graph as in *a*.
3. On your graph, plot the ten sample stars listed in *b*. Make one dot of the proper color for each of the 10 stars. The stars with greater absolute brightness are at the top of the graph.
4. Connect the dots to make a smooth line.
5. Enter a newly studied star on your graph. Its temperature is 3,500°C and its brightness is 100. Use the proper color dot.

Analysis
1. How does color relate to a star's position on the graph?
2. What is the name of the line connecting the stars on your graph? (See the graph in 3–4.)
3. What type of stars have you graphed on the line?
4. Why did you select the color you used for the unknown star? What kind of star is it?

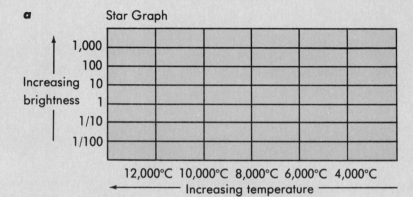

a Star Graph

b

Star	Temperature	Brightness	Color
A	3,500	1/10	red
B	13,000	1,000	blue
C	11,000	100	blue
D	3,000	1/10	red
E	4,500	1/10	orange
F	10,000	10	blue
G	4,000	1/10	red
H	6,000	1	yellow
I	7,000	1	green
J	5,000	1/10	red

Did You Know?

Stars Come in Pairs

When you look at a star at night, you see a bright spot in the sky. But if you look at some stars through a telescope, you might see two spots. Each of these stars is really two stars so close to each other that they look like one. Groups of two, three, or even more stars are called binary stars.

Our sun has no other stars near it in space. But most stars have companions. Stars in a binary star system orbit each other. A binary star system may be so faint or so far away that only one bright spot can be seen even through a telescope. In some of these systems, the bright star seems to dim regularly. The regular dimming occurs when one star passes in front of the other, just as the moon shuts off the light of the sun during a solar eclipse.

Sometimes astronomers can tell that a star is part of a binary star system by the way it moves. The star snakes through space on a wavy path. Something invisible seems to be pulling it back and forth.

If the stars in a binary star system are very close together, one star can pull streams of hot gases from the other, as shown in the picture.

In some binary star systems, one star is a white dwarf and the other is a giant. Gravity is not strong at the surface of the giant, so the dwarf can pull mass from it. Occasionally, the matter is pulled onto the surface of the white dwarf and fusion starts. From the earth, the star appears to grow brighter for a few weeks. We call this brightened star a nova—or newly visible star.

Astronomers know the life stages well only for stars that do not change much in mass. But one member of a binary star system can pull mass from another. So the life stages of binary stars may be different from those of a single star like the sun.

For Discussion
1. Explain two ways astronomers find double stars.
2. What can happen when one star in a double star system pulls mass from the other?
3. Why are the life stages of binary stars less predictable than the life stages of single stars?

The dwarf pulls mass from the giant

3–5
Black Holes

The strangest ending of all happens to stars that have many times the mass of the sun. They may become black holes. As you read about black holes, keep in mind:

a. What is a black hole?
b. How can astronomers detect black holes?

Nothing Can Escape a Black Hole

The mass remaining after a star explodes as a supernova may be much greater than the sun's mass. Astronomers believe that if five or more times the mass of the sun remains after a star collapses, it will continue to collapse forever. The pull of its gravity is so great that its nuclei are forced even closer together than in a neutron star. But this does not stop the collapse. The star continues to shrink. Einstein's theory of gravity explains what happens when so much mass collapses into such a small region. Even light cannot escape! Such a star is called a **black hole.**

How Astronomers Detect Possible Black Holes

Astronomers cannot see a black hole directly. Instead, they observe the behavior of a visible star near what may be a black hole. They believe the tremendous gravity of the black hole pulls matter from the visible star toward the black hole. The picture shows how this matter may orbit around a black hole.

Gravity gradually pulls the matter into the black hole. As the matter is pulled, it becomes hot and gives off X rays. Space telescopes can detect these X rays.

Astronomers carefully observe the movement of the visible star. The black hole and the star are like two ice skaters holding hands and twirling around an ice rink. Imagine that each skater is pulling on the other, just as each star's gravity pulls on the other star. Even if one skater were invisible, as shown in the drawing, you could tell that the visible skater had a partner. Astronomers can tell if a visible star has a "partner" by how much it moves. They can also tell how much mass the invisible partner has.

Space telescopes detect many sources of X rays. But not all sources of X rays are near black holes. For an invisible star to be a black hole, it should fulfill several conditions. First, the X rays must come from an area in space where one star is visible and another is invisible. Second, the invisible star must have more than five times the mass of the sun. Finally, the pair of stars must be close enough to the earth that if the invisible star were an ordinary dwarf star, telescopes would detect it. An invisible star that fulfills these conditions probably is a black hole.

One of the strongest X-ray sources detected by space telescopes is in the constellation Cygnus (sig′nəs). A visible star there is being twirled around. The unseen star pulls on the visible star so much that it must have more than five times the mass of the sun. Most astronomers think that the unseen star in Cygnus is a black hole.

Astronomers also believe that black holes can form from masses of gas much larger than the mass of dying stars. For example, the center of a galaxy may contain a black hole with millions of times more mass than the sun. Also, some astronomers think a powerful explosion in space might cause small amounts of matter to compress so much that they form extremely small black holes.

The invisible skater

Have You Heard?

Some black holes may contain as much mass as a mountain but be less than a millimeter across. If the earth were compressed enough, it would form a black hole about the size of a small marble!

Review It

1. How does a black hole get its name?
2. How might astronomers detect a black hole?

Chapter Summary

- Stars begin to form when gravity pulls together gas and dust in space. (3–1)

- Astronomers measure the distances to stars in light years. (3–1)

- The parts of the sun include the surface, the interior, and the corona. (3–2)

- Sunspots are regions of magnetic activity on the sun's surface. (3–2)

- During a solar eclipse, the moon blocks the light from the sun's surface. (3–2)

- Stars shine because nuclear fusion within them changes small amounts of mass into large amounts of energy. (3–3)

- Characteristics of stars include color, temperature, brightness, and mass. (3–4)

- Stars with different masses have different stages in their life cycles. (3–4)

- The force of gravity is so great in a black hole that even the nuclei are forced close together. (3–5)

- Astronomers hope to detect a black hole by watching how it affects a nearby visible star. (3–5)

Interesting Reading

Asimov, Isaac. *How Did We Find Out About Black Holes?* Walker & Co., 1978. Tells how scientists figured out what a black hole is, how it forms, and how to detect it.

Branley, Franklyn M. *Black Holes, White Dwarfs, and Superstars.* Crowell, 1976. Compares stages in the life history of the sun and other stars.

Mitton, Jacqueline, and Mitton, Simon. *Concise Book of Astronomy.* Prentice-Hall, 1978. Illustrates the life and death of stars.

Questions/Problems

1. How is a total eclipse related to the phases of a partial eclipse?

2. What might happen to a spaceship as it neared a black hole?

3. Why do astronomers graph stars by absolute brightness rather than apparent brightness?

4. Explain how the mass of a star affects its life stages.

5. How do astronomers find forming stars in nebulae?

6. Will the sun ever become a supernova? Explain your answer.

Extra Research

1. Find out how the astronomer Henrietta Leavitt used special kinds of stars called Cepheid (se′fē əd) variables to determine the distances of faraway stars.

2. Study a map of the stars or visit a planetarium to learn what some constellations look like. Find at least three constellations in the sky. Find stars of different colors.

3. Using information from the library, prepare a report on the discovery of pulsars.

4. Write or analyze a science-fiction story that uses knowledge of the life cycle of stars.

5. Look up the Ursa Major and Ursa Minor Groups (Big and Little Dippers) in an astronomy book. Find them in the night sky. Make a poster showing the brightest stars in both groups. Use your poster to deomonstrate to the class how to find the direction *north*. Tell some of the myths about the Big and Little Dippers to the class.

Chapter Test

A. Vocabulary   Write the numbers 1–10 on a piece of paper.
Match the definition in Column I with the term it defines in Column II.

Column I

1. 9,500,000,000,000 kilometers

2. apparent shift in position of nearby stars with respect to distant stars

3. halo of glowing gas around the sun

4. an ordinary star on the main sequence

5. a region of space from which light cannot escape

6. explosions that erupt from the sun's surface

7. a neutron star that gives off beams of radiation

8. the combining of two or more nuclei

9. the central part of an atom that contains most of the mass

10. a type of star that is brighter than main sequence stars of the same color

Column II

a. black hole

b. corona

c. dwarf

d. fusion

e. giant

f. light year

g. nucleus

h. parallax

i. pulsar

j. solar flare

B. Multiple Choice   Write the numbers 1–10 on your paper.
Choose the letter that best completes the statement or answers the question.

1. A cloud of glowing gas and dust is a
a) constellation.   b) nebula.   c) sunspot.
d) supernova.

2. Light reaches us most quickly from   a) the
sun.   b) the moon.   c) Proxima Centauri.
d) the Orion Nebula.

3. Most sunspots are   a) bigger than the
earth.   b) hotter than the rest of the sun's
surface.   c) hotter than the sun's interior.
d) visible only during a solar eclipse.

4. All pulsars give off   a) solar flares.
b) visible light.   c) X rays.   d) beams of radiation that appear as regular pulses.

5. The sun is a   a) white dwarf.
b) supergiant.   c) dwarf.   d) giant.

6. All black holes   a) form as stars die.
b) contain less than five times the mass of the
sun.   c) give off radio pulses.   d) collapse a
great deal of mass into a small region.

7. Fusion produces energy because the helium
nucleus formed has   a) less mass than four
hydrogen nuclei.   b) more mass than four hydrogen nuclei.   c) only protons.   d) only neutrons.

8. When all its energy is gone, the sun will
become a   a) supergiant.   b) neutron star.
c) black dwarf.   d) black hole.

9. A supernova is   a) a star on the main sequence.   b) a brilliant explosion.   c) a pulsating star.   d) an X-ray source.

10. The most massive stars   a) are as much as
50 times more massive than the sun.   b) can
become supergiants.   c) can become supernovae.   d) a, b, and c.

Chapter 4
Galaxies, Quasars, and the Universe

Luke Skywalker and his friends are looking from their spaceship toward a spiral of light. The light is coming from gas, dust, and a tremendous number of stars. Our sun and its solar system are in a spiral of light like the one in the picture.

This chapter tells you how stars belong to groups and how these groups are different from each other. You will learn about our own star group and the ones farthest from us in the universe. Finally, you will discover how astronomers think the universe began and what they think its future will be.

Chapter Objectives

1. Describe the Milky Way and why we see it as we do.

2. Define four types of galaxies.

3. Explain why astronomers think quasars are so far away.

4. Explain how the universe may have begun and how it may change in the future.

4–1
Our Galaxy

Each person belongs to groups of different sizes. For example, you belong to a family group, a state, and a nation. You also belong to the large group of human beings. Likewise, the earth belongs to a variety of groups, beginning with the solar system. Keep the following questions in mind as you read about a much larger group our solar system belongs to:

a. What is included in the Milky Way?
b. What does the Milky Way Galaxy look like to an observer outside the galaxy?

The Milky Way

The photograph shows part of a broad band of light that crosses the night sky. The ancient Greeks called this band of light the **Milky Way.** They thought the light was drops of milk splashed across the sky. Some of the light from the Milky Way comes from billions of stars. They are so close together in the sky that we cannot even count them. The remaining light comes from nebulae (neb′yə lē)—clouds of gas and dust. Some of the nebulae in the Milky Way glow brightly. Others are dark and prevent us from seeing the stars behind them.

The Milky Way

Observing the Milky Way

Almost everything in the sky that we can see with just our eyes is part of the **Milky Way Galaxy.** This **galaxy** is a group of hundreds of billions of stars, gas, and dust that are relatively close together. The galaxy is so large that it takes light 100,000 years to travel from one side to the other. The band of light the Greeks named the Milky Way is just part of that galaxy. Earth and our star, the sun, are also part of the Milky Way Galaxy.

The diagram shows that our sun is located in one of the spiral arms that unwind from the center of the Milky Way Galaxy. The arrows show how the entire galaxy is spinning. To understand why you see the Milky Way as a band of light, look at the side view of the galaxy in the diagram. If you try to see outside our galaxy along the dashed line A, there are not many stars to block your view. However, if you look toward or away from the center along line B, you see many more stars. The stars seem closer together and look like a band of light—the Milky Way.

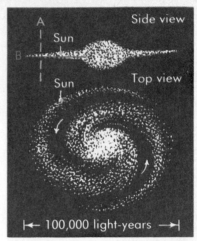

The Milky Way Galaxy

Review It

1. What is the Milky Way made of?
2. Why does the Milky Way appear as a band of light?

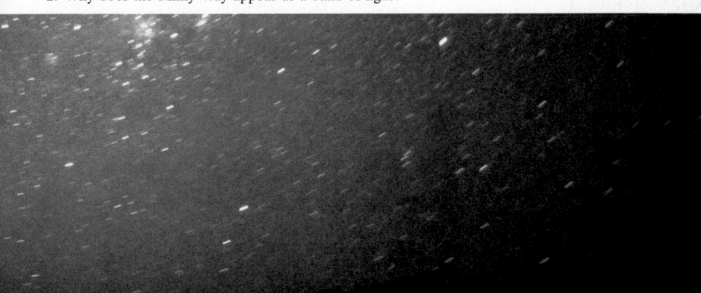

Activity

Milky Way Model

Analysis
1. From which view does your arrangement of stars appear to be more crowded?
2. Which view appears to show more space between the stars?
3. Which view represents what you see when you look at the Milky Way?
4. Suppose our galaxy were shaped like a sphere with our solar system located in the center. Would we see stars in a band like the Milky Way? Explain your answer.

Purpose
To observe why the Milky Way appears as it does.

Materials
• 15 paper cups (any size)
• paper and pencil

Procedure
1. Arrange the paper cups upside down on the desk or table, as shown in *a.* Do not line the cups in rows; scatter them around. The cups represent stars in our own galaxy.
2. Draw a diagram of what you see when you look down on your arrangement of stars. Label this diagram "view from above." This diagram represents a view of the night sky as you look downward through our galaxy.
3. Imagine what you would see if you looked up at your arrangement from beneath a glass desk or table. Draw what you would see and label it "view from below."
4. Look at your arrangement from the side at eye level, as in *b.* Draw a picture of your arrangement. Label this picture "side view."

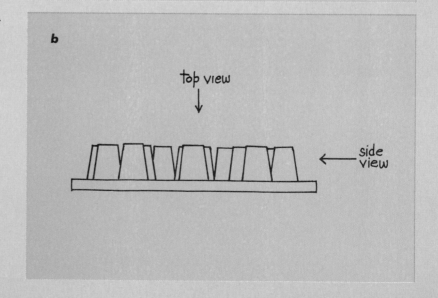

Breakthrough

What Is in the Center of the Galaxy?

In Williamsburg, Virginia, there is a copy of an English maze. The maze is a network of paths hidden between tall, thick hedges. It is very difficult to find out where you are in a maze like this because you cannot see through the hedges. But there are other ways besides seeing to find out where you are. For example, sound travels through the hedges and can help you find your way out.

Trying to look through our galaxy is like trying to see through a maze. We cannot use visible light to study where we are in our galaxy because light is blocked by dust before it reaches us from our galaxy's center. But other types of radiation, such as radio waves, infrared radiation, and X rays, *can* penetrate the dust.

Most of our galaxy is hydrogen. Hydrogen gives off radio waves. Astronomers can use these radio waves to make maps of our galaxy.

The group of radio telescopes in New Mexico known as the Very Large Array (VLA) observes radio waves from the center of our galaxy. Radio astronomers have found a small region at the center of our galaxy that is a very bright and very strong source of radio waves. This energy source is so strong and so small that scientists think it might be a black hole. The black hole could contain thousands of times the mass of the sun.

The Einstein Observatory was a spacecraft that observed X rays from space. Astronomers observe infrared radiation through telescopes. The illustration below is an infrared picture of the galaxy's center.

Dust no longer completely hides interesting parts of the galaxy. By means of X rays, infrared radiation, and radio waves, astronomers can now "see" through the dust.

For Discussion
1. Why is it useful to use other kinds of radiation besides visible light to observe our galaxy?
2. Why do astronomers think a black hole may be in the center of our galaxy?
3. What is the Einstein Observatory?

Infrared picture of the galaxy's center

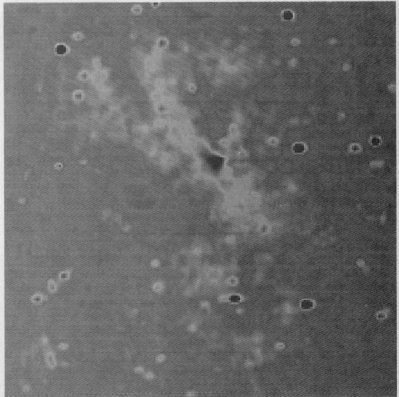

4–2
A Universe of Galaxies

Each star in the universe belongs to a certain galaxy. Galaxies are the basic building blocks of the universe. As you read about galaxies, keep in mind:

What shapes of galaxies are found in the universe?

Galaxies Have Different Shapes

Some galaxies, such as the one on the left below, look like pinwheels. Their large arms, which unwind from their centers, led to the name **spiral galaxies.** Our own Milky Way is a spiral galaxy. The other picture below shows a view of a spiral galaxy at an angle. The dots in the pictures are nearby stars in our own galaxy.

The galaxy on the left above is shaped like an oval. It is an **elliptical** (i lip′tə kəl) **galaxy.** The two small ovals in the view of a spiral galaxy at an angle are also elliptical galaxies.

Spiral galaxy—top view

Spiral galaxy—view at an angle

Elliptical galaxy

Irregular galaxy

Some galaxies have regular but unusual shapes. These are simply called **peculiar galaxies.** The picture in the margin shows a peculiar galaxy in the constellation Centaurus (sen tor′əs). It has dark material, probably dust, wrapped around it.

Some galaxies have no regular shape. They are **irregular galaxies.** The picture at the right above shows a view of the sky that you can see only from the Southern Hemisphere. The two fuzzy regions are irregular galaxies. They are called the Large Magellanic (maj′ə lan′ik) Cloud and the Small Magellanic Cloud. Although these galaxies are closer to our own Milky Way Galaxy than any others, they are still very far away. It takes light from these galaxies 170,000 to 200,000 years to reach the earth.

Just as stars belong to galaxies, galaxies belong to larger groups and clusters. The Milky Way Galaxy, another large spiral galaxy, and two dozen elliptical and irregular galaxies form our Local Group of galaxies. The Local Group and other nearby galaxies make up one of many clusters of galaxies in the universe.

Peculiar galaxy

Review It

1. List and describe four types of galaxies.
2. What are the two galaxies closest to our own galaxy?

Have You Heard?

The galaxies are so far apart that the density of matter in space is very low. One scientist has said that if one fly's breath spread through the Empire State Building, the gas in the building would be more dense than it is in space.

4–3
Quasars and the Expanding Universe

How do we learn about the most distant parts of the universe? From the light from faraway objects, astronomers can calculate how fast the distant objects are moving. As you read about these distant objects, keep these questions in mind:

a. What does a red shift tell us about moving objects?
b. What are quasars?

What a Red Shift Tells Us

Sound travels through the air in waves. When an ambulance passes you with its siren on, you can hear the pitch of the siren change. The pitch of the sound depends on whether the source of the sound waves is coming toward or moving away from you. As it approaches you, the siren has a high pitch because the sound waves are jammed together. As the ambulance moves away from you, the siren has a low pitch because the sound waves are stretched apart.

Light waves behave much like sound waves as the source of the light comes toward or moves away from you. Just as sound changes pitch, light changes color. When a distant object that gives off light moves toward you, the light waves jam together and the object's light shifts toward the blue end of the spectrum. When a distant object moves away, the light waves stretch and the object's light shifts toward the red end of the spectrum. This change of each light wave from retreating objects to a slightly redder color is called a **red shift.**

All the distant galaxies have red shifts. Therefore, these galaxies are all moving away from us. In 1929, Edwin Hubble discovered that the farther away a galaxy is, the faster it is moving from us. The photograph shows Hubble beside a telescope on Palomar Mountain in California.

The photographs at the top of the page show information from two galaxies. When scientists photograph the light from each of these galaxies, they break the starlight into the colors of the spectrum. Each photograph above shows the spectrum of a galaxy.

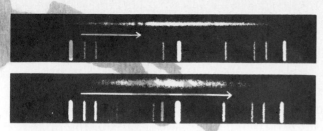

Galaxy 1.5 billion light-years away

Galaxy 4 billion light-years away

Length of arrow indicates amount of red shift

It is easy for astronomers to pick out the lines marked on each spectrum. The arrows show how far the lines have shifted from where they would appear if the galaxies were not moving. The larger the shift, the faster the galaxy is moving away.

Distant galaxies in all directions appear to be rushing away from the Milky Way Galaxy. This does not mean that our galaxy is the center of the universe. Imagine that you are inside a raisin cake that is rising. No matter what raisin you are on, all the other raisins in the cake would be moving away from you. In the same way, the galaxies are moving away from us. But they are moving away from all the other galaxies as well. Therefore, scientists believe the universe is expanding. If you imagine the raisin cake as unending, the cake has no center. In the same way, scientists believe the universe has no center.

Edwin Hubble

Quasars

Stars in our galaxy are relatively close to us, so they do not have large red shifts. In 1963, astronomers were surprised to find that some objects that look almost like stars had large red shifts. The objects gave off radio waves. Since "quasi-" means *almost* and "stellar" means *star* the objects were called quasi-stellar radio sources, or **quasars** (kwā′särz) for short.

Hubble had shown that objects with larger red shifts are farther away than objects with smaller red shifts. Quasars have the largest red shifts known. Therefore, astronomers think that quasars are the farthest objects from us. Some quasars are twelve billion light years away. This means that the light we are seeing now left the quasars twelve billion years ago! When scientists look at this "ancient light," they are looking back in time to those early days of the universe.

At first, quasars were studied only by the light or radio waves they give off. Now that we have satellites above the earth's atmosphere, we can also study X rays from quasars. The picture shows an X-ray view of a quasar.

Astronomers know that the farther away objects are, the dimmer they appear. Since we can see quasars, even though they are so far away, quasars must be giving off amazing amounts of energy.

Scientists do not know exactly what quasars are or where all their energy comes from. Many astronomers think quasars are early stages of galaxies. Most of these scientists think quasars are in the middle of galaxies whose arms are too faint to see. Perhaps the energy comes from a giant black hole in the middle of each quasar. A black hole does not release any energy. But matter that is being swallowed by a black hole heats up and gives off a great amount of energy.

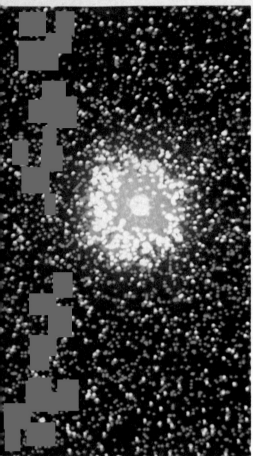

X-ray picture of a quasar

Review It

1. What does a red shift show?
2. Why do astronomers think quasars are far away?

Activity

The Expanding Universe Model

Purpose
To illustrate why galaxies travel away from us at different speeds and to show how the universe is expanding.

Materials
• one rubber band
• cm ruler
• pen

Procedure
1. With your pen, make two marks—one toward each end of the rubber band, as in a. The two marks represent galaxies G and X in the diagram. The observer in the model is at 0, shown at the left end of the rubber band in a.
2. Lay the rubber band against the cm ruler, as in a. Record the length of the rubber band to the nearest half cm.
3. To the nearest half cm, record the positions of G and X. For example, in a, the position of G is at 1.5 cm.

4. Hold the rubber band at 0 with your left hand and pull the rubber band to the right. Stretch it to three times its original length, as shown in b. This stretching represents the expansion of the universe.
5. At this new length, record the new positions of G and X. Unlike galaxies, the marks will stretch out, so use the middle of the mark to record the mark's new position.
6. Record the differences between the old and new positions for G and X.

7. Assume it takes two seconds to stretch the rubber band in step 4. Record the rate of speed in cm/sec for G. Do the same for X.

Analysis
1. By about how many times did the distance from the observer increase from the first to the second position of G? of X?
2. By how many cm did the distance from the observer increase from the first to the second position of G? of X?
3. In this activity, what represented our Milky Way Galaxy?
4. Predict what would happen if you started with marks in different places.

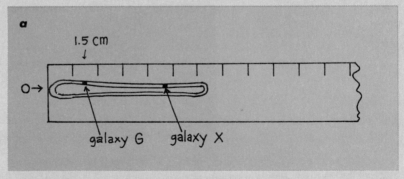

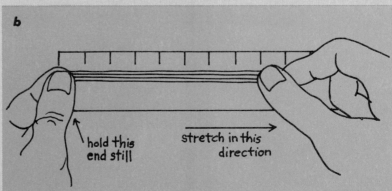

4—4
The Past and Future of the Universe

Since you were born, you have constantly grown and changed. The universe, too, has grown and changed since its beginning. As you read about changes in the universe, keep in mind:

a. What is the big bang theory?
b. What could happen to the universe in the future?

The Big Bang Theory

The theory of how the universe began that scientists accept today is called the **big bang theory.** It states that the universe formed about 15 billion years ago. At first, matter and energy in the universe were heavily concentrated. A gigantic explosion—the big bang—sent matter and energy traveling through space, as shown in the drawings. This explosion had no center. It took place everywhere at the same time. For a short time, matter and energy changed back and forth into each other. After millions of years, the matter that was left over formed the galaxies. They have continued to move away from each other in all directions.

Scientists have figured out that as a result of the big bang, the universe should contain faint radio waves traveling in all directions. The waves should reach us from all directions, since the explosion occurred everywhere. In 1965, astronomers discovered these faint radio waves coming to the earth from all directions. The discovery of these radio waves is strong evidence for the big bang theory.

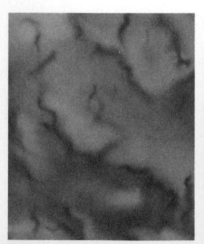  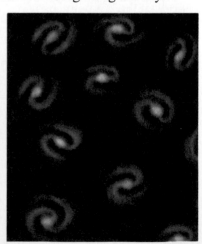

The Future of the Universe

The picture above shows many galaxies. What will happen to the universe and its galaxies in the distant future? Scientists think the universe will expand for at least another 50 billion years. But will it keep expanding forever?

Astronomers are trying to answer this question by estimating whether there is enough gravity in the universe to stop the expansion. If there is enough mass present in each region of space, the total amount of gravity will eventually pull the universe back together. The universe will contract. If there is less than that certain amount of mass in each region of space, the universe will expand forever.

Scientists do not yet know how much mass all the gas, dust, and stars—including black holes—contain. More mass can be present in several invisible forms. So far, evidence seems to indicate there is not enough mass and gravity to pull the universe back together. But this may change as our knowledge of the universe increases. As of now, we are still uncertain about the future of the universe.

Review It

1. Describe the big bang theory.
2. How might gravity affect the future of the universe?

Have You Heard?

If there is enough mass for the universe to contract, there could be another explosion. The universe would then start expanding all over again.

Chapter Summary

- The Milky Way is a band of light that stretches across the sky. The Milky Way Galaxy includes our solar system, gas, dust, and billions of stars. Some of the gas, dust, and stars make the Milky Way. (4–1)

- Galaxies are the basic building blocks of the universe. The major types of galaxies include spiral, elliptical, peculiar, and irregular. (4–2)

- All the distant galaxies have red shifts and are, therefore, moving away from us. The most distant galaxies have the greatest red shifts, so scientists believe the universe is expanding. Quasars have the largest red shifts known. (4–3)

- Astronomers think that the universe formed with a big bang about 15 billion years ago. It has been expanding ever since. The universe will continue to expand, unless gravity pulls it back together. (4–4)

Interesting Reading

Asimov, Isaac. *The Universe.* Walker, 1980. Includes current information on black holes and quasars.

Knight, David C. *Galaxies, Islands in Space.* Morrow, 1979. Explains current theories on the evolution and future of the universe.

Mitton, Jacqueline and Mitton, Simon. *Concise Book of Astronomy.* Prentice-Hall, 1978. Contains beautiful illustrations and discusses the Milky Way, galaxies, quasars, and the origin of the universe.

Questions/Problems

1. What is the difference between the Milky Way and the Milky Way Galaxy?

2. Why are we unable to photograph the shape of our own galaxy?

3. What did Hubble find out about the motion of galaxies?

4. Explain the evidence for the big bang theory.

5. If light from a certain galaxy was shifted toward the blue end of the spectrum, what would that tell you about that galaxy's movement? Explain your answer. Do any distant galaxies with blue-shifted light exist?

Extra Research

1. Look up the term *cosmology* (koz mol′ə jē) in reference books in the library. Find out what the steady-state theory is. Explain why it lost out to the big bang theory.

2. Using reference materials such as newspapers and magazines, write a one-page report on quasars.

3. Make a list of the vocabulary words in this chapter. Write a short science-fiction story using as many of the new terms as you can.

Chapter Test

A. Vocabulary   Write the numbers 1–10 on a piece of paper.
Match the definition in Column I with the term it defines in Column II.

Column I

1. clouds of dust and gas in space

2. a group of hundreds of billions of stars, gas, and dust

3. includes the Milky Way Galaxy, another spiral galaxy, and two dozen elliptical and irregular galaxies

4. two irregular galaxies close to the Milky Way Galaxy, visible from the Southern Hemisphere

5. shift in wavelength that indicates that objects are moving away

6. galaxies that have no definite shape

7. objects with the largest known red shifts

8. can provide the energy for quasars

9. band of light across the sky from stars, gas, and dust in our own galaxy

10. event that may have marked the beginning of the universe

Column II

a. big bang

b. black hole

c. galaxy

d. irregular galaxies

e. Local Group

f. Magellanic Clouds

g. Milky Way

h. nebulae

i. quasars

j. red shift

B. Multiple Choice   Write the numbers 1–10 on your paper.
Choose the letter that best completes the statement or answers the question.

1. Some nebulae   a) glow brightly.   b) are dark.   c) are in the Milky Way.   d) a, b, and c.

2. Galaxies with regular, but unusual, shapes are called   a) irregular.   b) peculiar.   c) spiral.   d) elliptical.

3. How many light-years across is the Milky Way Galaxy?   a) 5,000   b) 30,000   c) 100,000   d) 170,000 to 200,000

4. According to the big bang theory,
a) matter was once heavily concentrated.
b) faint radio waves can be detected from all directions.   c) galaxies continue to move away from each other.   d) a, b, and c.

5. The galaxy that most resembles our own galaxy in shape is   a) elliptical.   b) irregular.   c) spiral.   d) peculiar.

6. As an object approaches you, its light waves
a) are jammed together.   b)-are stretched apart.   c) remain the same.   d) slow down.

7. The farther a galaxy is from us,   a) the slower it is moving.   b) the faster it is moving.   c) the brighter it is.   d) a and c.

8. Quasars   a) give off much energy.   b) are near the Milky Way Galaxy.   c) are a type of star.   d) have the smallest red shifts known.

9. Galaxies with arms that appear to unwind from a central region are called   a) unusual.   b) clusters.   c) elliptical.   d) spiral.

10. So far, evidence seems to indicate that the universe   a) will contract.   b) will contract and then expand.   c) will continue expanding.   d) will expand only for another ten million years.

Chapter 5
The Solar System

For hundreds and thousands of years, people have studied the movements of the planets across the sky. Many of the laws of science were discovered as a result of these observations. Because of our knowledge of these laws, we can build cars or jet airplanes. By using these laws, we were able to send spacecraft to take pictures like these of Saturn and some of its moons.

In this chapter, you will learn how people developed laws about the planets and their motions. You will find out how scientists think the solar system formed. You will discover how spacecraft have added to our knowledge about the solar system. By the time you finish this chapter, you will have read about all the planets of our solar system and many of their moons.

Chapter Objectives

1. Describe Kepler's laws, Newton's laws, and gravity.
2. Explain how scientists think the solar system formed.
3. List some ways the inner planets—Mercury, Venus, Earth, and Mars—are alike and some ways they are different from each other.
4. Describe some features of our moon, such as what it looks like, its phases, and lunar eclipses.
5. Compare the outer planets—Jupiter, Saturn, Uranus, Neptune, and Pluto.
6. Describe asteroids, meteoroids, and comets.

The Background of Modern Astronomy

The laws about planets that were discovered in the 1600s explain the movements of satellites we use for communication. As you read about these and other laws, keep in mind:

a. How did ideas about the planets' movements change?
b. What are Newton's three laws of motion?
c. How may the solar system have formed?

The Planets and Their Movements

The ideas of the ancient Greeks had a widespread and long-lasting influence on astronomy. Aristotle, a Greek who lived about 300 B.C., believed that the earth was the center of the universe and that everything in the sky revolved around it. For more than a thousand years, most people thought that the earth was the center of the universe.

Then, in 1543, the Polish astronomer Copernicus stated that all the planets—including the earth—moved in circular orbits around the sun. Sixty-seven years later, the Italian scientist Galileo used one of the first telescopes and discovered moons rotating around Jupiter. His observation proved that all bodies did not revolve around the earth.

In the early 1600s, Johannes Kepler, a German astronomer, proposed three laws that described the movements of planets. First, Kepler said the orbit of each planet is an **ellipse** (i lips'). As the picture shows, an ellipse is an oval that has two special points—**foci** (fō'sī). The length of a line from one focus to any point on the ellipse and then to the other focus is always the same. Kepler found that the sun is located at one of the foci in the elliptical orbit of a planet. Nothing is at the other. If the two foci fall in one place, then the ellipse is a circle.

Second, Kepler stated that an imaginary line stretching from a planet to the sun moves across equal areas in equal times. Although the two shaded areas in the diagram are not the same shape, they are equal in area. It takes a planet the same length of time to move from A to B as it takes to move from C to D.

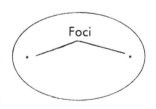

Foci

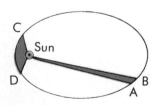

C
Sun
D
B
A

Therefore, the planet moves faster when it is closer to the sun than it does when it is farther from the sun.

Third, Kepler showed how the size of a planet's orbit is related to its **period.** The period is the length of time it takes a planet to orbit the sun. The earth's period is about 365 days.

Newton's Laws of Motion

In the mid-1600s, the English scientist Isaac Newton developed three laws about motion. From these laws, he could explain Kepler's planetary laws.

Newton's first law says that objects tend to continue moving as they have been moving. If objects are at rest, they remain at rest. If they are moving, they keep moving at the same speed and in the same direction—unless something changes their motion. In space, there is little to change an object's motion. So once the object starts moving, it will keep on moving forever. After the *Voyager* spacecraft in the picture was launched, it kept on moving toward Jupiter for over a year without using additional power. Now it is past Saturn and it will keep moving in the same direction for thousands of years.

Voyager

Newton's second law explains how forces affect objects. When a force acts on an object, the object will change speed, direction, or both. Suppose, for instance, that a bat makes contact with a baseball. The force exerted by the bat will cause the baseball to change speed and direction.

Newton's third law states that, when you push on any object with a force, the object pushes back at you with a force of the same strength. This law is often stated: "For every action there is an equal and opposite reaction." Newton's third law explains how rockets and jets work. Gas is forced out of the back of rocket and jet engines by a force pushing backward. A force of equal strength in the opposite direction, therefore, pushes the jet or rocket forward.

Gravity and the Origin of the Solar System

The moon moves through space. Newton wondered why it did not keep moving in a straight line and escape from the earth. He realized that a force must pull the moon toward the earth to keep it from escaping. He called this force "gravity."

Newton described the strength of gravity and told us that it always pulls objects together. But Newton did not know why gravity existed.

In 1915, Albert Einstein presented a theory that explains why gravity exists. His theory says that a mass makes a sort of dent in space, just as a heavy object dents a mattress. A ball placed on the mattress tends to fall into the dent. This tendency to fall toward the dent in space is what we call gravity.

The force of gravity once pulled the solar system together. Scientists think that about five billion years ago, gravity pulled together a large cloud of dust and gas. A nearby exploding star—a supernova—may have helped start the collapse. The cloud of dust and gas was spinning slightly.

As the cloud collapsed, its spin speeded up. Because of this high spin, the cloud took the shape of a pancake. The pancake shape developed because the cloud's spin acted to push gas and dust outward toward the side edge—against gravity. However, nothing kept gravity from pulling the cloud in from top and bottom.

Eventually, gravity pulled small bits of gas and dust together. These smaller bits then collected to make a few large clumps. The largest clump became the sun, as shown in the drawing. Smaller clumps became planets and other objects.

Review It

1. What did the discovery of Jupiter's moons show astronomers?
2. Why do spacecraft not need power to move in space?
3. What is the effect of Einstein's "dent in space"?

Activity

Model of Planets' Orbits

Purpose
To construct ellipses that represent the orbits of planets.

Materials
- sheet of unlined paper
- two push pins
- 26 centimeters of thin string
- heavy cardboard, 30 cm by 30 cm, or larger
- pencil

Procedure
1. Find and mark the center of the paper by folding it as shown in *a*.
2. Place the paper on the cardboard. Stick a push pin into the center of the paper.
3. Securely tie the two ends of the string together to make a loop. Place the loop around the push pin.
4. Put a pencil inside the loop and carefully pull the loop tight, with the pin at one end of the loop and the pencil at the other. Draw a pattern on the paper by moving the pencil, which is within the loop, around the push pin. Label the drawn figure #1.

5. To draw an ellipse you need more than one center, or focus (singular of foci). Stick the second push pin into the paper along a fold line, 2 cm away from the first pin.
6. Place the loop of string around both pins.
7. Repeat step 4, but this time, keep the pencil and both pins within the loop, as in *b*. Label the second figure #2.
8. Move the second pin 5 cm away from the first, but along the same fold line. Repeat step 7, moving the loop around both pins. Label the figure #3.
9. Now move the second pin 8 cm away from the first pin, along the same fold line. Repeat step 7 and label the figure #4.

Analysis
1. What shape did you draw when you used only one pin?
2. What happened to the shape of the figure you drew when you switched from one to two pins (foci)?
3. What happened to the shape of the ellipse when you changed the distance between the pins?
4. What parts of the solar system did the following items in your model represent: the ellipses, the pencil and one of the two pins used?
5. Is a planet always the same distance from the sun? Explain your answer.

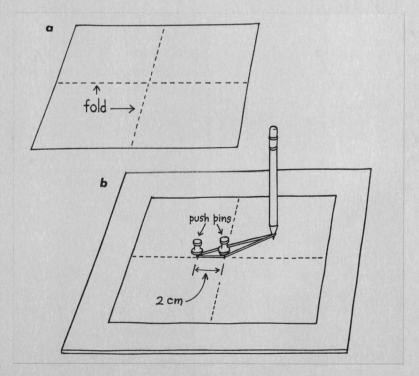

5–2
The Inner Planets of Our Solar System

The sun shines with its own light and energy. It is surrounded by planets and other objects. These members of the sun's family do not shine by their own light. As you read about the inner two planets and our moon, ask yourself:

a. What is the surface of Mercury like?
b. How do we know what is under Venus' clouds?
c. Why is the moon of special interest to us?

Mercury—Planet of Craters

The four planets closest to the sun—Mercury, Venus, Earth, and Mars—are alike in many ways. These inner planets are all small, rocky worlds. But there are many differences among them.

The innermost planet, **Mercury,** is so close to the sun that its surface is very hot. This planet is only 40 percent as large as Earth and has no atmosphere.

Mercury is sometimes visible for about an hour just after sunset or just before sunrise. But it is never high enough in the sky for us to see it well. Only when a spacecraft flew by did we find out what Mercury really looks like. It is covered with craters, as shown in the picture below, and it has scarps—or cliffs. The scarps are wrinkles that probably appeared soon after Mercury formed, when the planet shrank a little.

Mercury

Challenge!

The ancients called the planets "wandering stars" because they seemed to move in relation to the stars. All of the planets but one are named for a Roman god or goddess. Find out about the god or goddess for which each planet was named. See if you can figure out why the planets were named as they were.

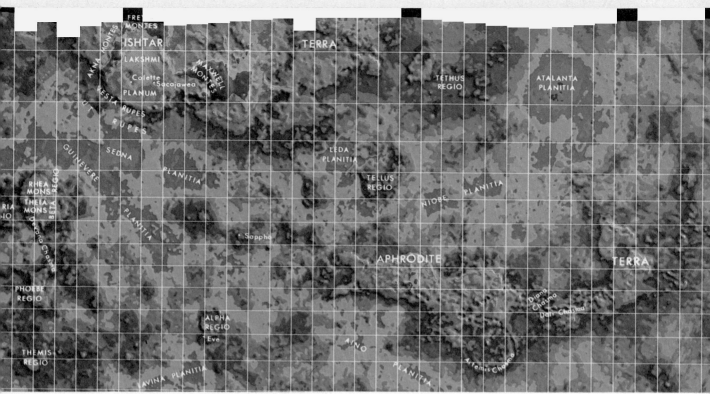

Radar map of Venus

Venus—Covered by Thick Clouds

By Earth's standards, **Venus** is an unpleasant place. Its temperature is 475°C, and the weight of its atmosphere is 100 times greater than Earth's blanket of air.

Venus is covered by clouds that keep us from seeing the planet's surface. The clouds are made of droplets of sulfuric (sul fyùr′ik) acid. Carbon dioxide and other gases in Venus' atmosphere trap sunlight inside. The trapped sunlight makes the planet's surface very hot.

A NASA spacecraft sent radio waves to penetrate Venus' clouds and make the radar map shown above. Each color stands for a different height. Venus is mostly covered by a rolling plain. It has two highlands that are each as big as a small continent on Earth. One highland has a giant mountain that is larger than any mountain on Earth.

Have You Heard?

Venus can be brighter in the sky than any other planet. It can be 25 times brighter than the brightest nighttime star. At its brightest, Venus can even cast shadows of objects on Earth.

83

Our moon

The Moon—Our Natural Satellite

Earth is the third planet from the Sun. Our natural satellite, the **moon,** is our closest and most visible neighbor in space. As a result, the moon has always been of great interest to people.

When we look at the moon in the sky, we see a pattern of light and dark on the moon's surface. This pattern, which you can see in the picture, sometimes looks a bit like a face. The light parts of the moon's surface are highland regions where there are a lot of craters. The dark parts are maria (ma′rē ə), which means "seas" in Latin. But there is no water on the moon. Instead, maria are places where molten material flowed out of the moon's interior billions of years ago. The molten material covered parts of the moon with a smooth layer.

The picture below illustrates the **moon's phases** (phā′zəz). The moon circles the earth once every 29.5 days. When the moon is in the opposite part of the sky from the sun, the side of the moon that faces the earth is completely lighted. We see a **full moon.** When most but not all the lighted side of the moon is visible, we see a **gibbous** (gib′bəs) **moon.** When only a sliver of the moon is visible, people call it a **crescent** (crəs′sənt) **moon.** When the moon is very close to the sun in the sky, only the side of the moon that faces away from us is lighted. The side that faces us is dark. This phase is a **new moon.**

Phases of the moon as seen from earth

Full moon   Gibbous   Crescent   New moon

The diagram shows you that the earth's shadow in space is very large. When the moon is on the opposite side of the earth from the sun, it usually passes above or below the earth's shadow. But sometimes the moon passes through the shadow. This event, which takes more than an hour, is a **lunar eclipse.** People anywhere on the half of the earth from which the moon is visible can see the lunar eclipse.

Six pairs of astronauts in NASA's *Apollo* program landed on the moon between 1969 and 1972. They carried out many experiments, such as measuring the flow of heat from the moon's interior. They brought back 400 kilograms of rocks for analysis. Scientists found that all the rocks were about 4 billion years old. They discovered that most of the craters on the moon formed when rocks from space bombarded the moon. The picture below shows craters on the backside of the moon.

The moon has no air or water on it. Thus, its surface has not been worn and changed the way the earth's surface has. The moon, therefore, is a laboratory where we can see how the solar system looked billions of years ago.

Review It

1. What are two features found on Mercury?
2. Why is Venus unpleasant by Earth's standards?
3. Describe the moon's phases.

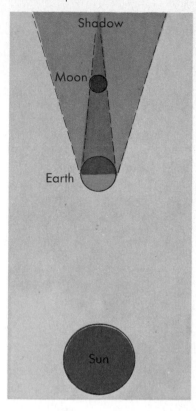

Lunar eclipse

The backside of the moon

85

5–3
Mars, the Red Planet

Mars, the fourth planet from the sun, looks reddish in the night sky. It has been a center of attention for many years. As you read about Mars, ask yourself:

a. What did spacecraft learn about life on Mars?
b. How is Mars like Earth?

The Exploration of Mars

About 100 years ago, some astronomers thought they saw straight lines crisscrossing **Mars'** surface. These lines, which they called canals, sparked the interest of people for many years. Because the canal lines seemed straight and regular, some people assumed that intelligent beings on Mars must have built the canals. Photographs of Mars, such as the one in the margin, did not show canals. But people were still very eager to explore Mars, and find out if life existed there.

Both the United States and the Soviet Union sent spacecraft to Mars between 1965 and 1976. In 1976, the United States *Viking* spacecraft went into orbit around Mars and landed on Mars' surface as well. The photograph to the left and the one to the right were taken by *Viking* spacecraft.

The spacecraft carried experiments to see if Mars had life. Because all life on Earth is based on the element carbon, the experiments looked for carbon-based life. Each *Viking* lander carried a small biology laboratory, packed into a cube only 0.3 meter on each side. *Viking* experiments searched for signs of life in Martian soil, but found no definite signs of life on the planet.

What Mars Is Like

Mars has a thin carbon dioxide atmosphere and two small, rocky moons that revolve around it. Like Earth, Mars has seasons and is warmer at its equator than at its poles. But average temperatures on Mars are much lower than on Earth. The polar regions of Mars are dotted with ice caps made of frozen water and frozen carbon dioxide.

Mars

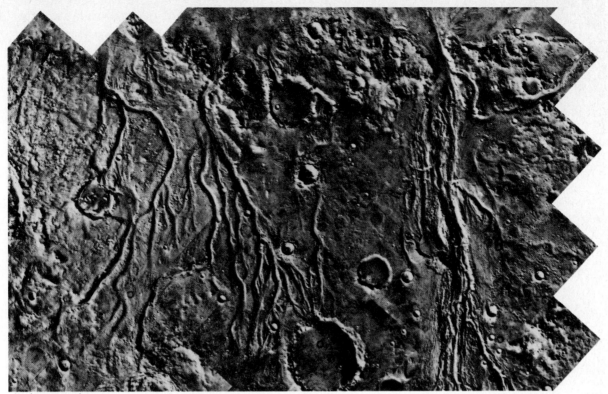
A closeup of Mars

Some people compare the rocks and sand dunes in the Martian landscape to those of deserts in the American Southwest. The rocks and sand of Mars are stained red by iron compounds. Mars' sky is pink because winds blow so much red dust around the planet.

The orbiters photographed huge canyons and volcanoes. The volcanoes are larger than any mountains on Earth, even though Mars is only about half the size of Earth. Pictures of Mars, such as the one above, show depressions that look like dry riverbeds. These depressions probably indicate that water once flowed on Mars.

Review It

1. How do we know so much about Mars?
2. Why do scientists think water once flowed on Mars?

Have You Heard?

The Italian astronomer who saw the lines on Mars named them "canali," which is Italian for channels—not canals. The lines the astronomer saw were a type of optical illusion. Many imaginative drawings of the so-called canals and the strange Martians who dug them created a sensation in newspapers and books. Later, good, sharp photographs from space proved that no such lines on Mars really exist.

5—4
Beyond Mars—Jupiter and Its Family

The *Voyager* missions to Jupiter sent back information and pictures like the one below. These events were as exciting to sky watchers as the discovery of a new solar system. In many respects, Jupiter and its moons are a miniature solar system. As you read about Jupiter, consider the following questions:

a. How is Jupiter different from Earth?
b. How are Jupiter's moons like worlds?

Jupiter, the Sun's Giant Planet

Jupiter often gleams brilliantly in the sky at night. It is a giant planet, 11 times larger in diameter than Earth. It contains over 300 times Earth's mass.

Jupiter was not massive enough to become a star, but the interior of Jupiter is very hot and gives off energy. Some people call Jupiter a near-star. Like a star, Jupiter is made of hydrogen and helium. Pictures show only the tops of Jupiter's thick clouds. The planet does not have a solid surface like Earth. Deep inside Jupiter there may be liquid and solid levels.

A pair of *Voyager* spacecraft passed close by Jupiter in 1979. Their closeup views showed Jupiter in much more detail than we had ever seen it.

Have You Heard?

Under Jupiter's clouds may be a strange, liquid hydrogen ocean that is 70,000 kilometers deep. Seventy thousand kilometers is nearly one-fifth the distance from here to the moon.

Jupiter

The Great Red Spot

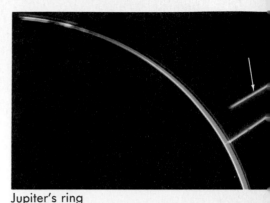

Jupiter's ring

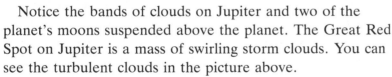

Lightning

Notice the bands of clouds on Jupiter and two of the planet's moons suspended above the planet. The Great Red Spot on Jupiter is a mass of swirling storm clouds. You can see the turbulent clouds in the picture above.

The photograph taken by spacecraft cameras shows lightning flashes on Jupiter's surface. The glow of auroras was visible at Jupiters edge. Scientists were surprised to discover a faint ring around Jupiter. You can see part of the ring in the *Voyager* photograph above.

Both *Voyagers* have on board golden records that carry hours of greetings in many different languages, music from many different cultures, and a set of over 100 photographs of Earth and of life here. The *Voyagers* are leaving the solar system. They will not travel the distance to the nearest star for another 40,000 years. The *Voyager* records are a message for life on planets around other stars, if any exists. They also remind all the nations on the earth of their common human heritage.

Have You Heard?

Clouds and weather features last longer on Jupiter than on Earth. Astronomers have been watching the Great Red Spot through telescopes on Earth for more than 150 years!

Jupiter's Moons

In 1610, Galileo discovered four spots of light moving around Jupiter. They were Jupiter's largest moons. The discovery supported Copernicus' idea that the sun is at the center of our solar system.

These moons remained only specks of light until the *Voyagers* flew close to them and took their pictures. Because the moons are about as large as some planets, they seem more like "worlds" than moons.

The red surface of the second moon out, Io (ē′ō), is the most interesting. Scientists were suprised to see active volcanoes erupting on Io. The volcanoes are much larger and more active than any on Earth. They erupt constantly and cover the moon's surface with reddish sulfur compounds.

Io

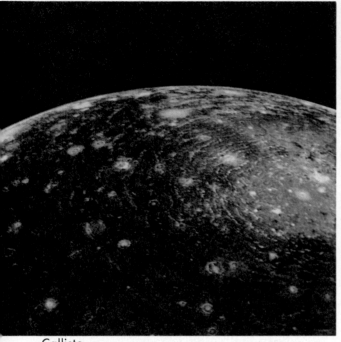

Callisto

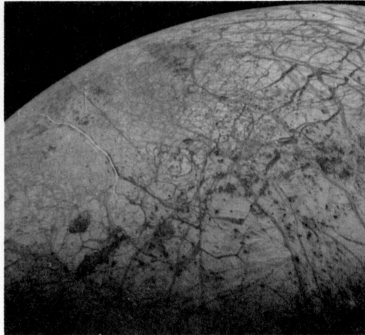

Europa

Jupiter's next three moons are covered with ice. Europa (yù rō′pə) has cracks in the smooth ice.

The next two moons out are Jupiter's largest— Ganymede (gan′ə mēd) and Callisto (kə lis′tō). They are about as large as Mercury. Both moons probably consist of large amounts of water and ice surrounding a rocky center. Ganymede has many craters and also a strange set of grooves. Callisto is completely covered with craters. Notice the bull's-eye formation on Callisto. It probably formed when a large object hit this moon.

The densities of Europa, Ganymede, and Callisto are so low that some scientists think they are made of mixtures of ice and dust. These moons are like icy mud balls.

Jupiter also has another dozen moons. Some are less than a hundred kilometers across.

Ganymede

Review It

1. What prevented Jupiter from becoming a star?
2. How is Io different from the rest of the moons?

5–5
Beyond Jupiter—Saturn and the Outer Planets

The rings of Saturn are among the most fantastic sights in our universe. You can see the rings through even a small telescope. As you read about Saturn and the remaining outer planets, keep in mind:

a. What is the most outstanding feature of Saturn?
b. What is unusual about Saturn's moon Titan?
c. How are Uranus and Neptune similar?
d. What did the discovery of Pluto's moon tell us?

Saturn, the Ringed Planet

Saturn is smaller than Jupiter, but the rings of Saturn are wider than Jupiter and its ring. Saturn, like Jupiter, is entirely covered by clouds. But Saturn's clouds are much less colorful than Jupiter's.

Like Jupiter, Saturn is made almost entirely of hydrogen and helium. Saturn, too, has no solid surface. The core of Saturn contains more mass than all of Earth.

The *Voyagers* went on to Saturn after they passed Jupiter. They reached Saturn in 1980 and 1981. The picture below is a view of Saturn from the first *Voyager*. The *Voyagers* found that Saturn and Jupiter give off more energy than they receive from the sun because of the heat within them.

Have You Heard?

Imagine a phonograph record four kilometers across, but the same thickness as a regular record. This record would have a shape similar to that of Saturn's rings.

Saturn

Saturn's ringlets

As the first *Voyager* got close to Saturn, it discovered that the broad rings we see from Earth are each composed of many small rings—or **ringlets.** Observers had thought that Saturn had about half a dozen rings. Instead, Saturn has thousands of ringlets! The colors in the photograph are exaggerated to show that different parts of the rings are made of slightly different amounts of material. Scientists discovered that some material exists even where the view from Earth seemed to show gaps in Saturn's rings.

Each ring is made of chunks of rock covered with ice. Most are probably from a few centimeters to a meter across. Each chunk orbits Saturn by itself, in an orbit following Kepler's laws.

The *Voyagers* did much more than just take pictures as they flew by Jupiter and Saturn. They measured temperature on the planets, found out what kinds of matter were present, and measured the amount of magnetism. Now, we have a much better understanding of what the two planets are like.

Have You Heard?

Saturn is so far away that radio waves from *Voyager* took 90 minutes to come back to Earth. Compare this time with radio waves from astronauts on the moon, which took only 1.2 seconds to reach Earth.

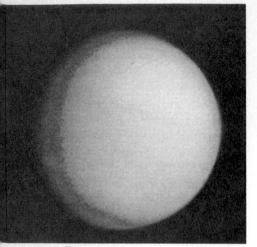

Titan

Iapetus

Hyperion

Dione

Saturn's Moons

The *Voyagers* also took the photographs that you see of Saturn's moons. Saturn's largest moon, Titan, is larger than the planet Mercury. Titan is the only moon of any planet known to have an atmosphere. Thick layers of clouds surround Titan. The temperature below the clouds is only −180°C. Clouds and a form of smog on Titan are so thick that the *Voyagers* could not see the moon's surface.

The moon Dione (dē ō′nē), has an icy crust and many craters. Dione and three other moons are each between 500 and 700 kilometers across, about the length of Texas. These moons have craters and canyons on them.

For unknown reasons, one moon of Saturn's, Iapetus (ē äp′ə təs), is snow white on one side and very dark-colored on the other.

Mimas

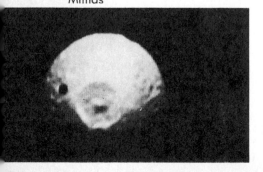

Another moon, Mimas (mē′məs), has such a large bull's-eye crater that it reminds people of the "Death Star" in the movie *Star Wars*. Notice how large the crater is compared to the size of the moon. The large object that hit Mimas and made the crater probably came close to destroying this moon.

One moon of Saturn, Hyperion (hī pēr′ē ən), has an irregular shape that resembles a hamburger patty! Saturn has a dozen more moons.

Uranus and Neptune

Beyond Saturn are two more giant planets made almost entirely of gas. They are **Uranus** (yùr′ə nəs) and **Neptune.** Each is four times larger than Earth.

Uranus and Neptune are so far away that telescopes show no details on their surfaces. Uranus has five moons and Neptune has two, but we know little about them. Scientists were surprised in 1977 when they discovered a set of nine rings around Uranus. They were observing Uranus as it passed in front of a star, and noticed that the star dimmed briefly many times. Each dimming occurred when a ring went between the observers and the star. We may learn more about Uranus in 1986 and Neptune in 1989 when *Voyager 2* reaches these planets.

Pluto

The farthest planet, **Pluto,** was not discovered until 1930. Pluto is 40 times farther from the sun than Earth, and it takes almost 250 years to make a single orbit around the sun.

In 1979, an astronomer noticed a slight bulge in the picture of Pluto on the right. This bulge is a moon. From studying how long it takes the moon to orbit Pluto and how far it is from Pluto, astronomers calculated Pluto's mass. Pluto contains only 1/400 the mass of Earth. Other measurements show that Pluto is only about the size of our moon. Perhaps Pluto was once a moon of Neptune's, which escaped.

Review It

1. What did *Voyager* discover about Saturn's rings?
2. What is special about Saturn's largest moon?
3. What surprising discovery was made about Uranus?
4. How did scientists calculate the mass of Pluto?

Have You Heard?

Attention fortune-hunters of the solar system! Great temperatures and pressures inside Uranus and Neptune may change carbon atoms into diamonds or diamond flakes. The diamonds would slowly drift down onto the cores of the planets.

Pluto's bulge

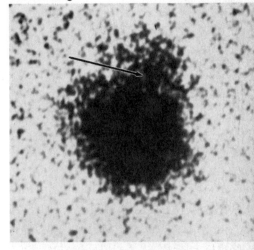

Have You Heard?

Until 1999, Pluto, the planet with the largest orbit, will be closer to the sun and to us than Neptune. This happens because Pluto's orbit around the sun is a skinnier ellipse than Neptune's—even though Pluto's ellipse is longer.

5–6
Between the Planets

Around August 11 every year, you can see spectacular showers of shooting stars. These shooting stars are also members of our solar system. As you read more about objects other than planets, keep in mind:

a. What is an asteroid?
b. How do meteoroids, meteorites, and meteors differ?
c. What is a comet?

Asteroids Are Minor Planets

Thousands of small, rocky objects orbit the sun. Astronomers call them minor planets—or **asteroids** (as′tə roidz′). The largest asteroids are 1,000 kilometers across. Most of them are in the **asteroid belt,** which is between the orbits of Mars and Jupiter. But the orbits of some small asteroids are even closer to the sun than the earth's orbit. One of these small asteroids probably hits the earth and makes a large crater every few million years.

Shooting Stars Are Meteors

A shooting star

Many chunks of rock, named **meteoroids** (mē′tē ə roidz′), are found between the planets and asteroids. When meteoroids pass through the earth's atmosphere, they burn. Note in the picture that they look like streaks of light as they move across the sky. The burning rocks are called **meteors,** or shooting stars. Sometimes pieces of meteors do not burn. Instead they hit the earth. When these rocks land, they are renamed **meteorites** (mē′tē ə rīts′). Some meteorites are rocky, and some are mostly iron. Meteorites and moon rocks are the only matter from space that scientists can analyze on the earth.

If a meteorite is a meter or more across, it may make a large crater where it hits the ground. A large meteorite was destroyed when it gouged out Meteor Crater in Arizona about 25,000 years ago.

Comets Grow Tails

Thousands of balls of ice and gas exist around the outside of the solar system, beyond Pluto. Sometimes one of the balls of ice falls in toward the sun. Its orbit becomes a very long, thin ellipse. Such an object is a **comet.**

As a comet comes near the orbit of Jupiter, the energy in sunlight melts some of the ice. Gas and dust released from the melted ice make a beautiful tail that extends in the opposite direction from the sun. Sometimes the tail of a comet extends over a large part of the sky.

Some comets appear unexpectedly, disappear, and are not seen again. Other comets return time and time again. In 1705, the English astronomer Edmond Halley realized that the bright comets that had been seen every 75 years or so were really reappearances of the same comet. **Halley's Comet** was last seen in 1910. The photographs show how its tail changed over a period of weeks. Halley's Comet will return in 1985 and 1986. You will be able to see it without binoculars or a telescope.

Review It

1. Where is the asteroid belt located?
2. What is a shooting star?
3. How does the tail of a comet form?

Fireball

Have You Heard?

A fireball is a spectacular meteor. Hundreds of fireballs probably pass through the air every day. Some are brighter than the moon and can be seen even in daylight. Occasionally, people on the earth can even hear a fireball explode.

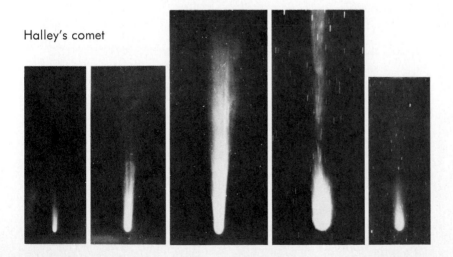
Halley's comet

Activity

Solar System Model

Purpose
To construct a scale model of the solar system.

Materials
- 6-meter strip of adding machine tape
- ball about 5 cm in diameter
- meter stick
- tape

Procedure
1. Roll out the adding machine paper and tape it to the floor.
2. Place the ball at one end of the paper, as shown in *a*. Tape the bottom of the ball to the paper to hold the ball in place. The ball represents the sun.
3. Use table *b* and the meter stick to mark off the positions of the planets on the strip of paper. Make one dot for each planet and label the dot with the planet's name. For example, Mercury is shown by a dot 6 cm from the sun.

4. Each cm on the paper tape represents 10 million km in space. Next to each planet on your model, record its distance in km from the sun.
5. The asteroid belt starts about 330 million km from the sun and extends to about 480 million km from the sun. Draw two lines on the model to show the location of the asteroid belt. (1 cm = 10 million km)

Analysis
1. Compare your solar system model to an atom model. (See the oxygen atom diagram on page 124.)
2. Between which two planets is the asteroid belt?
3. Study the solar system model to see if there is any pattern in the distances between the planets. Describe your observations.
4. Explain two ways that your model is *not* an accurate representation of the planets.

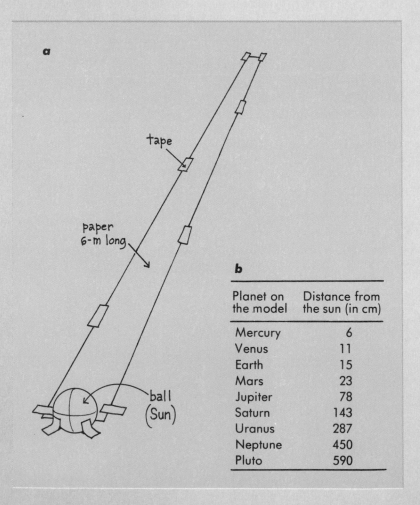

a

tape

paper
6-m long

ball
(Sun)

b

Planet on the model	Distance from the sun (in cm)
Mercury	6
Venus	11
Earth	15
Mars	23
Jupiter	78
Saturn	143
Uranus	287
Neptune	450
Pluto	590

Breakthrough

Satellites and Kepler's Laws

Kepler's laws, discovered almost 400 years ago, help us in many ways. Since 1957, people have sent satellites, such as Skylab 2, into orbit around the earth. Kepler's laws apply to all objects that orbit another body—satellites as well as planets. All earth satellites, therefore, have elliptical orbits.

When the satellites are closer to the earth, they move faster, as Kepler's second law says. Satellites with cameras can take better close-ups when they are lower in their orbits. Because they are moving so fast, they have to snap pictures quickly or the pictures will be blurred.

The first satellites were only a few hundred kilometers above the earth's surface. These satellites orbited the earth in 90 minutes, which means their periods were 90 minutes long. Kepler's third law states that the period of the orbit gets longer as the satellite gets higher and the ellipse gets larger.

We are now able to launch a satellite so high—about 40,000 kilometers above the earth—that its period is 24 hours long. The earth also rotates on its axis once every 24 hours. Therefore, the satellite appears to hover above some point on earth.

Because overhead satellites remain over one spot on earth, they can relay television and telephone signals long distances. It is less expensive to transmit television and telephone signals by satellite than by wires or cables.

Overhead satellites can take clear pictures of spots on the ground that are only ten meters across—about as large as your schoolroom.

These pictures have many uses, such as monitoring changes in crops, changes caused by growth of cities, or tracking fish in the sea.

For Discussion
1. In what part of its orbit does a satellite go faster?
2. Explain why some satellites seem to hover over one place on the earth.

Skylab 2

Chapter Summary

- Kepler found laws of planetary orbits. Newton developed laws of motion and of gravity. Einstein developed a theory of gravity. (5–1)

- About five billion years ago, the force of gravity pulled the solar system together. (5–1)

- The inner planets—Mercury, Venus, Earth, and Mars—are small, rocky bodies. (5–2)

- Our moon appears to go through phases as it travels around the earth. Unlike Earth, it has no atmosphere or flowing water. (5–2)

- Mars' landscapes look like barren places on Earth, but no life exists on Mars. (5–2)

- The first of the outer planets, Jupiter, is a large gaseous planet with many moons. Some of its moons are as large as planets. (5–4)

- Saturn, the next planet after Jupiter, is also a large, gaseous body. It has a thousand ringlets and many interesting moons. (5–5)

- Uranus and Neptune are gaseous giants too. Uranus has rings. (5–5)

- Pluto is a small planet. Pluto's moon allowed us to calculate the mass of the planet. (5–5)

- Asteroids, meteoroids, and comets are also members of our solar system that move around the sun. (5–6)

Interesting Reading

Gallant, Roy A. *National Geographic Picture Atlas of Our Universe*. National Geographic, 1980. Contains good pictures and discussions about the solar system.

Gore, Rick. "What *Voyager* Saw: Jupiter's Dazzling Realm." *National Geographic,* January 1980, pages 3–29. Describes discoveries from *Voyager* spacecraft.

Questions/Problems

1. Why does studying the moon help us understand the history of the solar system?

2. What evidence indicates that water once flowed on Mars?

3. How are Saturn and Jupiter alike?

4. Meteor Crater in Arizona is incorrectly named. What would a correct name for it be? Explain your answer.

5. Give an example of each of Newton's three laws that you might see at an ice hockey game.

Extra Research

1. Look at a star map in magazines such as *Sky and Telescope* or *Astronomy*. Find out which planets are visible at this time of year. Sketch where they are in the sky. If you can use a telescope, describe how the planets appear. Report your findings to your class.

2. Observe the moon's phases as often as possible during the next month. Sketch and name the phases and record the dates and times. Turn in your data and sketches.

3. Demonstrate to the class why we see only one side of the moon at all times. Bear in mind that it takes the moon 29.5 days to revolve once around the earth. It also takes 29.5 days for the moon to rotate once on its axis. Select one student to represent the earth and another to represent the moon in your demonstration. You may wish to start by showing the class what side they would see if the moon revolved around the earth but did not rotate on its axis. Think about and plan this demonstration carefully before trying it in class.

Chapter Test

A. Vocabulary   Write the numbers 1–10 on a piece of paper.
Match the definition in Column I with the term it defines in Column II.

Column I

1. rocky body, smaller than an asteroid, that travels through space

2. moon that appears more than half full but less than full

3. Saturn's moon that has an atmosphere

4. minor planet

5. Jupiter's moon that has erupting volcanoes

6. an icy object that travels in a long, thin ellipse

7. the time it takes a planet to make one complete orbit

8. a mass of clouds on Jupiter

9. an oval-shaped figure with foci

10. the dark phase of the moon

Column II

a. asteroid

b. comet

c. ellipse

d. gibbous moon

e. Great Red Spot

f. Io

g. meteoroid

h. new moon

i. period

j. Titan

B. Multiple Choice   Write the numbers 1–10 on your paper.
Choose the letter that best completes the statement or answers the question.

1. The moons of Jupiter were discovered by
a) Einstein.   b) Newton.   c) Galileo.
d) Copernicus.

2. According to Kepler's second law, Earth moves faster in its orbit when it is   a) farthest from the sun.   b) closest to the sun.
c) farthest from Mars.   d) closest to Mars.

3. Most scientists think the solar system formed   a) about 5 billion years ago.
b) from a large cloud of dust and gas.   c) as a result of the force of gravity.   d) a, b, and c.

4. Mercury has   a) an atmosphere.
b) craters.   c) a great deal of mass.   d) a, b, and c.

5. The sky on Mars is   a) white.   b) blue.
c) yellow.   d) pink.

6. The space program that studied the moon was   a) *Apollo.*   b) *Voyager.*   c) *Pioneer.*
d) *Mariner.*

7. All of the following planets have rings around them *except*   a) Uranus.   b) Saturn.
c) Venus.   d) Jupiter.

8. Pluto   a) was discovered by the Greeks.
b) completes its orbit around the sun in half a year.   c) is more massive than Earth.   d) has a moon.

9. Most asteroids are found between the orbits of   a) Earth and Mars.   b) Mars and Jupiter.
c) Jupiter and Saturn.   d) Saturn and Uranus.

10. Which of the following planets gives off more energy than it receives from the sun?
a) Venus   b) Saturn   c) Jupiter   d) b and c

Careers

Toolmaker

Imagine that you just developed a new life-saving device, but you lack the right equipment for testing it. You need the expertise of a scientific toolmaker.

A scientific toolmaker produces hundreds of special parts that experimenters need for their work. They may also create tools, instruments, or machines from the ideas and sketches they receive.

Before a toolmaker can make a new instrument, he or she must have a mental picture of the object. So, besides being good at working with their hands, good toolmakers are imaginative and inventive.

Most toolmakers have a trade or high school education. During a four-year, on-the-job apprenticeship, the toolmakers develop their mechanical skills.

Career Information:
National Tooling and Machining Association, 9300 Livingston Rd., Washington, DC 20022

Satellite technician

Satellites pass overhead everyday, far out in space. You cannot see the satellites, but satellite technicians on earth constantly monitor them. Satellite technicians use electronic equipment at earth stations to track satellites in orbit.

A technician operates the controls on a communications panel. This person takes readings and sends messages to the computerized satellite. A technician must always be ready to handle an emergency, such as a breakdown in communication between the satellite and earth.

For this type of work, a person must have a radio-telephone operator's license. This requires at least two years of satellite and electronics training. On-the-job training is also necessary.

Career Information:
COMSAT, Office of Public Information, 950 L'Enfant Plaza, SW, Washington, DC 20024

Astronomer

Astronomers try to understand and explain the past, present, and future of objects in our universe.

If you are curious about what lies beyond the earth and are interested in math and science, you may want to become an astronomer.

As an astronomer, you do more than look through large telescopes. You analyze the light coming from distant stars. To do this, you may use photographic or electronic equipment. Measuring, mapping, and studying data may take up much of your time.

Most astronomers combine teaching duties in universities with their research. Astronomers generally earn a doctor's degree, following many years of science courses in college.

Career Information:
Education Officer, American Astronomical Society, Sharp Laboratories, Univ. of Delaware, Newark, DE 19711

Aerospacecraft assembler

You can build a spacecraft that may travel to the moon and beyond. As an aerospacecraft assembler, you will be in charge of everything from attaching tiles on the outside of a spacecraft to mounting the engines inside the craft.

You may specialize in putting together one section of the spacecraft. Welding, riveting, and drilling may be part of the job.

Often, an assembler inspects the parts or reads the blueprints. Every detail must be considered because people's lives as well as scientific data can depend on the operation of the finished machine.

The aerospacecraft assembler needs both technical and on-the-job training.

Career Information:
NASA, Education Services Branch, LCG-9, 400 Maryland Ave., SW, Washington, DC 20546

Astrogeologist

"What are moon rocks made of?" an astrogeologist asks, while studying the geology of the moon and other planets.

By applying what we know about the earth, astrogeologists learn more about other planets in our solar system.

Satellite photos and rock samples collected from meteorites and the moon hold important clues about other planets for astrogeologists.

These scientists analyze the data collected by satellites and space flights. Many years will pass before all the information from the *Voyager* missions to Jupiter and Saturn are completely sorted and sifted.

These earthbound space detectives need at least four years of college-level courses in geology, astronomy, and math.

Career Information:
American Geological Institute, 5205 Leesburg Pike, Falls Church, VA 22041

Solar equipment technicians

Five billion years will go by before the sun burns out. In the meantime, people use the sun's energy to heat and cool their homes. Solar equipment technicians handle the solar installations for both new and old buildings.

These workers put in solar collectors—the long, black metal sheets that trap the sun's heat. They may also install insulation, arrange backup systems for cloudy days, and put in sun-powered air conditioners.

People who are interested in this type of work may want to go to a two-year technical school after high school. They can learn more skills on the job.

Career Information:
Solar Energy Institute of America, 1110 Sixth St., NW, Washington, DC 20001

UNIT TWO
THE EARTH

Some people think the picture to the left looks like stones grouted together in a wall or floor. Other people look at it and see a leather or suede patchwork that is part of a purse or jacket. What do you think it is?

You may have guessed that the picture—taken from an airplane—is a view of fields of some sort. What kind of fields, however, is more difficult to guess. They are salt fields near San Diego, California. The salt is harvested when shallow ponds of sea water evaporate. Tiny organisms in the sea water cause the colors you see. The Earth's rich crust gives us salt and thousands of other materials that we take for granted. You will learn about the materials of the earth in this unit.

Chapter 6 Outside and Inside the Earth
Gravity, the magnetic field, and latitude and longitude are discussed in this chapter.

Chapter 7 Atoms to Minerals
Minerals are the natural materials of the crust. We can identify these minerals by examining their special features.

Chapter 8 Rocks and Ores
All the minerals of the earth's crust form three basic types of rocks.

Chapter 9 Learning About the Earth's Past
Fossils, radioactive dating, and some geologic laws have been used to make a time scale.

Chapter 6
Outside and Inside the Earth

The picture shows our earth as it looked to the astronauts on the moon. They noticed how friendly, yet isolated, the earth seemed. This view plus measurements taken on earth have improved our understanding of our planet.

This chapter has many "vital statistics" about the earth. The first section discusses the shape of the earth and what is inside it: There is information about gravity—the force that holds you to the ground. You will learn why you can use a compass to find north. The chapter ends by describing imaginary lines you can use to find locations and to keep track of time.

Chapter Objectives

1. Describe the shape of the earth.

2. List and describe the layers of the earth.

3. Explain how the earth acts like a bar magnet.

4. Explain why the weight of an object is different at different locations in the solar system.

5. Describe how time changes around the earth after each new day begins at the International Date Line.

6–1
The Earth

One young child, upon learning that the earth was round, decided to dig a hole to the other side of the world. This section explains why this is not possible. Answer the questions below as you read:

a. What is the earth's shape?
b. What are the three layers of the earth?

The Shape of the Earth

The earth is a ball that turns from west to east around an imaginary line that passes through it, as shown in the drawing. This line is the earth's **axis** (ak′sis). At one end of the earth's axis is the geographic North Pole. The South Pole is at the other end. The imaginary line that circles the earth midway between the poles is the equator. The distance around the equator is about 40,000 kilometers.

Viewed from space, the earth looks spherical, or ball-shaped. But the earth is not a perfect sphere. It bulges a little around the equator.

Axis
North Pole
40,000 km
Equator
South Pole

Layers of the Earth

The earth has three major layers. These layers—the crust, mantle (man′tl), and core—are shown on the next page.

The outer layer—or **crust**—of the earth, is a skin of solid rock. The crust varies in thickness from about 8 kilometers under the ocean bottom to 35 kilometers or more under the continents, as you can see in the picture below. The ocean crust is usually denser and darker in color than the crust of the continents.

Have You Heard?

The ancient Greeks knew that the earth is shaped like a sphere. They observed the earth's circular shadow when it fell on the moon during an eclipse. In addition, they noticed that, when ships sailed away from land, the ship disappeared from view before the tops of the sails. Ships and sails would not disappear if the earth were flat.

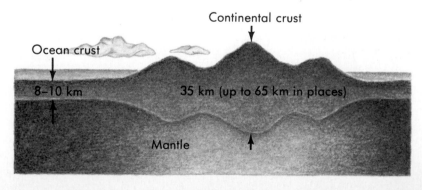

Continental crust
Ocean crust
8–10 km
35 km (up to 65 km in places)
Mantle

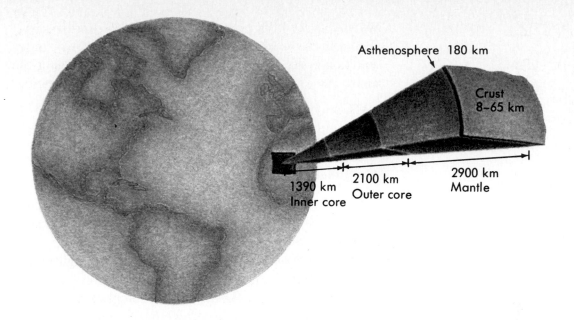

Asthenosphere 180 km

Crust
8–65 km

1390 km
Inner core

2100 km
Outer core

2900 km
Mantle

The earth gets hotter as you dig down into the crust. That is why the oil pumped from deep wells is very warm. Also, the air is very hot at the bottom of deep mines. The temperature rises 2°C or 3°C for every 100 meters you go down into the crust. Pressures also increase with depth because of the weight of rocks above.

The second layer of the earth, the **mantle,** lies below the crust. Within the mantle is a region that seems to be partly melted. This region, which you can see on the diagram, is the **asthenosphere** (as thēn′ə sfir). The mantle appears to be solid above and below the asthenosphere.

The third layer of the earth, the **core,** is beneath the mantle. The outer core is made mostly of melted iron. At the center of the earth is an inner core of almost solid iron. The **inner core** may reach temperatures as high as 5,500°C. Temperatures keep increasing from the mantle to the core, but the increase is slower than in the crust.

Review It

1. Name two ways that continental crust is different from ocean crust.
2. What arc the three layers of the earth?

6–2
The Earth's Magnetism

When you are hiking or riding in a car, you sometimes need a compass to guide you. The compass shows the direction north because of the magnetic properties of the earth. As you read, try to answer the following questions:

a. How do magnets behave?
b. How does the earth resemble a giant bar magnet?

The Behavior of Magnets

In many ways the earth acts like a giant magnet. To understand the earth's magnetism, you need to know more about magnets.

The simplest magnet is in the shape of a straight bar. One end of the magnet is called the south pole. The other end is the north pole. Look at the photographs below. When two magnets are close together, the south poles of the magnets repel each other, which means they push each other away. The two north poles also repel each other. However, the north pole of a magnet attracts the south pole of another magnet. "Like" poles of magnets repel, and "unlike" poles attract.

Every magnet is surrounded by a region in which its magnetism is felt. This region is the **magnetic field** of the magnet.

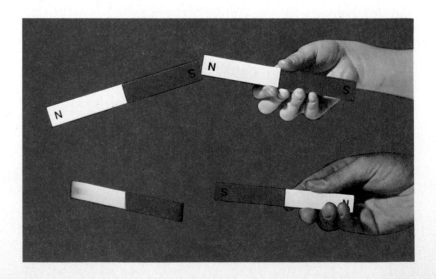

The Earth Resembles a Magnet

The earth, like a bar magnet, has magnetic north and south poles. However, the earth's magnetic north and south poles are not at the geographic North and South Poles. The magnetic north pole is near Hudson Bay in Canada. The position of the magnetic poles changes slightly through the years, as you can see on the right.

The needle of a compass is a bar magnet. The earth also acts like a bar magnet. Therefore, the earth's magnetic north and south poles attract the opposite poles of a compass needle.

The earth's magnetic north and south poles have reversed many times in the past. If the poles reversed today, the north-seeking needle of a compass would point to the south instead of the north. But the reversal does not happen overnight. It takes thousands of years for the magnetic poles to reverse. The flip-flop of the poles occurs an average of once every 500,000 years.

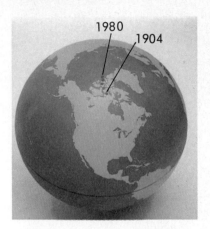

The poles wander

1980
1904

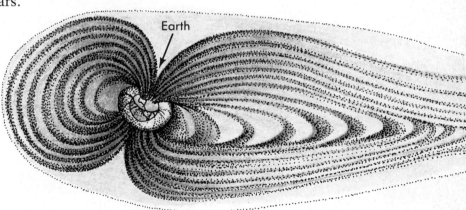

The magnetosphere of the earth

Earth

Like the bar magnet, the earth has a magnetic field. This field is called the **magnetosphere** (mag nē′tō sfir). The diagram shows that the magnetosphere has a long tail extending away from the sun. The magnetosphere protects life on earth by trapping powerful radiation from space.

Review It

1. Where is the magnetic north pole?
2. List two ways that the earth acts like a bar magnet.

Activity

The Earth's Magnetism

Purpose

To study the use of compasses and how the earth acts as a magnet.

Materials

- 1 small compass
- 1 bar magnet
- 1 sheet of thin cardboard
- shaker of iron filings
- two sheets of paper

Procedure

Part A

1. Place the magnet on a table and place the cardboard over it.
2. Put a paper over the cardboard.
3. Draw an outline of the shape of the magnet on the paper.
4. Leave the paper on the magnet. Rest the compass on the paper at one end of the magnet, as shown in *a*.
5. Draw two dots on the paper—one at each end of the compass needle.
6. Draw a line connecting the two dots. This shows the direction of the compass needle.

7. Repeat steps 5 and 6 several times, moving the compass along the magnet until you reach the other end. By doing this, you have mapped out an entire line of magnetic force.

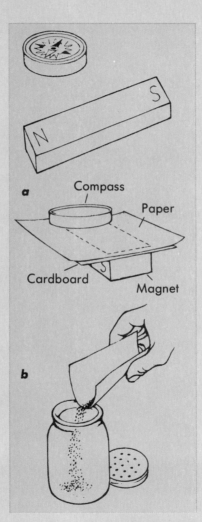

a

Compass

Paper

Cardboard

Magnet

b

Part B

1. Carefully shake the iron filings over the paper. Gently tap the edge of the paper to keep the filings from sticking.
2. On another paper, sketch the pattern of the magnetic field around the magnet.
3. Carefully pick up the paper, curve it, and pour the iron filings back into the container, as in *b*.

Part C

1. On a piece of paper, draw a circle 8 cm in diameter to represent the earth. Label the geographic North and South Poles and the axis.
2. Draw an imaginary bar magnet that forms a small angle with the axis inside the circle.
3. Draw a magnetic field for the magnet that resembles the magnetic field you found in Part B. Draw the field so that it extends outside the circle.

Analysis

1. Which is stronger close to a bar magnet—the magnetic field of the bar magnet or the magnetic field of the earth?
2. Why do you use a compass for finding north if the compass does not point to true north?
3. Does a compass point directly to magnetic north if the compass is located near a large metal object?

Breakthrough

The Northern Lights—Neon Signs in the Sky

The auroras—the northern and southern lights—are among the most fantastic displays of light seen on earth. The picture shows how the rippling curtains, arcs, and bands of colors fill the entire night sky. These natural but silent fireworks are from 100 to 400 kilometers above the earth. They form a ring around each magnetic pole.

Only people who live in the far north in this hemisphere or in the far south in the southern hemisphere can see the lights often. But sometimes the auroras are strong enough to be seen far from the poles.

Strong auroras are a beautiful kaleidoscope of shifting colors. You can see red, yellow, green, blue, and violet lights flickering across the sky. Weaker auroras show striking patterns that appear white.

The cause of the auroras had mystified people for thousands of years. Ancient Norse stories told about an eternal fire that burns around the edge of the earth. Norsemen thought this fire, shining up into the sky, created the northern lights.

Scientists are finally unlocking the mystery of the lights. The auroras are particularly strong when sunspots are very active. Solar flares that erupt from the sun shoot streams of gas, known as the solar wind, into space. When a powerful gust of solar wind hits the magnetosphere around the earth, the magnetosphere and the solar wind react. This reaction speeds up streams of particles in the magnetosphere. The rapidly moving particles descend into the earth's atmosphere only over the magnetic poles. When the particles hit oxygen and nitrogen atoms in the upper atmosphere, the atoms give off colored light. Neon lights work in a similar way!

What we learn about the magnetosphere and the solar wind has exciting practical applications. These studies may speed the day when scientists on earth can make fusion energy—the energy that powers the stars.

For Discussion
1. Where can you see the northern lights?
2. When are northern lights strongest?

Northern lights

6-3
Gravity and Weight

You remain fixed to the surface of the spinning earth because of gravity. But what is gravity? As you read, ask yourself:

a. How is weight related to gravity?
b. How does gravity vary from one planet to another?

Gravity Causes Objects to Have Weight

You walk and move around easily because you are used to the earth's **gravity.** You would need to relearn how to walk on the moon where the gravity is much less. The astronauts found that a little jump on the moon's surface lifted them much higher off the ground than it did on Earth. On the other hand, if the earth's gravity became stronger, you would feel weighted down. Walking would be tiring and difficult until you became used to the increased gravity.

Gravitation is one kind of attraction of one body for another. Because of gravitation, the earth attracts all other objects. A planet's gravitational attraction for objects is its force of gravity. The **weight** of an object on Earth or any of the other planets is the force that gravity exerts upon the object. Weight is not the same as mass. The amount of material in an object is its mass.

Have You Heard?

If you could go to the center of the earth, you would weigh nothing. The mass above you would pull equally in all directions.

Earth

Earth's moon
.17 Earth's gravity

Jupiter
2.5 X Earth's gravity

Gravity Varies from One Planet to Another

The strength of an object's gravity depends on how much mass it contains. The greater the mass, the greater the gravity. Our moon and each of the planets and their moons have a different mass and a different size. Thus planets and moons have different gravitational pulls on objects near their surfaces. As a result, an object will not weigh the same on Earth as it does on the moon or on one of the other planets.

The spring scales in the diagram show how a person's weight is different at different places in the solar system. Gravity at our moon's surface is one-sixth (.17) of the gravity at the earth's surface. Therefore, weight on the moon is one-sixth of the weight on Earth. The mass of a person never changes, because mass is the amount of matter an object contains.

Your Weight in the Solar System

	Multiply your weight on Earth by
Sun	28
Moon	.17
Mercury	.38
Venus	.89
Mars	.38
Jupiter	2.5
Saturn	1.1
Uranus	.8
Neptune	1.2
Pluto	.01

Review It

1. What is gravity?
2. How are weight and gravity related?

6—4
Using Place to Determine Time

You know where you live and what time it is. You know because people have set up ways to find locations and to keep track of time. As you read, consider the following questions:

a. How do we locate points in space and time?
b. How do we use the International Date Line?

Finding Locations and Time on the Earth's Crust

Every point on earth is located where two imaginary lines cross each other. These lines are called latitude and longitude lines.

The east-west lines on the diagram are **latitude** lines. Latitude, which is measured in degrees, indicates distance north or south of the equator. The equator is halfway between the North and South Poles. It is at 0° latitude. The highest latitudes are those of the North and South Poles. They are at latitudes 90° north and south.

The north-south lines on the diagram are lines of **longitude,** or **meridians** (mə rid′ē ənz). These lines run from the North Pole to the South Pole. Meridians are also described in degrees. The distance between two meridians marks off degrees in an east-west direction.

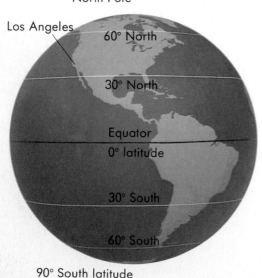

90° North latitude
North Pole

Los Angeles

60° North

30° North

Equator
0° latitude

30° South

60° South

90° South latitude
South Pole

90° East

Prime Meridian

North Pole
180° longitude   0° longitude

90° West

The meridian that runs through Greenwich, England, is the Prime—or first—Meridian. The **Prime Meridian** is 0° longitude. The highest possible longitude is 180°, which is halfway around the world from the Prime Meridian. The half of the earth that is east of the Prime Meridian has an east longitude. The half that is west of the Prime Meridian has a west longitude. Los Angeles, California, is 118° west of the Prime Meridian. It is also 34° north of the equator. Los Angeles is located at 118° west longitude and 34° north latitude.

Longitude and the time of day are closely related. Noon is the time of day when the sun is highest in the sky. It is noon at the same time at all points along a line of longitude.

An international conference set up **time zones,** which are bands of longitude that are 15° wide. There is one time zone for each of the twenty-four hours of the day. Notice in the picture that the time is the same within one band, or time zone. On either side of the zone, time is ahead or behind by one hour. The meridians on the diagram are 15 degrees apart. Each of the meridians lies in the center of a time zone.

Challenge!

Find the latitude and longitude for the farthest points north, south, east, and west in the United States.

Time zones

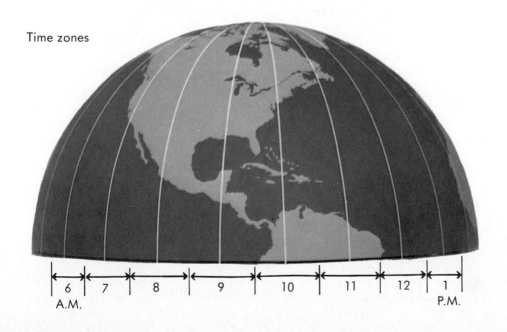

The International Date Line

The nations of the earth have chosen an imaginary line to mark the place where a new day begins. This line is the **International Date Line.** Because the change of date at the International Date Line could be confusing, the International Date Line does not run through heavily populated areas. The picture shows how the line runs along, or close to, the 180° meridian in the Pacific Ocean. The Date Line bends to avoid large land masses.

The day changes at the International Date Line

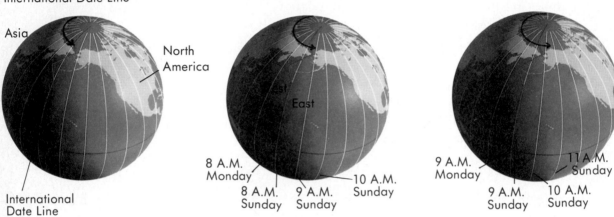

We can think of the time of day starting at the International Date Line and moving westward around the globe. Imagine that it is 8 A.M. Sunday just west of the International Date Line, as we see in the picture. Follow time around the earth through the 24 time zones. After 24 hours it is 8 A.M. Sunday on the east side of the Date Line. But now it is 8 A.M. *Monday*—the next day—on the west side of the Date Line. When it is Sunday just east of the International Date Line, it is Monday just west of the International Date Line. Imagine the confusion there would be if the Date Line ran through New York City instead of through the Pacific Ocean!

Review It

1. What lines mark 0° latitude and 0° longitude?
2. What is the International Date Line?

118

Activity

Time Zone Model

Purpose
To practice making the hour and day changes that occur when you cross time zones and the International Date Line.

Materials
- empty can
- sheet of paper
- tape
- pencil or pen
- cm ruler
- scissors

Procedure
1. You will be making a time zone model of the world. To begin, measure the height of the can in cm. *CAUTION: Cover any sharp edges on the can with tape.*
2. Cut out a rectangular piece of paper that is the height of the can and just long enough to wrap around the can.
3. You will make 24 columns on the paper. To begin, measure the length of your paper and divide this number by 24.
4. Use your answer in step 3 to draw 23 equally spaced marks at the top of the paper.
5. Now, using your marks, draw 23 lines from top to bottom as in *a*.
6. Tape the paper to the can, making sure your end lines meet to form the seam.
7. Label the can as in *b*. The seam represents the Prime Meridian. Label *all* the meridians and mark the 180° meridian IDL (International Date Line). Finally, label Monday and Tuesday.
8. Place a dot anywhere on the following five meridians and label A, B, C, D, and E: A) 15°W; B) 30°W; C) 90°W; D) 105°E; E) 165°E.
9. Assume it is 2:00 P.M. on Monday, November 15, at the Prime Meridian. Find the time and date at points A-E. Label them on the model.

Analysis
1. How do you change your watch and calendar when you cross the International Date Line going west?
2. Which meridian is closest to your home?
3. In the United States, why are the time zones divided by jagged, instead of straight, lines?

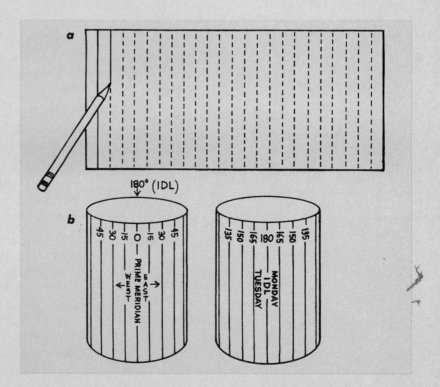

119

Chapter Summary

- The earth is shaped almost like a sphere. The distance around the earth is about 40,000 kilometers at the equator.   (6–1)

- The layers of the earth, from the outside in, are the crust, the mantle, and the core. (6–1)

- The earth acts like a giant bar magnet with a magnetic north pole and south pole.   (6–2)

- A planet's attraction for objects is called its force of gravity. The weight of any object is the force gravity exerts upon the object. (6–3)

- An object has different weights on different bodies in the solar system. But its mass does not change from planet to planet.   (6–3)

- Imaginary lines of latitude and longitude help us find the exact location of any place on the earth's surface.   (6–4)

- The earth is divided into twenty-four time zones. The International Date Line, where each new day begins, runs close to the 180th meridian.   (6–4)

Interesting Reading

Gallant, Roy A. *National Geographic Picture Atlas of Our Universe.* National Geographic Society, 1980. Contains good diagrams and descriptions of the earth's interior and magnetic field.

Our Earth. Banner Press, 1977. Good description of what the earth is made of.

Wyckoff, Jerome. *The Story of Geology.* Golden Press, 1976. Discusses layers of the earth and the earth's magnetism.

Questions/Problems

1. Describe the three layers of the earth.

2. Explain how the earth behaves like a giant bar magnet.

3. How does the location of the magnetic north pole change?

4. What is gravity?

5. Why does an object's weight change even though its mass does not change?

6. When a baseball game begins at 8 P.M. in San Francisco, what time do people in New York turn on their televisions to watch?

7. Find the latitude and longitude of New York City; Cairo, Egypt; Sydney, Australia; and Moscow, U.S.S.R.

8. Find the time and day in Cairo, Sydney, and Moscow, when it is noon Monday, New York Time.

Extra Research

1. On a map or globe, locate your town or city. Find its longitude and latitude.

2. Using the table in 6–3, calculate how much you would weigh on the moon, the sun, and the different planets.

3. Write a one-page report on James Van Allen's contribution to our understanding of the magnetosphere. You can find the information in an encyclopedia.

4. Calculate what the temperature at the center of the earth would be if the rate of temperature increase of 2°C for each 100 meters from the crust continued through to the center of the earth. The radius of the earth is 6,370 kilometers. Let 15°C be the starting temperature of the crust. Compare your result with the suggested temperature of the earth's core, which is 5,500°C.

Chapter Test

A. Vocabulary Write the numbers 1–10 on a piece of paper.
Match the definition in Column I with the term it defines in Column II.

Column I

1. the amount of matter in an object *h*

2. an imaginary circle around the earth that is parallel to the equator *e*

3. an imaginary north-south line, marking degrees of longitude *i*

4. an imaginary line separating one day from the next *d*

5. the magnetic north pole becomes the magnetic south pole *c*

6. a layer of the earth that varies in thickness from 8 to 35 kilometers *b*

7. a measure of the force of gravity *j*

8. the layer of the earth between the core and the crust *g*

9. the innermost layer of the earth *a*

10. region in which the earth's magnetic field is important *f*

Column II

a. core

b. crust

c. magnetic reversal

d. International Date Line

e. latitude

f. magnetosphere

g. mantle

h. mass

i. meridian

j. weight

B. Multiple Choice Write the numbers 1–10 on your paper.
Choose the letter that best completes the statement or answers the question.

1. The earth's crust is   a) the same thickness everywhere.   b) thicker under the continents than under the oceans.   c) liquid.   d) very cool in its deepest parts. *b*

2. The earth's core   a) is the same through-out.   b) lies directly beneath the crust.   c) is made mostly of iron.   d) is cool. *c*

3. The International Date Line   a) runs along or close to the Prime Meridian.   b) is an imaginary line where each new calendar day begins.   c) divides two time zones that are separated by 1 year.   d) divides two time zones that are separated by 12 hours. *b*

4. The force of gravity   a) works only on the earth.   b) causes objects to have weight. c) causes objects to have mass.   d) is greater on the moon than on Earth. *b*

5. The weight of an object   a) is the same as the mass.   b) is always less than the mass. c) is the same on all planets.   d) depends on gravity. *d*

6. The earth's magnetosphere   a) traps harm-ful radiation from space.   b) is shaped like a sphere.   c) is located in Greenwich, England. d) was discovered by Newton. *a*

7. The earth's magnetic field   a) has never changed.   b) is only imaginary.   c) has no ef-fect on life on earth.   d) has changed direc-tion many times in the earth's history. *d*

8. A time zone   a) is one of twelve in num-ber.   b) is measured by latitudes.   c) has time one hour later than the time zone to the east. d) has time one hour earlier than the time zone to the east. *d*

9. Most countries measure longitude east and west of the   a) Prime Meridian.   b) the equa-tor.   c) the International Date Line.   d) the Southern Hemisphere. *a*

10. The mantle   a) is the same throughout. b) contains the asthenosphere.   c) is solid rock.   d) is a thin layer. *b*

Chapter 7
Atoms to Minerals

At the left is one of the Crown Jewels of England. They are worth millions of dollars and are guarded at all times. The gold, silver, diamonds, and emeralds in this jewelry are all made of materials that come from the earth's crust. They are minerals. You have probably not seen the Crown Jewels, but you do see and touch minerals of some kind every day.

In this chapter you will learn what minerals are made of. The second section explains why a substance is called a mineral. Later, you will read about and do some simple lab tests on minerals. When you finish this chapter, you should be able to identify some common minerals.

Chapter Objectives

1. Explain the relationship between atoms, elements, compounds, and minerals.
2. List four features of all minerals.
3. Describe at least five tests used to identify minerals.

7–1

Atoms to Elements to Compounds

What do you and the Crown Jewels of England have in common? Both you and the jewels are made of combinations of the same basic substances. As you read, try to answer the following questions:

a. How can you describe an atom?
b. What is meant by the properties of elements?
c. What are compounds?

The Atom—A Building Block

Everything on earth and in the universe is made of building blocks called **atoms.** Although an atom is too small to see, we know that it has three kinds of particles—**electrons, neutrons,** and **protons.**

It is impossible to take an ordinary picture of an atom because it is too small. The diagram below is simply a model. It gives you an idea of how the parts of an atom are related. The nucleus contains neutrons and protons. The electrons form a cloud outside the nucleus. The parts of an atom are so small that the atom is mostly empty space!

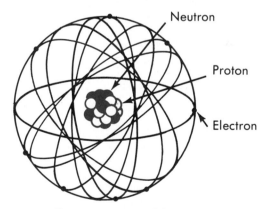

Oxygen atom model

Challenge!

Neutrons and protons are made up of still smaller particles called quarks. Find out about quarks.

Common elements	Number of protons
Helium	2
Carbon	6
Nitrogen	7
Oxygen	8
Silicon	14
Iron	26
Gold	79
Uranium	92

One or more atoms that contain the same number of protons are an **element.** All atoms of the element oxygen, for example, have eight protons. The table shows the number of protons in some common elements. About 90 elements occur naturally on earth. At least 16 other elements have been artificially created in laboratories.

124

Some Properties of Elements

Each of the 90 elements found on earth has its own special properties. The properties tell what an element is like and how it acts when it is with other elements. Hydrogen, for instance, is a colorless, odorless gas at normal earth temperatures. People who work with hydrogen are cautious because this gas can explode in the presence of oxygen.

There are many ways to describe and group elements by similar properties. In order to study rocks and what they are made of, earth scientists often group elements into **metallic** and **nonmetallic elements.** What are some properties of a metallic element? First, metals are good conductors of heat. For this reason, you use a potholder to touch the handle of a hot metal pan because the heat from a fire quickly moves throughout the pan. Second, metals are good conductors of electricity. The element copper is used for electric wiring because electric current moves through it easily. Third, metals have a shiny luster. Metals, like aluminum foil, look shiny because of the way they reflect light. Fourth, metals can be pounded into thin sheets or even drawn out into a thin wire. Because of these qualities, metals are used to make tools, equipment, and products such as those in the picture.

Nonmetals, on the other hand, do not conduct heat and electricity easily. They are often soft solids or gases, like oxygen or nitrogen.

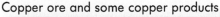

Copper ore and some copper products

Elements Form Compounds

A **compound** is a substance with new properties that forms when two or more elements join always in the same way. Most of the things around you are made of one or more compounds.

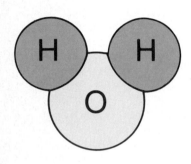

In the picture to the left two atoms of hydrogen unite with one atom of oxygen to form a compound—water. If you could look inside each atom, you would see that the electrons react in making compounds. The nucleus plays no part in compound-making. Oxygen, which is a gas in the air that you breathe, and the gas hydrogen become liquid water when they join. Water is unlike either gas.

Another common compound, table salt, forms when one atom of sodium unites with one atom of chlorine. Sodium is a metal that burns if it is exposed to air and explodes when water touches it. It must be kept under kerosene or oil to keep it from reacting with other elements. Chlorine (klôr′ēn′) is a poisonous greenish-yellow gas with a sharp odor. You smell chlorine when you open a bottle of house-hold bleach. These two elements combine to form a white, solid—table salt. The properties of salt are unlike those of either sodium or chlorine.

Scientists often need to describe very small amounts of substances. They use the term **molecule** (mol′ə kyul) for the smallest part of a substance that has the properties of the substance. A molecule of water is two atoms of hydrogen and one atom of oxygen. If you could break this strong molecule, you would no longer have the compound water. You would have atoms of hydrogen and oxygen.

Review It

1. Each of two atoms has 15 protons and 15 electrons. What does this tell you about the two atoms?
2. What are three properties of a metallic element?
3. What part of the atom is active in forming compounds?

Activity

Atom Models

Purpose
To construct and compare models of atoms found in some elements in the earth's crust.

Materials
- construction paper—blue, red, and green
- five paper plates
- hole puncher
- compass
- centimeter ruler
- glue

Procedure
1. Each paper plate represents an atom of one of the elements listed in table a. Label each of the plates with the name of one of the five elements listed in table a.
2. Use the ruler to measure the diameter of a plate. Divide the diameter by two to find the center of the plate. Mark the center of each plate with a point.
3. Use the compass to draw four circles around the center point of one plate, as shown in b. The radii of the circles are 3 cm, 5 cm, 7 cm, and 9 cm.

a

	Protons	Neutrons
Hydrogen	1	0
Carbon	6	6
Nitrogen	7	7
Oxygen	8	8
Silicon	14	14

	Electrons in orbit		
	#1	#2	#3
Hydrogen	1	0	0
Carbon	2	4	0
Nitrogen	2	5	0
Oxygen	2	6	0
Silicon	2	8	4

b

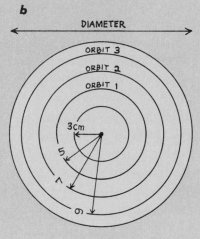

4. The inside circle represents the nucleus of the atom. The remaining circles represent the paths of the electrons, which are called orbits. Label the circles as they are in b.
5. Repeat steps 3 and 4 for each of the other plates.
6. Use the hole puncher to punch out 36 paper circles from each sheet of art paper.
7. The blue paper circles are protons. Glue them inside the nucleus. Do not glue one circle on top of another. The red paper circles are neutrons. Also glue them inside the nucleus. Do not glue one paper circle on top of another.
8. The green circles are electrons. Space the green circles at equal distances on each orbit, as indicated in a. Glue them on the different orbit circles.

Analysis
1. How are the atom models alike?
2. How are they different?
3. You made very simple atom models. Explain three ways that your models are *not* like the real atoms they represent.

7–2
Properties of Minerals

Minerals, which are elements and compounds, make up rocks. The flecks in the photograph of the rock are pieces of minerals. This section describes what a mineral is, and identifies two of the most common minerals. As you read, ask yourself:

a. What four features do all minerals have?
b. What are two abundant minerals in the crust?

Four Features of All Minerals

A **mineral** is an element or compound that is found in rocks and soil. Although some minerals are single elements, most of the 2,500 known minerals are compounds.

Some minerals, like diamonds, are used as ornaments. When these minerals are valuable, they are called gems. But whether or not a mineral is a gem, it shares four features with all other minerals.

First, all minerals are found in nature. The emeralds shown below were found in the mountains of South America. Imitation gems of high quality are made in laboratories. Imitation gems, however, are not true minerals.

Second, the substances that make up a mineral were never part of a living thing, nor were they formed by life processes. The carbon in a diamond comes from deep inside the earth. It was never part of a life process. On the other hand, the carbon in coal is what is left of ancient plants. Therefore, diamonds are minerals, but coal is not.

Rocks are made of minerals

Emeralds

128

Third, each mineral has a definite composition and its own special properties. The mineral pyrite (pī′rīt) is sometimes called fool's gold. Whether the pyrite comes from Spain or Colorado, it is a compound containing one atom of a metal for every two atoms of sulfur.

Last, the atoms of minerals are connected in an orderly arrangement that repeats itself regularly. You can see the orderly atomic pattern in the X-ray photograph of pyrite. **Crystals** of a mineral are the *outward sign* of an orderly atomic arrangement within the mineral. The crystals in the photograph are visible proof of the orderly arrangement of atoms in calcite and quartz. Minerals develop good crystals, if the mineral grows freely and undisturbed. The mineral samples in your classroom may or may not have visible crystals.

Some elements or compounds develop more than one arrangement of atoms. Thus the same element or compound can produce different minerals. Pencil lead is the mineral graphite. Both the pencil lead and the diamond, shown below, are made of the element carbon. Graphite, unlike diamond, is black, soft, and slippery to touch. The two minerals—graphite and diamond—and their properties are different because the arrangement of carbon atoms in each is different.

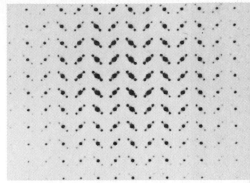
X-ray photograph of pyrite

Calcite and quartz crystals

Graphite (pencil lead) and a diamond

The Most Abundant Minerals

All four features necessary for a substance to be a mineral are present in the **silicate** (sil′ə kāt) **minerals.** Most rocks are made of silicate minerals. These minerals are compounds containing the elements silicon and oxygen. The **feldspars** (feld′sparz) are a group of silicate minerals. They are very common in rocks. Feldspars slowly break down into small pieces of new minerals, called clays, in the presence of air and water. Much of the soil on earth came from the clay minerals in feldspars. **Quartz** (kwôrtz) is also a common silicate mineral in rocks. The tan-colored sand at many beaches is tiny pieces of quartz. You can see samples of quartz and feldspar below.

Silicate minerals are common because of the great amount of silicon and oxygen in the earth. The table shows the relative weights of elements in the crust.

The Most Abundant Elements in the Crust

Oxygen	46%
Silicon	28%
Aluminum	8%
Iron	6%
Magnesium	4%
Sodium, potassium, calcium, and other elements	8%

Review It

1. Define mineral using the four features as part of your definition.
2. What is a silicate mineral?

Feldspar

Quartz

Did You Know?

The Story of a Diamond

There is an episode from the old Superman television series in which the Man of Steel crushes a chunk of coal in his hand and makes a diamond.

This story is not as far-fetched as you might think. Like coal, diamonds are made of carbon.

Natural diamonds form deep within the mantle of the earth, where the temperature and pressure are so great even rocks are melted.

Tremendous explosions drive the diamonds and other hardened material up through the mantle and out of the crust from pipes—or passages—in volcanoes.

In Africa, most diamonds are mined directly from ancient volcanic pipes. If the pipes are worn away by running water, the diamonds can be found nearby in river beds. Most diamonds from India were recovered from river beds.

The history of certain large diamonds is filled with mystery and adventure.

Perhaps no gem has as colorful a history as the Koh-i-noor diamond. The Koh-i-noor first belonged to a rajah —a prince—in India in the 1300s. At that time, the diamond weighed 186 carats —about two hundred times bigger than the diamonds in most engagement rings!

From that time on the gem was captured and held by a number of kings. In the 1700s, a Persian ruler, Nadir Shah, found the diamond hidden in an Asian emperor's turban. Nadir Shah called the gem Koh-i-noor, which means Mountain of Light.

The Koh-i-noor passed to Queen Victoria in England in 1849. Because it looked dull, the Queen had the diamond cut and polished. The cutting did not improve its brilliance and it reduced its size to 109 carats.

The Koh-i-noor now rests with the crown jewels of England in the Tower of London.

For Discussion
1. What conditions are necessary for a diamond to form?
2. Does cutting always increase the beauty of a diamond?

7–3
Mineral Identification

How can you tell the pyrite in the photograph from gold? The answer is in this section, which also describes ways to identify minerals. Consider this question as you read:

What tests are used to identify minerals?

Identifying Minerals

The tests that follow are fairly simple ones that you can perform in the laboratory. Mineralogists (min′ə rol′ə jists), who are mineral experts, use these tests as well as more complicated ones to identify minerals.

Hardness   You can tell gold from pyrite because gold is much softer than pyrite. Earth scientists use the **hardness scale,** shown on this page, to help them identify minerals.

On this scale, 1 is the softest mineral and 10 is the hardest mineral. The softest mineral, talc, is used for crayons and talcum powder. The hardest mineral, diamond, has industrial uses as a grinder or cutter because it is the hardest known substance.

Each mineral on the hardness scale can leave a scratch on any other mineral that has the same number or a lower number. Also each mineral on the hardness scale can be scratched by any mineral with a higher number.

You can do the hardness tests on minerals in ways other than scratching one mineral with another. Your fingernail · (hardness 2.5), a copper penny (hardness 3), and a knife-blade (hardness 5.5–6) will all scratch minerals softer than they are. In addition, any mineral harder than 6.5 will scratch a piece of glass.

Pyrite

Scale of Mineral Hardness

1. Talc	6. Orthoclase
2. Gypsum	7. Quartz
3. Calcite	8. Topaz
4. Fluorite	9. Corundum
5. Apatite	10. Diamond

Hematite's streak is red

Color A few minerals can be identified by color. The mineral sulfur, for example, is bright yellow. But the color of most minerals is caused by the presence of small amounts of impurities. Quartz occurs in a variety of colors, depending on what elements were added as the quartz formed.

Streak For many minerals, a reliable test is **streak** or the color of the mineral when it is ground into a fine powder. The color of a mineral may vary from sample to sample, but the color of the streak usually remains the same. The iron ore hematite (hem′ə tīt) in the picture to the left below was rubbed across a streak plate made of unglazed porcelain. Although hematite samples are different colors, the streak is always dark red. The streak plate has a hardness of 7. Therefore, minerals harder than 7 will not leave a streak on the plate. Instead, they will scratch the plate.

Cleavage or Fracture Observing the way a mineral breaks can help you identify it. If a mineral breaks along one or more smooth, flat surfaces, it has **cleavage** (klē′vij). Notice that mica "cleaves" in flat sheets that look like thin pieces of plastic. Often, however, a mineral may lack cleavage because it does not break along flat surfaces. As you can see, obsidian (ob sid′ē ən) breaks along a curved surface like a piece of glass. Other minerals may splinter or break unevenly. Minerals that break along curved surfaces, splinter, or break unevenly are said to have **fracture** rather than cleavage.

Luster A mineral's **luster** is the way the mineral's surface reflects light. Notice in the picture that galena (ga lē′nə) has a metallic luster. You can describe nonmetallic lusters as greasy, glassy, pearly, silky, or diamondlike, depending on how the mineral looks. For instance, quartz often has a glassy luster, and gypsum may have a silky luster. Luster alone, however, is not a reliable test because the luster of a mineral may vary from sample to sample. A piece of quartz, for example, may have a glassy, a greasy, or a sparkling luster.

Mica cleaves in sheets

Obsidian breaks along a curved surface

Galena has a metallic luster

Challenge!

Demonstrate double refraction to the class, using a type of calcite called Iceland Spar. Find out how to do this by looking up minerals or refraction in an encyclopedia.

Magnetite

Magnetic Properties A few minerals that contain iron are magnetic. They can be identified because they are attracted to a magnet. Magnetite (mag′nə tīt), sometimes called lodestone, is the most common magnetic mineral. It is attracted to the magnet in the picture.

Specific Gravity The weight or **heft** of a mineral may be helpful for mineral identification. Galena feels much heavier than the same size piece of talc.

The **specific gravity** of a mineral is the comparison of the density of a mineral with the density of water. The density of water is 1 gram/cubic centimeter. Silver has a specific gravity of 10.5. This number means that silver is 10.5 times more dense than water.

The acid test

The Acid Test The acid test may show whether a mineral sample contains carbon and oxygen. Minerals that contain joined groups of carbon and oxygen atoms are called carbonates (kar′bə nāts). Most carbonates give up carbon and oxygen as carbon dioxide gas when drops of hydrochloric acid are added to the sample. You will see bubbles when you put drops of the acid on calcite (kal′sīt), a carbonate mineral. The bubbles on the calcite, shown to the left, form as the carbon dioxide gas leaves the mineral.

Quartz crystals

Crystals All crystals of a mineral resemble each other in the angles that form between corresponding crystal faces. If you know the crystal shape of a mineral, it will help you identify that mineral. The photograph of quartz shows the characteristic shape of quartz crystals.

Hornblende

Sulfur

Olivine

Halite

Graphite

Fluorite

Other Tests   Some minerals can be identified by taste, feel, and smell. The table salt halite (hā′līt) tastes salty. If you rub talc, it feels soapy or greasy. A few drops of water on kaolinite (kā′ə lə nīt) bring out a musty smell.

You can see examples of some common minerals in the photographs on this page.

Review It

1. How can you prove that a diamond is harder than quartz?
2. What is the best way to identify calcite?
3. Calculate the mass of a 5 cubic centimeter sample of galena (specific gravity = 7.5).

Activity

Identifying Minerals

Purpose
To learn how mineral properties are used to identify minerals.

Materials
- unidentified minerals, numbered 1 through 7
- unglazed porcelain streak plate
- copper penny (hardness 3)
- nail (hardness 6)
- piece of glass (hardness 7)
- magnet
- dilute hydrochloric acid

Procedure
1. Fold a piece of notebook paper lengthwise three times as in a. When you open the paper, it is divided into 8 long columns. With a straight edge, draw a line in each crease to separate the columns. Write the numbers 1–7 in the columns across the top of the paper as in b.
2. List mineral properties in the left-hand column, as in b. Skip a line between each property.
3. Do the tests and make the observations necessary to determine the mineral properties of mineral #1.

Record your results in column #1 on your data table. Use the terms in the Table of Minerals, on the opposite page, as a guide for recording results.

NOTE: When doing the hardness test: if the mark the mineral makes on the piece of glass rubs off, the mineral is softer than glass. If the mineral has a hardness above 7, you will record it as >7.

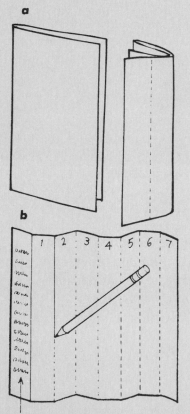

Mineral properties

Color · Streak · Hardness · Heft (light, med., heavy)
Luster · Magnetic · Acid test · Cleavage/Fracture observed
Other properties · Name of mineral

4. Repeat step 3 for each of the remaining 6 minerals.
5. When you have completed your table, identify each of the numbered minerals by matching the information on the Table of Mineral Properties with the results you recorded on the data sheet. Since mineral samples vary, your tests may not agree exactly with the Table of Mineral Properties. Hunt for the best match of properties. (Orthoclase, which is listed on the table, is a member of the feldspar group of minerals.)

Analysis
1. How can you tell the difference between calcite and quartz?
2. Which is a more reliable test—color or streak? Explain your answer.
3. Why is it difficult to get an accurate observation for heft?
4. An unknown mineral sample cannot be scratched by a penny but can be scratched by the nail. Estimate its hardness.

Table of Mineral Properties

Mineral	Hardness	Streak	Cleavage/ fracture	Heft—light, medium, heavy, (specific gravity)	Luster	Color	Other properties
Calcite	3	White	Cleavage or fracture	Light (2.7)	Glassy	Clear	Fizzes in acid *double refraction
Hematite	5.5–6.5	Red-brown	Fracture	Heavy (5.30)	Dull or earthy	Red-brown	Source of iron
Corundum	9	Colorless	May look like it has cleavage	Medium (3.9–4.1)	Glassy or sparkling	Brown, green, red, blue	Some varieties used as gemstones. Samples may be 6-sided
Magnetite	6	Black	May look like it has cleavage	Heavy (5.2)	Metallic	Black	Attracts magnet/ source of iron
Quartz	7	Colorless	Fracture (like glass)	Light (2.65)	Glassy or waxy	Colorless unless impurities added	Often shows well-formed crystals
Halite	2.5	Colorless	Good cleavage	Light (2.1)	Glassy to dull	Colorless unless impurities	Tastes salty
Graphite	1–2	Black	Good cleavage	Light (2.3)	Greasy	Steel gray-black	Feels greasy, soft. Blackens fingers
Talc	1	Colorless	Good cleavage	Light (2.8)	Pearly soapy	Greenish-white (varies)	Soft, feels greasy
Galena	2.5	Gray/black	Good cleavage	Heavy (7.6)	Metallic	Blue to black to lead gray	Often looks like metallic cubes
Pyrite	6.5	Greenish-black	May show cleavage	Heavy (5.0)	Metallic	Brassy yellow	May resemble gold
Orthoclase	6	Colorless	Good cleavage	Light (2.5)	Often looks pearly or glassy	Usually white to gray	Common in rocks
Mica	2–3	Colorless	Good cleavage	Light (3)	Glassy or pearly or shiny	Varies white to dark	Light colored mica, trans- parent, in thin sheets; dark colored mica; smokey looking in thin sheets

*A double image is produced when Iceland Spar, a type of Calcite is placed over printed material.

Chapter Summary

- The basic building blocks of all materials on earth and in the universe are atoms. (7–1)

- An element is one or more atoms that contain the same number of protons. (7–1)

- Elements combine to form compounds. (7–1)

- Minerals are naturally occurring elements or compounds. They form from materials that were never alive. Minerals have a definite chemical composition, and an orderly arrangement of atoms, which results in a characteristic crystal structure. (7–2)

- Feldspar and quartz are two common minerals. (7–2)

- Minerals can be identified by tests of several properties, such as hardness, color, streak, cleavage or fracture, luster, magnetism, specific gravity, and characteristic crystal structure. (7–3)

Interesting Reading

Chesterman, Charles W. *The Audubon Society Field Guide to North American Rocks and Minerals*. Knopf, 1978. Presents a good introduction to minerals.

Kerrod, Robin. *Rocks and Minerals*. Warwick, 1977. Written in a colorful and informative way.

Pough, Frederick H. *A Field Guide to Rocks and Minerals*. Houghton Mifflin, 1976. Contains interesting facts about many common minerals.

Shedenhelm, W.R.C. *The Young Rockhound's Handbook*. Putnam, 1978. Explains how to cut and polish minerals and how to prospect for gold.

Questions/Problems

1. Name and describe the location of the three major parts of an atom.

2. Describe three properties of a metallic element.

3. List and explain four features of all minerals.

4. Explain what is meant by a silicate mineral and give two examples.

5. List five properties of minerals that can help identify a mineral.

6. What does specific gravity tell about a mineral?

7. How can you identify calcite when it is with a group of similar-looking minerals?

Extra Research

1. Use the library to find out about particles inside the atom smaller than electrons, protons, and neutrons.

2. Find the volumes of three mineral samples in cubic centimeters. Hint: 1 milliliter of water equals 1 cubic centimeter. Determine how much water the mineral displaces.

3. Find out about the mineral properties of your birthstone or favorite gem.

4. List the minerals that are of economic importance in your state, and give the uses of each.

5. Report on the six major crystal systems by defining and drawing each system, and identifying a mineral example. You will find a good description of the crystal systems in an encyclopedia or a geology book in your library.

6. Use an encyclopedia or mineralogy book to find out what qualities a mineral has to possess to be called a gem.

Chapter Test

A. Vocabulary   Write the numbers 1–10 on a piece of paper.
Match the definition in Column I with the term it defines in Column II.

Column I

1. substance formed by one or more atoms of the same kind

2. how the surface of a mineral reflects light

3. property of breaking along surfaces that are not flat

4. compound or element that is found in nature, formed of materials that never lived

5. comparison of the density of a mineral to the density of water

6. participates in making compounds

7. outward sign of the orderly arrangement of atoms in minerals

8. the powder produced when a mineral is rubbed on a hard surface

9. property of breaking along one or more smooth, flat surfaces

10. substance formed when two or more elements combine

Column II

a. cleavage

b. compound

c. crystal

d. electron

e. element

f. fracture

g. luster

h. mineral

i. specific gravity

j. streak

B. Multiple Choice   Write the numbers 1–10 on your paper.
Choose the letter that best completes the statement or answers the question.

1. Atoms   a) are usually found alone in nature.   b) can be seen with a magnifying glass. c) always have the same number of protons. d) are mostly empty space.

2. The streak and the color of a mineral are a) always the same.   b) never the same. c) sometimes the same.   d) none of the above.

3. The properties of every mineral are determined by   a) the arrangements and types of atoms in it.   b) cleavage.   c) fracture. d) luster.

4. The smallest part of many substances that retains the properties of the substance is called a   a) crystal.   b) molecule.   c) mineral. d) none of the above.

5. Metals   a) do not conduct heat.   b) have a shiny luster.   c) are often gases.   d) cannot be drawn into a thin wire.

6. An orderly arrangement of atoms in a mineral is illustrated by the mineral's   a) color. b) crystal.   c) fracture.   d) luster.

7. All of the following are minerals except a) talc.   b) halite.   c) fluorite.   d) coal.

8. Feldspar and quartz are   a)compounds containing silicon and oxygen.   b) rare minerals.   c) not common in rocks.   d) both unaffected by contact with air, water, and living things.

9. The hardest mineral is   a) diamond. b) talc.   c) lodestone.   d) calcite.

10. A mineral that fizzes when acid is poured on it must be   a) magnetic.   b) a carbonate. c) nonmetallic.   d) made mostly of silicon.

Chapter 8
Rocks and Ores

The picture shows the largest hole in the ground that people have ever made. This excavation is the copper mine at Bingham Canyon, Utah. It is about three kilometers across and .8 kilometers deep. At one time, 300 kilometers of railroad track wound around inside the mine. Now, both trains and trucks carry rocks, which contain copper, silver, gold, platinum, and many other valuable minerals, up from the bottom of the mine.

In this chapter you will learn about the three families of rocks and how they are related. The last section deals with valuable products we take from the earth's crust. You will read about miners who found diamonds in the bottom of a stream. Their knowledge of rocks and geologic processes enabled them to find a large diamond deposit.

Chapter Objectives

1. Explain how you can identify igneous rocks by their crystal size and the minerals they contain.

2. Describe and give three examples of sedimentary rocks that formed in different ways.

3. Describe conditions that can cause metamorphic rocks to form.

4. Explain how the three rock families are related by the rock cycle.

5. Identify three ways that valuable minerals are concentrated in a small area.

6. Explain how oil and gas form and accumulate into large deposits.

8–1
The Family of Igneous Rocks

Rocks belong to families just as people do. The rocks in this section all belong to the family of rocks born in fire. They are the oldest rocks in the crust. As you read, ask yourself:

a. How can you describe intrusive rock?
b. How does extrusive rock differ from intrusive rock?
c. How can you identify igneous rock?

Intrusive Igneous Rocks Are Born Inside the Earth

The big family of fire-born rocks is called **igneous** (ig′nē əs) **rock.** The name is from the Latin word *ignis,* which means "fire." Many igneous rocks form from the molten (mōl′tən)—or melted—material that is deep within the earth. This molten rock is **magma** (mag′mə). It may reach temperatures of over 1,000°C.

Magma pushes its way into the openings and cracks of surrounding rocks. When magma cools and hardens, it is igneous rock. **Intrusive** (in trü′siv) **rock** is the name given to igneous rock that forms inside the earth. These rocks usually have large crystals because magma that is buried deep in the ground cools slowly. Large crystals develop when magma has time to cool slowly.

You can see the large crystals of pink feldspar, clear quartz, and some dark minerals in the photograph of **granite** Many buildings are made of granite because it is very strong and can be highly polished. Granite is a common intrusive igneous rock. Much of the continental crust is made of granite. It is the foundation of the continents.

Extrusive Igneous Rocks Form on the Earth's Surface

Sometimes magma pours out onto the earth's surface through a volcano or a crack in the ground. Magma that reaches the surface is renamed **lava.** Igneous rock that forms on the earth's surface is **extrusive** (ek strü′siv) **rock.**

Granite

Extrusive rock usually has small crystals because lava cools quickly. In fact, the crystals are so small that they can generally be seen only if they are magnified.

The **basalt** (bə sôlt′) in the picture is a common extrusive igneous rock with small crystals. The basalt may have come from an ancient lava flow like the one that covers hundreds of square kilometers in the states of Washington and Oregon. The black rocks in Hawaii and the black sand found in a few places there are basalt. The Hawaiian Islands are the tops of volcanoes that rose from the ocean bottom. Just as continental crust is mostly granite, ocean crust is mostly basalt.

Sometimes lava cools so quickly that no crystals develop. Obsidian looks like black glass. It is an extrusive rock with no crystals. The obsidian shown below flowed down the side of a volcano and cooled quickly. Volcanic materials without crystals are described as glassy.

Pumice (pum′əs) is another glassy rock that explodes from volcanoes. Some pumice is so light-weight that it floats on water. Notice the holes in the pumice. These holes formed when gases escaped from the lava.

Basalt   Obsidian   Pumice

Identifying Igneous Rock by Crystal Size and Minerals

Igneous rocks are made mostly of silicate minerals. These minerals are mainly silicon and oxygen plus other elements. Feldspars, quartz, and mica are light-colored silicate minerals. Rocks made of these minerals are often pink, tan, or another pale color. Dark-colored igneous rocks may also contain some light-colored minerals. But they are mostly hornblende (horn′blend), olivine (ol′ə vēn), or other dark silicate minerals. The element iron makes the minerals dark.

Geologists identify igneous rocks by their crystal size and mineral content. The table shows the relationship between three light and two dark igneous rocks. Imagine that this table was stretched so that all of the many kinds of igneous rocks in the world could fit on it. Many of them would lie somewhere between the rocks on the left and those on the right.

Notice that granite, rhyolite (rī′ə līt), and obsidian are "first-cousins" because they contain similar silicate minerals. The three kinds of rock, however, do not look alike.

How to identify igneous rocks

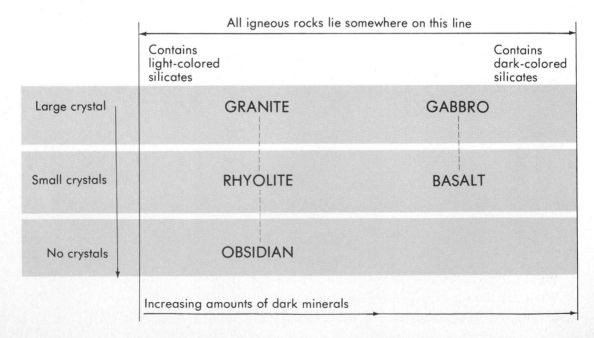

	Contains light-colored silicates	Contains dark-colored silicates
Large crystal	GRANITE	GABBRO
Small crystals	RHYOLITE	BASALT
No crystals	OBSIDIAN	

All igneous rocks lie somewhere on this line

Increasing amounts of dark minerals

Rhyolite   Gabbro

Rhyolite, which you see in the photograph, is light-colored. Most granite seems speckled because it has large crystals of different colors. Obsidian looks much darker than the other two rocks. If, however, you look at a thin slice of obsidian, you will see that it is almost colorless—not dark.

The three "first-cousin" rocks all formed in different ways. We know granite formed from cooled magma because it has large crystals. Rhyolite came from lava and has very small crystals. Obsidian cooled too quickly to have any crystals.

Gabbro (gab′rō), which is also pictured, is an intrusive rock with large crystals. Gabbro and basalt are closely related, just as granite and rhyolite are.

There are many kinds of igneous rocks that vary in crystal size and color. But all igneous rocks are made of materials that come from deep inside the earth.

Review It

1. What do large crystals in igneous rock tell you?
2. What are the crystals in extrusive rock like?
3. In what two ways do granite and basalt differ?

8–2
Sedimentary Rocks, the Second Family of Rocks

Have you ever walked along a sandy beach or over gravel in a brook? Some sedimentary rocks—the second family of rocks—are made of sand and gravel. As you read, ask yourself:

a. What are the three types of sedimentary rocks?
b. How do animal remains and water form rocks?
c. What are two outstanding features of sedimentary rocks?

Three Types of Sedimentary Rocks

Most of the rocks you see around you belong to the **sedimentary** (sed ə men′tər ē) **rock** family. They are usually one of three types. The most common type is made of materials that are carried and dropped by water, wind, or ice. Millions of years may pass before the materials are cemented or pressed together and harden into rocks. A second type of sedimentary rock develops chemically from minerals that were once dissolved in water. A third type of sedimentary rock forms when plant or animal remains harden into rocks.

The sedimentary rock story begins when air and water break large rocks into smaller pieces in a process called weathering. Weathering acts slowly but continuously on the earth's surface.

Sandstone

Shale

Conglomerate

Breccia

When you walk along a sandy beach or through mud, you see products of weathering—sand, soil, and pebbles. These are types of **sediments** (sed′ə məntz). They may be as small as dust or as large as boulders. Running or moving water in rivers, lakes, or oceans shifts many sediments to other places. Eventually, the sediment settles out of the water. Usually the larger pieces drop first and become the bottom layer of a rock bed.

Finally, the sediments harden into rock. Sometimes the sediments are cemented together by minerals in the water that flows over them. Quartz and calcite are common cements. The sandstone in the photograph to the left below formed when quartz, which was dissolved in water, filled the spaces between the grains of sand and hardened. The quartz acts as the cement for the sand grains. The "brownstone" used to build many houses in cities of the eastern United States is a sandstone.

Conglomerate (kən glom′ə rit) and breccia (brech′ē ə), both shown above, develop when pebble-sized sediments are cemented together. Breccia is like conglomerate except that the pebbles are angular instead of round.

The mud and clay sediments in shale, the most common sedimentary rock, are not cemented like sandstone. Instead, they are squeezed and pressed by the weight of the material above them until they harden into rock. The sediments of the shale in the photograph to the left are so fine that you can not see them. The color of shale varies from gray to greenish-black.

Rocks from Animal Remains and Water

Limestone, another common sedimentary rock, usually forms from animal remains or by a chemical process. All limestone is made of the mineral calcite, which is calcium carbonate. Sometimes limestone forms when dissolved calcium carbonate sinks to the bottom of a body of water as calcite crystals. However, most limestone is the hardened remains of dead sea animals. For instance, chalk is limestone made from many tiny seashells pressed together. Large pieces of seashells cemented together are a type of limestone called coquina (kō kē′nə). Along the beaches of Florida, you can see coquina that looks like the photograph in the margin.

Many fine buildings and homes in the United States are built of limestone from Indiana. Limestone is also essential to the building industry as an ingredient in cement and mortar.

Rock salt (halite) and gypsum (jip′səm) form from minerals that were left behind when a large body of water evaporated. The white gypsum sand in the White Sands National Monument of New Mexico formed in this way. Both rock salt and gypsum are widely used in industry and in your everyday life. Salt, which you use to season food, has been used for thousands of years to preserve food. Gypsum, shown below, is used to make plaster walls and insulation for homes and buildings.

Coal is sedimentary rock made of decayed plant life buried in the earth. The soft coal in the picture is bituminous (bə tü′mə nəs).

Coquina

Gypsum

Bituminous

Outstanding Features of Sedimentary Rocks

Sedimentary rocks have special features that may help you identify them. The most outstanding feature is the layering in sedimentary rocks. Layers—or beds—of rock look different because they contain sediments of different types or sizes. Perhaps differences in the size of the sediments created the layering of the rocks in the picture above. A section of rock that contains alternating sandstones and shales also looks layered. This is true because sandstone and shale are made of different sediments—sand or clay.

Fossils, which are evidence of past life, are very common in sedimentary rocks. A cover of sediments protects plant and animal remains from decay. The normally cool temperature of sediments helps preserve plants and animals. Limestone often contains fossils of sea animals. Chalk and coquina are made entirely of sea fossils. Shale, which was once mud and clay, may have fossils such as the imprint of a fern leaf seen in the picture.

Have You Heard?

A geode (jē′ōd), shown below, is a beautiful small feature occasionally found in limestone or other sedimentary rocks. A geode occurs where water fills a round hole or cavity in a rock and deposits crystals of quartz or calcite.

Review It

1. How do mud and clay become shale?
2. What are two ways that limestone forms?
3. Explain why sedimentary rocks look layered.

8–3
Rocks Can Change

Can you change limestone into another type of rock? This section describes how rocks can change. Consider these questions as you read:

a. What are metamorphic rocks?
b. How are rocks related in the rock cycle?

Metamorphic Rocks

Igneous and sedimentary rocks that are buried deep inside the earth may change in appearance or in mineral content. The new rocks that result are called **metamorphic** (met ə mōr′fik) **rocks.**

Many conditions cause metamorphic rocks to form from older rocks. Heat from nearby magma may change the original minerals of rocks into other minerals. Liquids and gases escaping from the magma also can change minerals in the rocks that surround the magma. In addition, pressure from the weight of rocks above can rearrange the atoms in the minerals of a rock.

Heat and pressure usually change the appearance of a rock. Often the crystals of minerals in metamorphic rock are coarser than those in the original rock. The minerals in metamorphic rocks may line up in colored bands that bend and fold as a result of great pressure. Notice the light and dark bands of metamorphic rock in the photograph below. The picture was taken near the bottom of the Grand Canyon.

Common metamorphic rocks

Original rock	Changes into	Metamorphic rock
Limestone	⟶	Marble
Granite	⟶	Gneiss
Shale	⟶	Slate
Basalt	⟶	Schist
Sandstone	⟶	Quartzite

Bands of metamorphic rock

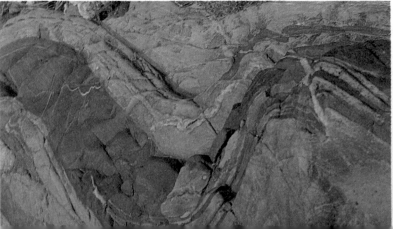

There are many types of igneous and sedimentary rocks and many ways that they can change. As a result, there are many types of metamorphic rock. The chart to the left below lists five common metamorphic rocks and the types of rock from which they may come. The pictures on this page show some characteristic samples.

Most slate comes from shale. Slate splits easily into thin, smooth layers. Because of this quality, slate is used to make roofs, floors, and chalkboards.

Marble is altered limestone. It is much stronger than limestone and ideal for buildings and monuments. Marble is normally white, but impurities in the rock produce marble of different colors.

A great deal of gneiss (nīs) forms from the igneous rock granite. Gneiss may be identified by the light- and dark-colored bands such as the ones in the picture below.

Most schist (shist) has stretched, interlocking crystals. Notice the shimmering, crystalline appearance of the schist sample. The stretched crystals may break away, giving the schist a platey or flakey look.

Slate

Gneiss

Schist

Marble

151

More Changes in the Rock Cycle

The changes that lead to metamorphic rock are only one paragraph of the big story of what happens to rocks on the earth. The name of this story is **The Rock Cycle.** It tells how rocks are related. You can look at the diagram as you read about the rock cycle.

In the first stage of the rock cycle, igneous rocks form. They are the ancestors of all rocks. These rocks may harden from lava that pours out onto the earth's surface, or they may form beneath the earth's surface from cooled magma.

In the next stage of the rock cycle, igneous rocks break down into sediments in the process called weathering. Running water, wind, or ice carry the sediments away and deposit them in layers. The layers of sediments harden. They may be cemented together by the minerals in water, or they may be pressed together by the weight of the material above them.

The sedimentary rocks may be buried deep within the earth. There they can be changed into metamorphic rock by heat, pressure, and the action of liquids and gases.

Rock cycle

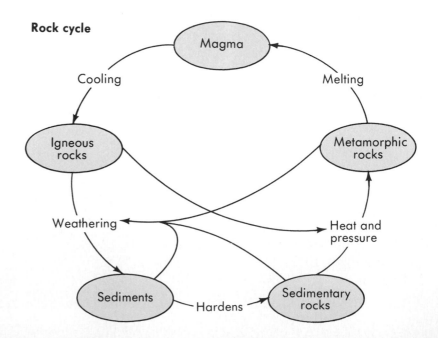

The Green River—100 years ago

The Green River—today

If the metamorphic rocks are exposed to more heat and pressure, they may melt into a magma. When the magma cools, igneous rocks form. The rock cycle begins again.

Sometimes the rock cycle is interrupted. Intrusive igneous rocks, for example, may not be exposed at the earth's surface. If heat and pressure act on them, they may change directly into metamorphic rocks. But the basic flow of the rock cycle is always the same. As one type of rock is destroyed, other types of rock are formed.

The rock cycle acts continuously but very slowly. Big changes in rocks usually take millions of years. Hundreds of years from now, the land around you may look the same as it does today. The two photographs show the Green River in Utah as it looked more than 100 years ago and as it appears today.

Review It

1. What causes sedimentary or igneous rocks to change into metamorphic rocks?
2. Explain what the rock cycle is.

153

Activity

A Variety of Rocks

Purpose
To identify rocks.

Materials
• unknown rocks, numbered
• dilute hydrochloric acid
• knife blade or nail
• hand lens
• colored pencils or crayons

Procedure

Part A
1. Divide a sheet of paper into five columns as shown in *a*. Notice that the columns are different widths. The fourth and fifth columns are the widest.
2. At the head of the first column write UNKNOWN SAMPLE. Title the remaining columns as follows: ROCK NAME, ROCK FAMILY, DRAWING, OBSERVATIONS.
3. Write the number of each of the rock samples down the left side of the page, as shown.

4. Use the key, *b*, on the opposite page to identify the unknown rocks. Indicate whether the sample belongs to the igneous, sedimentary, or metamorphic family. Allow enough space in the fourth column to draw and color each rock.
5. Record any unusual features of the unknown sample in the OBSERVATION column.

Part B
1. Sometimes it is very difficult to tell whether a rock is igneous, sedimentary, or metamorphic. Make a table, such as that shown at the bottom of *a*.
2. List as many outstanding features as you can think of for each family of rocks. You may use information from the book or features that you have observed.

a

Unknown sample	Rock name	Rock family	Drawing	Observations
1.				
2.				
3				

Features that might help identify rocks

Igneous	Sedimentary	Metamorphic

b

Rock Identification Key

Name of rock	Description
1. Basalt	dark gray to black; crystals not usually visible; heavier than #10
2. Bituminous	soft, shiny coal; cannot be scratched by fingernail
3. Conglomerate	cemented pebbles
4. Gabbro	large, dark, interlocking crystals
5. Gneiss	bands of color that may or may not be bent; often visible crystals
6. Granite	interlocking pink, gray, and dark crystals
7. Limestone	may contain tiny shells or interlocking crystals; usually light-colored; fizzes in acid
8. Marble	color varies; may appear very crystalline; fizzes in acid
9. Obsidian	dark; glassy-looking; fractures with curved surface
10. Pumice	lightweight and holey; looks like a cinder; comes from volcanoes
11. Rhyolite	pinkish-tan; crystals not visible without magnification
12. Sandstone	cemented sand grains; color may vary
13. Schist	may have long stretched crystals; may shimmer or look flaky
14. Shale	color varies but usually dark; smells musty when it is moistened
15. Slate	looks like a piece of blackboard; harder than #14

Analysis

1. Suggest why two samples of one rock type may look different.
2. Why do both marble and limestone react with hydrochloric acid?
3. How is the formation of shale and slate different?
4. What might cause crystals to line up or bands of color to form in gneiss?
5. Why are most of the rocks that we see at the surface of the earth in the sedimentary family?
6. What family of rocks makes up most of the outer 16 km of the earth? Explain your answer.
7. Imagine that you are taking a hike and find two rocks that you want to identify. One light-colored rock has large crystals of various colors—pink, clear, and dark. The other rock is greenish-black and appears to be layered. It is not very hard and easily splits into thin pieces. Try to identify these rocks.

8–4
Valuable Minerals and Oil

Minerals are of great interest to earth scientists because they are vital to our lives. Cars, paper clips, and refrigerators are only a few items that are made of minerals taken from the ground. Except for food, almost everything we use is taken from the earth's crust. As you read, ask yourself:

a. What are some ways that minerals are concentrated in the crust?
b. How are oil and sedimentary rocks related?

How Are Valuable Minerals Concentrated in a Small Area?

The mineral deposits that we use today formed millions of years ago. Deposits that contain a large amount of metallic minerals are **ores.** Ores and important mineral deposits developed in many different ways.

Valuable minerals may separate from magma and crystallize just as crystals of sugar form in a pan of boiling fudge. These minerals are trapped when magma hardens. Many metals, such as copper and platinum, were concentrated in this way.

Many ores form when hot water or gases with dissolved minerals escape from the magma into the cracks and spaces in the rocks surrounding the magma. The minerals and fluids may harden into veins, such as the quartz vein in the picture. Often the minerals and fluids react with the minerals in the surrounding rocks and change them into valuable ore minerals.

Many ore deposits are the result of water and air acting on rocks. Water and air break down and change the minerals in feldspars. In tropical climates, aluminum ores may develop from the changed feldspar minerals.

Water moving through the ground can also concentrate ore minerals. This water can dissolve a valuable mineral that is scattered across a large region. If the water concentrates the mineral in a small area, the mineral becomes an ore. Copper ores that formed in this way are mined in Bingham Canyon, Utah.

A quartz vein

Inside a salt mine

Running water flushes gold, diamonds, and some heavy metals out of rocks and into rivers. Diamonds and metals are dense and théy do not break down. Therefore, they soon drop to the river bottom. In the late 1800s, miners in South Africa discovered diamonds in a stream. They followed the trail of the diamonds up the stream. There they found a large diamond deposit in igneous rocks.

Rock salt, gypsum, and other minerals are left behind when salty seas evaporate. This type of mineral deposit is common throughout the world. Buried rock salt deposits stretch across thousands of square kilometers in western Texas and New Mexico. The photograph shows workers in a salt mine in this region. Salt deposits are usually very thick. One mine in Europe has been producing salt for over 2,000 years.

We use sand and gravel deposits to make buildings and roads. Many of these deposits—especially across the northern United States—were left thousands of years ago when glaciers melted.

For the most part, the hundreds of minerals that we take from the ground have a one-time use. Once they are taken from the ground, they are gone forever. We are now using many low-grade ores of vital minerals. That means that the concentration of ore mineral in the deposit is not high.

Oil Forms in Sedimentary Rocks

Oil is our most widely used energy source. Oil and natural gas are commonly found together in sedimentary rocks. Both are compounds of carbon and hydrogen that are similar to the carbon compounds found in living animals and plants. For this reason, scientists think that oil and gas form where sea life dies and drops to the bottom of ocean water. Oil probably develops best in shallow, still water. Conditions favorable for oil formation are found in the shallow ocean water around continents. In time, the animal and plant remains are covered with sediments of mud, clay, and sand that later become sedimentary rocks.

After millions of years, the buried remains change into oil and gas. Oil will not form when heat and pressure on the buried remains exceed a certain limit. Instead, the deposit may yield natural gas, as well as carbon compounds that are of little value.

The muddy sediments that bury the remains often become shale. As sediments are pressed into shale, oil and gas are often squeezed out of the rocks. At this point, oil and gas may escape into **permeable** (per′mē ə bəl) **rock.** Permeable rock, such as sandstone, has pores, or spaces, that are connected. Fluids, such as oil and gas, can pass through the connected spaces and fill any permeable rock that happens to be nearby.

Just as oil floats on water in an unmixed salad dressing, oil and gas move above the water level in the sandstone. The drawing illustrates this.

Oil and gas in permeable sandstone

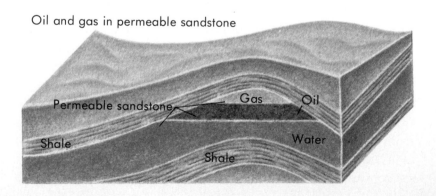

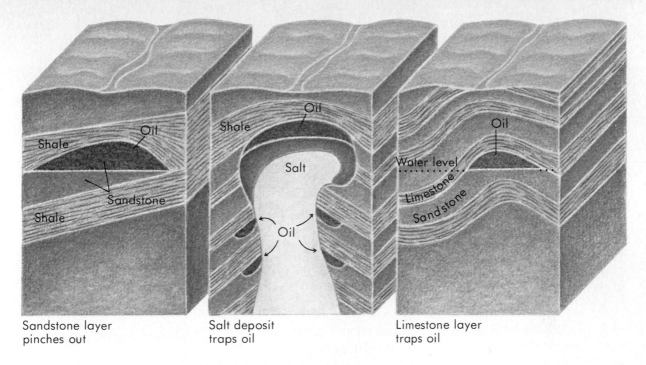

Sandstone layer
pinches out

Salt deposit
traps oil

Limestone layer
traps oil

For a large deposit of oil and gas to accumulate, there must be a "trap." A bed of rock, such as shale, can trap the oil and gas and keep it from moving away. Since the trap rock is not permeable, the oil and gas are imprisoned. The illustration shows three ways that oil is trapped. A large accumulation of oil in the pores and cracks of rock is called an oil pool.

Many rock structures provide ideal conditions for the accumulation of gas and oil. Oil and gas deposits are common throughout the world. In the United States, however, we have already discovered and used a great deal of our biggest deposits. It will take millions of years for big oil deposits to develop again.

Review It

1. Explain three ways that minerals can be concentrated into a small area.
2. Why is some kind of trap necessary for a large accumulation of oil and gas?
3. Why is oil stored in sedimentary rocks rather than in igneous or metamorphic rocks?

Activity

Permeable Layers

Purpose
To see how liquid moves through different materials.

Materials
- water
- sand
- gravel or small pebbles
- patching plaster
- modeling clay
- one empty glass jar
- stirrer or spoon
- small container
- graduated cylinder
- meter stick
- pencil, pen, or sharp, pointed tool

Procedure
1. You will make four layers of equal thickness in the glass jar, as illustrated in *a*. Decide how many cm thick each layer must be for all four layers to fill the jar about 3/4 full.
2. Pour a layer of sand to the desired thickness in the bottom of the jar.
3. Next, add the clay. Press it against the sides of the jar to seal any openings.
4. Third, add a layer of gravel.
5. In the small container, mix about 50 mL of plaster with just enough water to make the plaster *damp*. If the mixture is too wet, add a little more plaster. Now scoop the plaster into the jar.
6. Let the jar sit until the plaster hardens. While you are waiting, draw the jar and its contents. Label the layers.
7. Pour a small amount of water on the layers in the jar. Observe what happens. Indicate the results on your diagram of the jar.
8. Carefully pour off any water that has not soaked into the layers.
9. Use a pencil or pen point to crack the plaster in one or two small spots. Be very careful not to disturb the other layers.
10. Add a small amount of water again. Record on your diagram whether the water reached the bottom of the jar.

Analysis
1. Compare porous rock with permeable rock.
2. What type of sedimentary rock might each layer represent?
3. Which layers were permeable?
4. Which layers in your model might serve as a trap for oil and gas?
5. Draw an area on your diagram where a mineral ore might accumulate. Explain how it might happen.

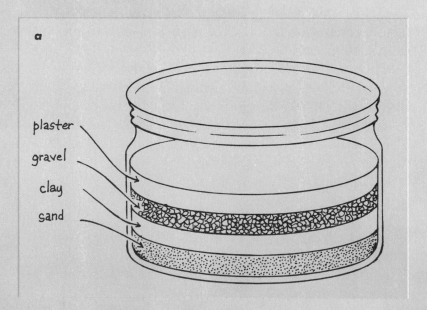

a

plaster
gravel
clay
sand

Did You Know?

The Great Ore Hunt

Many metals are in short supply. As a result, scientists have begun to look in some unusual places for ores. One of these places is the ocean.

Many nodules or clumps of metallic ores rest on the ocean bottoms. The nodules contain copper, cobalt, zinc, lead, manganese, and other metals. But nodules are found from 4,000 to 6,000 meters below the ocean's surface. Scientists have designed ships and special tools to scoop up minerals at this depth.

Another place we can tap large deposits of metals is Antarctica. This region does not look inviting to miners because more than 98% of the continent is covered with ice. But explorers have reported that the minerals are there in abundance. As minerals become more scarce, Antarctica looks more inviting.

The most remote place to search for ores and minerals is outer space. We know that the moon contains many of the same minerals found on Earth. NASA has suggested mining the moon's surface. The ores could be towed to Earth in "space trains."

Another idea calls for mining the small meteoroids that have orbits which intersect or come close to the earth's orbit around the sun. A meteoroid could be captured and towed into the earth's orbit. Then ores could be mined as the meteoroid orbits the earth.

Years ago these ideas were found only in science-fiction stories. Now scientists are seriously thinking about unconventional, new ways to get mineral resources.

For Discussion
1. What are some unusual places to find minerals?
2. What are some advantages of mining in space?

Mining a meteoroid

Chapter Summary

- Intrusive igneous rocks, such as granite, form when magma cools below the earth's surface. (8–1)

- Extrusive igneous rocks, such as basalt, form when lava cools on the earth's surface. (8–1)

- Sedimentary rocks form when sediments are cemented or pressed together, minerals separate from the water in which they are dissolved, and animal or plant remains harden. (8–2)

- Metamorphic rocks form from older rocks that are changed by heat, pressure, or liquids and gases that escape from magma. (8–3)

- The rock cycle is a repeating process that changes one type of rock into another type. (8–3)

- Valuable minerals are concentrated into small areas in a variety of ways. (8–4)

- Oil and gas are the remains of sea plants and animals that are found in sedimentary rock layers. (8–4)

Interesting Reading

Kerrod, Robin. *Rocks and Minerals.* Warwick, 1977. Discusses the three rock families, mineral ores, and rocks from other worlds.

Shedenhelm, W. R. C. *The Young Rockhound's Handbook.* Putnam, 1978. Explains how to identify rocks and minerals, how to display a collection, and where to get various equipment and supplies.

Questions/Problems

1. What does the length of cooling time have to do with crystal size?

2. Peridotite (pə rid′ə tīt) is a very dark igneous rock. Predict two minerals that it may contain.

3. Name two rocks mentioned in this chapter that can be identified by the acid test.

4. How is the way that sandstone formed different from the way that shale formed?

5. The earth's crust is about 6% iron on the average. Does this mean that a mining company could mine iron anywhere on the crust? Explain.

6. Give one example each of a way an ore might form in an igneous, metamorphic, or sedimentary rock layer.

7. Suggest the history of a vein of copper in a mountain in Colorado.

Extra Research

1. Write one paragraph each about the rocks found at the Garden of the Gods in Colorado, the Palisades in New York and New Jersey, and the White Cliffs of Dover in England. Use an encyclopedia to find your information.

2. Identify and list four types of stone used in buildings in your area.

3. Write to your state geologic survey to learn what are the most important ores and nonmetallic minerals in your state. Find out how they developed and the type of rocks in which they are present.

4. Write a one-page report on the most important ores of iron. Tell how they formed and where the big deposits of the world are located.

Chapter Test

A. Vocabulary Write the numbers 1–10 on a piece of paper.
Match the definition in Column I with the term it defines in Column II.

Column I

1. molten rock material inside the earth

2. rock that allows water to pass through it

3. igneous rock that forms from cooled magma

4. igneous rock that forms from cooled lava

5. rock formed from pebbles or gravel cemented together

6. shale changed by pressure and heat

7. useful carbon and hydrogen compound

8. rock pieces of different sizes

9. strong building rock that can be highly polished

10. mineral or rock containing a large concentration of a valuable metal

Column II

a. conglomerate

b. extrusive igneous rock

c. intrusive igneous rock

d. magma

e. marble

f. oil

g. ore

h. permeable rock

i. sediment

j. slate

B. Multiple Choice Write the numbers 1–10 on your paper.
Choose the letter that best completes the statement or answers the question.

1. When hot magma cools slowly, the rocks that form a) have large mineral crystals. b) contain no minerals. c) are glass. d) have small mineral crystals.

2. All the following are extrusive igneous rocks except a) obsidian. b) basalt. c) volcanic glass. d) granite.

3. Dark igneous rock that contains iron and magnesium probably contains a large amount of the mineral a) calcite. b) fluorite. c) olivine. d) quartz.

4. A sedimentary rock that often contains fossils is a) rock salt. b) algae. c) granite. d) limestone.

5. Chalk is a) an igneous rock. b) a metamorphic rock. c) an ore. d) a sedimentary rock.

6. Metamorphic rocks form a) from igneous rocks only. b) from sedimentary rocks only. c) from igneous and sedimentary rocks only. d) from igneous, sedimentary, and other metamorphic rocks.

7. All of the following are metamorphic rocks except a) marble. b) schist. c) gneiss. d) shale.

8. All the following are important ores except a) iron. b) silver. c) diamonds. d) gold.

9. Valuable mineral and rock deposits may be concentrated by a) separation within magma. b) the action of fluids and gases that leave magma. c) water moving through the ground. d) a, b, and c.

10. This condition is *not* found at a large oil deposit. a) permeable rock to hold the oil b) gas c) a "trap" to stop the oil's escape d) high temperatures

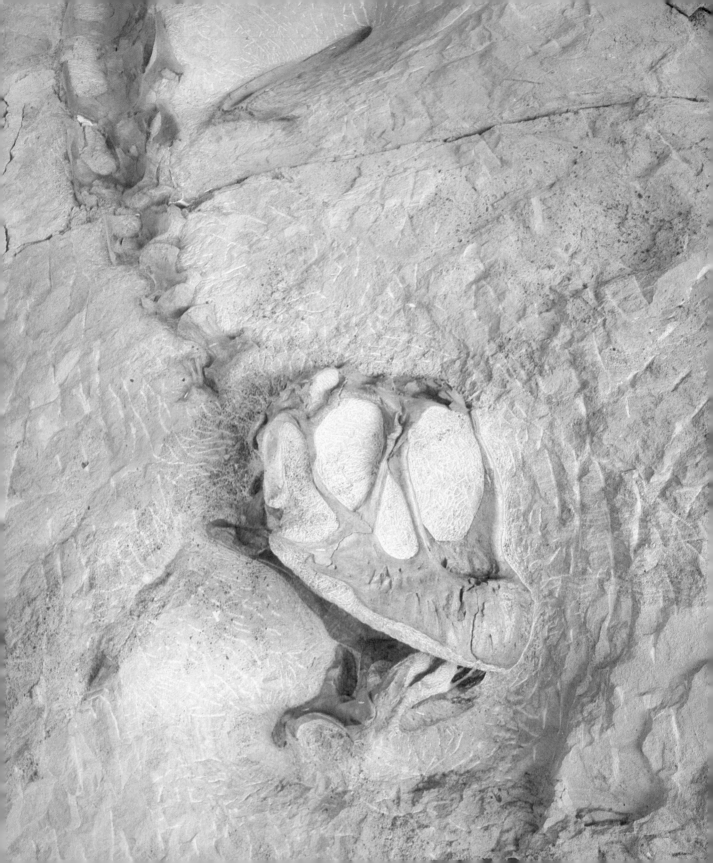

Chapter 9
Learning About the Earth's Past

The only records scientists have of things that happened on earth millions of years ago are the rocks that have been preserved since those times. Some rocks, like those shown at the left, contain the remains of dinosaurs. Dinosaur remains in these rocks tell us that these animals once lived where the rocks were found. Not all rocks tell their stories so clearly and dramatically, but most rocks can tell us something about the earth's past.

In this chapter you will discover how scientists have unfolded the earth's history. You will learn how fossils form and how they help us learn about the earth's history. You will also read about the eras of geologic time. In the last section, you will find out how radioactive dating allows scientists to determine the age of rocks and fossils.

Chapter Objectives

1. Explain the principle of superposition and the principle of uniform processes.
2. List four ways fossils form.
3. Explain how fossils help us learn about the earth's history.
4. Name the four eras of geologic time and describe a major event in each.
5. Explain how radioactive dating allows scientists to determine the age of rocks and fossils.

9–1
The Present Is the Key to the Past

The Grand Canyon is a striking sight to anyone who sees it. But what can a geologist learn from it? This section explains two principles that help geologists figure out the geologic history of specific places and how to extend that knowledge to other places on earth. As you read, keep the following questions in mind:

a. What is the principle of superposition?
b. What is the principle of uniform processes?

The Principle of Superposition

Look closely at the picture of the Grand Canyon. You can see the many horizontal layers typical of sedimentary rock. The layers of sediment that first settled and hardened into rock are at the bottom of the rock formation.

This simple observation applies to all rock formations that have not been overturned or changed since their original formation. The oldest rock layer is at the bottom. Each higher layer of rock is younger. Scientists call this observation the **principle of superposition** (sü′pər pə zish′ən), from the Latin words meaning *placed over*.

The Grand Canyon

The rock layers of the Grand Canyon are a record of its history, as though the earth had taken notes. By studying the rock layers, scientists learn about the climate and living things that existed long ago. A geologist "reads" the walls of the Grand Canyon as you might read a detective story.

The Principle of Uniform Processes

One clue about the origin of the Grand Canyon comes from the fact that a river, the Colorado River, flows deep inside the canyon. Scientists think that the river wore its way through solid rock to cut the canyon, which is now over a kilometer deep.

Running water carries away rock in the process called erosion (i rō'zhən). We know that erosion takes place around us today. Rivers deepen their channels and sometimes change their courses. Rain washes soil from lawns onto streets and sidewalks. Oceans make sand by pounding away at the shore.

Just as we see erosion taking place around us today, erosion has been taking place all through earth's history. The idea that the present tells us about the past is a principle of geology known as the **principle of uniform processes.** It tells us that the processes that are at work in changing the earth's surface today are the same processes that have been acting since the earth formed.

A very long time must pass for processes such as erosion to cause large changes. Scientists say the earth changed over "geologic time." We use this phrase to talk about changes that take many thousands to millions of years.

Review It

1. Where would you look to find the oldest rocks in the Grand Canyon? Why?
2. Explain the principle of uniform processes.

9–2
Fossils Tell Us About the Past

When geologists study the rocks of the Grand Canyon they may find fossils, the remains of living things from the past. Just as the oldest layers of rock are on the bottom of the canyon, the oldest fossils also lie close to the bottom. Scientists can tell from the fossils what life was like millions of years before people existed on earth. As you read, ask yourself:

a. How do fossils form?
b. What do scientists learn from fossils?

How Fossils Form

When living things die, they usually decay or are eaten by other living things. But, if a living thing has hard parts, such as wood, teeth, bones, or shells, it has a chance to survive. If it dies in a place where it will be quickly buried by sediment, it stands an even better chance of being preserved.

Fossils form in several ways. The plant or animal may become **petrified** (pet′rə fĭd), which means turned into stone. The wood pictured below was petrified when the substances in it were dissolved by water and replaced a molecule at a time by different minerals. Even the tiniest parts of the petrified wood were preserved.

Occasionally scientists find the **actual remains** of living things of long ago. The picture below shows an ant that was trapped in amber (am′bər), the sap of a tree from long ago. Notice that every part of the ant is preserved.

Petrified wood

Ant in amber

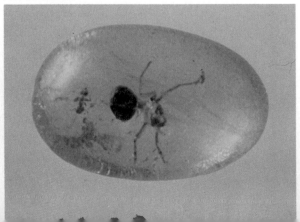

Some fossil remains are traces or **imprints** of the living thing. For example, the dinosaur footprints shown at the right were preserved in mud, which later became shale.

Fossils may form as a **carbon imprint.** Living things are composed mainly of carbon, hydrogen, and oxygen. Hydrogen and oxygen disappear after the death of the living thing. Occasionally, a thin film of carbon remains, leaving an imprint of the life form. The leaf shown to the right has been preserved in this manner as a "carbon copy."

Some fossils form when sediment buries a sea animal on the sea floor. Bit by bit, water dissolves the minerals that make up the original shell. The surrounding sediment hardens, making a hollow *mold* that has the features of the original shell. Sometimes other minerals slowly fill the mold, forming a *cast* that shows the original form of the animal.

The cast and the mold shown below are fossils of *trilobites* (trī⁄lə bīts), ancient sea animals that no longer exist. Trilobites are easy to identify because their bodies are divided into three parts.

Carbon imprint

Cast

Mold

What Scientists Learn from Fossils

The study of fossils gives clues to how living things have changed over time. We also learn a great deal about changes in geography and climate. For example, we know that Greenland once had a tropical climate, because fossil palm trees and magnolias have been found there.

Fossils found in the Grand Canyon also tell us about life millions of years ago. As you can see in the marginal picture, the oldest rocks have no fossils. Some of the early fossils that appear in the rocks are trilobites. Above the trilobites in the Grand Canyon, bones of fish and fossils of other sea life are found. Further up the rock layers, geologists have found remains of reptiles and land plants. Above these layers are tracks of other land animals. And above these fossils, more sea-life forms are found. This fossil record indicates that the sea covered the Grand Canyon three different times.

Fossils that help scientists determine the age of rocks are **index fossils.** These fossils represent forms of life that lived over a wide area for a short period of geologic time. Trilobites are index fossils. When scientists find fossils of trilobites anywhere in the world, they know that the rocks containing these fossils all formed during the same geologic time span.

The study of fossils also helps geologists in their search for oil and coal. Certain fossils appear in or near coal or oil deposits. Therefore, geologists hunt new deposits where rock layers contain the same fossils.

Review It

1. Name four ways fossils form.
2. How do index fossils help scientists determine the age of rocks?

Top of
main canyon rim

Sea life

Sea life

Land animal tracks

Plants

Reptiles

Sea life

Fish bones

Trilobites

Trilobites

No fossils

Colorado River

Activity

Making Fossils

Purpose

To make models of fossil casts and molds.

Materials

- 1 small seashell
- petroleum jelly
- plaster of Paris
- water
- 1 small plastic cup
- mixing container
- stirring rod
- food coloring
- graduated cylinder
- screwdriver

Procedure

Part A

1. Cover the outside of the seashell with a thin film of petroleum jelly as shown in *a*.
2. Pour about 75 mL of water into the container.
3. Slowly pour plaster of Paris into the water. Mix as you pour. Add plaster of Paris until the mixture resembles thick cream. If your mixture is too thick, add more water. If your mixture is too thin, add more plaster of Paris.
4. Pour the plaster of Paris mixture into the plastic cup. Tap the cup to eliminate air bubbles.

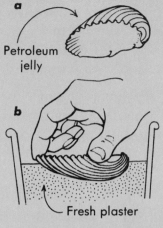

Petroleum jelly

Fresh plaster

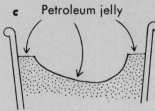

Petroleum jelly

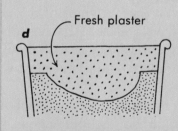

Fresh plaster

5. Press the greased outside of the seashell into the plaster of Paris, as shown in *b*. Do not let the plaster flow into the shell. Do not submerge the shell.
6. Let the plaster harden overnight. Then remove the shell from the plaster.

Part B

1. Coat the surface of the hardened plaster with petroleum jelly as in *c*.
2. Mix another batch of plaster according to the instructions in step 3, Part A. Add a little food coloring to the mixture.
3. Cover the plaster model you made of the outside of the shell in Part A with the fresh plaster, as shown in *d*. Let the plaster harden overnight.
4. Carefully separate the two blocks of plaster. You may need to use a screwdriver to pry them apart.

Analysis

1. What are the terms used to describe the models you made in Part A and Part B?
2. Suggest how a cast of a shell might be made in nature.
3. Why would you not expect to find a mold or cast of a jellyfish?
4. Name one way the plaster of Paris models differ from the formation of a fossil mold or cast found in nature.
5. Compare plants and animals that are petrified with your model. How do the results differ?

9-3
The Eras of Geologic Time

Perhaps your parents keep a "Baby Book" or your family keeps an album to record special events in your family's life. By studying rocks, earth scientists have put together a record of the earth's history. This record is the geologic time scale. As you read, think about these questions:

a. What major changes occurred during the Precambrian?
b. What important natural resources and life forms developed during the Paleozoic?
c. What forms of life were common during the Mesozoic?
d. What forms of life were common during the Cenozoic?

The Earth's Beginnings in the Precambrian Era

Scientists think the earth is about 4.5 billion years old. Earth scientists divide the history of the earth into four main geologic time periods called **eras** (ir′əz). The first era, the **Precambrian** (prē′kām′brē ən), was the longest and is least understood. Approximately 85 percent of all the earth's history occurred during the Precambrian era.

At the beginning of this era, the earth formed. Millions of years passed before a rock crust developed. Later, the oceans developed and air surrounded the earth. Simple life forms appeared, but most were not preserved in the fossil record.

Precambrian rocks, such as the granite in the photograph, are the foundations of continents. They are called **shields** (shēldz). Many great mineral deposits are located in these rocks, which are hidden under younger rocks.

Have You Heard?

Scientists have found tiny, threadlike fossil cells in some rocks of western Australia. These fossils, which are about 3.5 billion years old, are among the oldest known evidence of life. They lived in a shallow sea that covered western Australia during the Precambrian era.

The Precambrian rocks in the Canadian Shield of North America are the largest single region of Precambrian rocks in the world.

The Paleozoic Era

The **Paleozoic** (pā′lē ə zō′ik) era began about 600 million years ago with the appearance of sea life, such as trilobites, snails, and sponges. Before the era ended, 225 million years ago, the first land plants appeared. Animals such as amphibians and reptiles also appeared on land.

A variety of natural resources formed during the second half of the Paleozoic era. Coal, oil, and natural gas are called fossil fuels because they formed from things that were once alive, beginning in the Paleozoic era. Most of our coal formed during this era in swamp areas that covered much of the land.

Buried plants go through a series of changes before they turn into coal, as you can see in the picture. First, dead and decaying plants accumulate and form a soft material called **peat** (pēt). When peat is buried, layers of sediment change it into **lignite** (lig′nīt), a woody, brown coal. As heat and pressure increase, lignite forms soft coal, or **bituminous** (bə tü′mə nəs). This type of coal burns with a smoky flame. Where the heat and pressure are greatest, **anthracite** (an′thrə sīt), or hard coal, forms. Anthracite burns with a smokeless flame and produces a great amount of heat.

In addition to coal, some oil and gas are found in rocks of the Paleozoic era. Wells drilled into sandstone in western Texas have produced oil formed during this era.

Have You Heard?

Imagine meeting a dragonfly with a 73 centimeter wing span or a cockroach 10 centimeters long! Primitive insects of astounding sizes appeared in Paleozoic times.

How coal forms

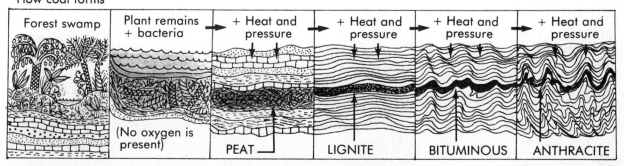

173

The Mesozoic Era

The **Mesozoic** (mes′ə zō′ik) era began about 225 million years ago and ended about 65 million years ago. The climate during this period was generally mild. Many forms of life flourished, as you can see in the picture.

Small mammals and birds first appeared during the Mesozoic. Most insects, such as flies, ants, termites, and moths, also lived in Mesozoic times. But this era is sometimes called the Age of Reptiles, because reptiles were so large and so numerous. Snakes, lizards, alligators, and turtles are all reptiles.

The ruling reptiles of this era were the dinosaurs. Scientists are able to reconstruct the skeletons of some of these animals from fossil bones found in the ground. By the end of the Mesozoic, the dinosaurs had died out completely.

Rocks formed during this era contain many important natural resources, including uranium ores used for nuclear fuels. Mesozoic rocks, especially those in the Middle East, hold about 25 percent of the world's supply of oil and gas. The Rocky Mountains, formed during this era, also contain oil and gas deposits.

Have You Heard?

Before the end of the Mesozoic era, forests of trees that shed their leaves seasonally sprang up. These modern trees—maple, birch, walnut, oak, beech, and others—competed for space. Before that, evergreen forests dominated the landscape.

174

From Early Cenozoic to the Present

We are living in the **Cenozoic** (sen/ə zō/ik), which began about 65 million years ago. Landforms that we see today developed in the Cenozoic.

During the Cenozoic, many mountain chains formed, including the Alps and Himalayas. In North America, the Coast Range of California and Oregon and the Cascade Mountains of Oregon and Washington formed.

About 60 percent of the world's oil has been found in Cenozoic rocks. Coal, gold, tin, copper, and silver also appear in Cenozoic rocks.

The climate late in this era became much colder than during the Mesozoic era. Several Ice Ages took place, where huge sheets of ice covered great expanses of land.

Changes in climate during the Cenozoic caused changes in life forms. Large mammals appeared that could live in the extreme cold, such as the woolly mammoth you see below. Remains of the woolly mammoths have been found frozen in northern Siberia. Other very large animals lived farther south where it was warmer. It was toward the end of the Cenozoic that humans first appeared.

Review It

1. In what era did the earth form?
2. In what era did most of our coal form?
3. In what era did the dinosaurs live?
4. In what era did many *large* mammals appear?

Trilobites
Snails
Ferns
Insects
Fishes
Amphibians
and Reptiles

Dinosaurs
Turtles
Crocodiles
Lizards
Snakes
Early mammals
Plants with seeds

Large mammals—
Woolly mammoths
Ancestors of modern mammals
Ancestors of modern plants

Simple one-celled organisms

Precambrian

Paleozoic

Mesozoic

Cenozoic

Years Since the Beginning of Era

← 4.5 Billion

600 Million ↗ 225 Million ↗ ↖ 65 Million

Did You Know?

What Happened to the Dinosaurs?

For 150 million years dinosaurs lived on every continent but Antarctica. Some were little chicken-sized dinosaurs. Others weighed as much as fifty tons. No larger animals ever lived on land.

Then a strange thing happened. About 65 million years ago, dinosaurs suddenly became extinct. All dinosaurs disappeared from the face of the earth.

Many ideas have been suggested to explain this catastrophe. Perhaps the earth's climate became too warm or too cold for dinosaurs. Or perhaps a terrible disease swept through the dinosaurs, killing them all. Possibly animals or plants basic to the dinosaurs' food chain became extinct, and the dinosaurs starved.

Many attempts have been made to explain the mystery of the dinosaurs. Now some exciting new information from the geologic record suggests another possible cause for the disappearance of dinosaurs.

Scientists working at Berkeley, California, proposed a startling reason for the disappearance. They found unusually high amounts of the rare element iridium in sedimentary deposits in Italy and Denmark. Iridium is rare in the earth's crust. The scientists believe it must have come from outer space. They suggest that the earth collided with an asteroid as large as 10 kilometers in diameter. This would explain the high concentration of iridium in certain places. Also, such a tremendous crash would cause a huge crater. Since no crater of the right size and age has been found, they suggest that the asteroid crashed into the ocean. The crash of an asteroid would probably send clouds of dirt and dust into the air for months.

Perhaps, they say, this darkening of the land began the changes that caused the extinction of the dinosaurs. Certainly it would cause severe changes in climate. Many answers to the dinosaur mystery may yet be locked in the rocks.

For Discussion
1. How long did dinosaurs rule the earth?
2. How could months of darkness cause dinosaurs to become extinct?

An asteroid hits the earth

9—4
Clocks in Rocks Tell Us About the Past

When earth scientists first began to construct the geologic time scale, they could tell only if one layer of rock was older than another. Today, scientists have methods for learning how old rocks actually are. Ask yourself these questions as you read:

a. How do radioactive elements behave?
b. How does carbon 14 help date fossils?

Radioactive Elements Decay

Rocks, like everything else, are composed of atoms. Some rocks contain forms of elements whose atoms change over time. These elements are **radioactive.** The atoms of radioactive elements break apart, or **decay**, to form other elements or other forms of the same element. The length of time that it takes for half the atoms of a radioactive element to decay is the **half-life** of the element.

Scientists measure the half-lives of elements in rocks to tell the ages of the rocks. It is as if the rocks had clocks inside them, ticking off the years since the rocks formed.

Mass spectrometers (spek trom/ə tərz) are instruments used to measure the decay rate of radioactive elements.

These instruments have revealed the ages of earth rocks and lunar—or moon—rocks. The photograph shows a mass spectrometer at the California Institute of Technology. Dr. Gerald Wasserburg jokingly calls it "Lunatic" because scientists used it to examine lunar rocks. Even microscopic pieces of moon rock are large enough to test with this sensitive instrument.

Uranium 238 (^{238}U) is a form of uranium. Scientists have learned that it takes 4.5 billion years for half of a given amount of ^{238}U to decay into a form of lead, lead 206 (^{206}Pb). The half-life of ^{238}U is therefore 4.5 billion years. If a rock sample contains as much ^{206}Pb as ^{238}U, then half the ^{238}U must have changed to this form of lead. (No ^{206}Pb was present at the beginning.) Therefore, the rock sample is 4.5 billion years old.

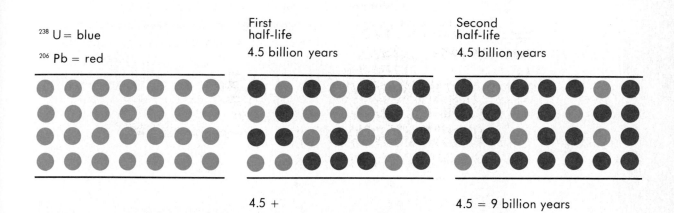

^{238} U = blue

^{206} Pb = red

First
half-life
4.5 billion years

Second
half-life
4.5 billion years

4.5 +

4.5 = 9 billion years

The diagram pictures the rate of decay of ^{238}U atoms into ^{206}Pb atoms. The blue dots represent atoms of ^{238}U. The red dots represent atoms of ^{206}Pb. After 4.5 billion years, or one half-life, the amount of ^{238}U decreases by half. Notice that one-half the blue dots have changed to red. At the end of a second half-life, or another 4.5 billion years, the amount of ^{238}U will decrease by one-half again. Notice that three-quarters of the ^{238}U has changed to ^{206}Pb. This process continues as time passes, regardless of what happens to the rocks.

Finding Ages with Carbon 14

Radioactive carbon is used to figure out the ages of materials that once lived, such as wood, bones, and shells. Carbon 14 (^{14}C), a radioactive form of carbon, decays into nitrogen 14 (^{14}N). ^{14}C has a half-life of 5,730 years, which means that half the ^{14}C will change to ^{14}N in 5,730 years.

All living things contain the same percentage of ^{14}C compared to other forms of carbon. But once a plant or animal dies, it takes in no more ^{14}C. Whatever ^{14}C is already within the plant or animal continues to decay, however. By comparing the amount of ^{14}C in the material to the amount of other forms of carbon, scientists can measure how long ago the sample died.

The diagram below shows how ^{14}C dating works. Remember that after each half-life, 5,730 years, the amount of ^{14}C has decreased by one-half. Notice that after one half-life, or 5,730 years, half the ^{14}C atoms are left, and so on.

^{14}C is used to measure the age of materials that lived within the last 50,000 years. In fossils older than this, almost all the ^{14}C has decayed. A study of the amount of ^{14}C in European and North American fossil wood led scientists to conclude that the last sheets of ice retreated from these areas around 11,000 years ago.

Review It

1. What is a radioactive element?
2. What is meant by the half-life of an element?

The leaf dies, but radioactive decay continues

^{14}C = red dots

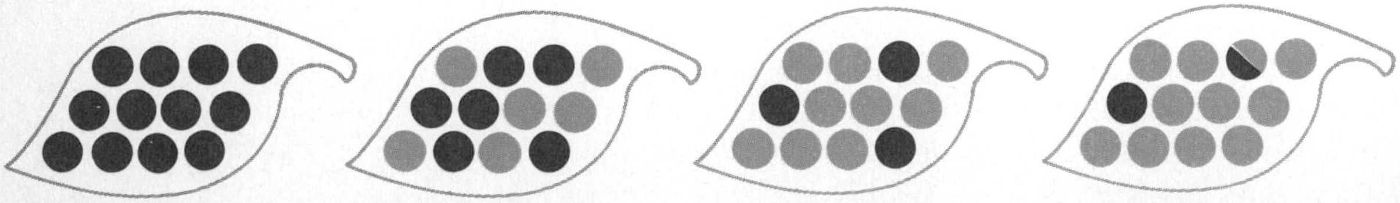

One half-life
½ the ^{14}C is left

5730 +

Second half-life
¼ the ^{14}C is left

5730 +

Third half-life
⅛ the ^{14}C is left

5730   = 17,190 years

Activity

Half-Life Model

Purpose
To demonstrate that radioactive decay takes place at a predictable rate.

Materials
- 100 white beans
- shoe box and lid
- felt-tip marker
- pencil
- graph paper

Procedure

Part A
1. Use the marker to put an "X" on one side of each bean. The beans represent radioactive atoms.
2. Put the beans in the box and put the lid on the box. The box represents anything that contains atoms, living or non-living.
3. Shake the box several times. Remove the lid and take out the beans that are "X" side up.
4. Count the beans that remain and record this number. Each counting represents one half-life.
5. Repeat this procedure four more times. Be sure to count and record the number of beans that are left each time.

Part B
1. Make a graph like the one shown in *a*. Label the horizontal and vertical axes as shown. Enter your five bean counts in the proper places on the graph. Put a dot at the 100 mark on the vertical axis.
2. Draw a line connecting the six points you marked on the graph.

Analysis
1. About what fraction of the 100 beans remained in the box after each count?
2. Suppose 2,000 years passed each time the beans were counted. Let the box with 100 beans represent an animal at the time of its death. If the animal contained 25 "beans" when it was found, how long has the animal been dead?
3. Suppose you put black beans in the box with the white beans. The black beans are not removed no matter how many times you shake the box. Do the black beans undergo radioactive decay? Explain.
4. Why does another kind of atom, instead of carbon 14, have to be used to date living things millions of years old?

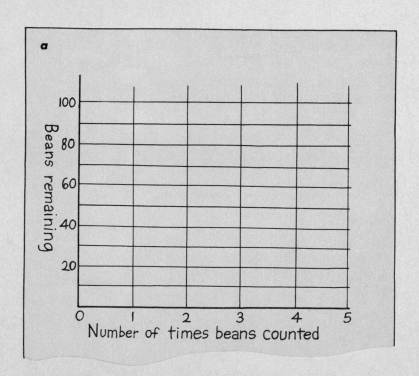

Chapter Summary

- The principle of superposition tells us that in all rock formations that have not been changed since their formation, the oldest rock layer is at the bottom. Each higher layer is increasingly younger. (9–1)

- The principle of uniform processes tells us that processes that are at work in changing the earth's surface today are the same processes that have been acting since the earth formed. (9–1)

- Fossils may be petrified by mineral replacement or carbonized. Fossils are also found as molds and casts and in impressions. Occasionally actual remains of living things of long ago are found. (9–2)

- Fossils teach us how life, land conditions, and climates changed over geologic time. Fossil study also helps in the search for oil and coal. (9–2)

- The earth formed in the Precambrian era about 4.5 billion years ago. In the Paleozoic era most of the earth's coal deposits formed. During the Mesozoic era, dinosaurs lived. The Cenozoic era saw several Ice Ages and the appearance of humans. (9–3)

- Radioactive decay of elements in rocks and fossils allows scientists to measure their actual ages. (9–4)

Interesting Reading

Gannon, Robert. "How Old Is it?" *Popular Science,* November 1979, pages 76-81. Describes carbon 14 and other methods of dating objects.

Lambert, David. *Dinosaurs.* Crown, 1978. Describes dinosaurs that lived during the Mesozoic era and explains the work of fossil-hunters.

Questions/Problems

1. Describe the principles of superposition and uniform processes.

2. What is a fossil? How are index fossils valuable to scientists?

3. Name the eras of the geologic time scale, and describe a major event or life form that occurred during the era.

4. Describe how coal forms.

5. A certain radioactive element has a half-life of 10,000 years. After 40,000 years, what fraction of the original amount of the radioactive element is left?

6. Hikers found a bone buried in a field. Scientists tested the bone and found that 75% of the carbon 14 was gone. The half-life of carbon 14 is 5,730 years. About how long ago did this animal die?

Extra Research

1. Use an encyclopedia to find three examples of index fossils. Draw and label the fossils. Write one paragraph about each fossil. Describe each fossil and tell when and where it lived.

2. Write a one-page report on the latest rock and fossil dating methods. You may use the *Readers' Guide* to find magazine articles about the subject. Look under "radioactive dating" techniques.

3. Make your own geologic time scale. On it mark eras, periods (smaller divisions of geologic time within eras), order in which plants and animals appear, and length of eras and periods in millions of years.

Chapter Test

A. Vocabulary   Write the numbers 1–10 on a piece of paper.
Match the definition in Column I with the term it defines in Column II.

Column I

1. widespread fossil that lived for a relatively short period of geologic time

2. radioactive element used to date dead plant material

3. hard coal

4. soft coal

5. the number of years it takes for half a given amount of a radioactive element to decay

6. radioactive element used to date ancient rocks

7. the current era of geologic time

8. the first era of geologic time

9. the age of the dinosaurs

10. the era of geologic time in which large coal deposits formed

Column II

a. anthracite

b. bituminous

c. carbon 14

d. Cenozoic

e. half-life

f. index fossil

g. Mesozoic

h. Paleozoic

i. Precambrian

j. uranium

B. Multiple Choice   Write the numbers 1–10 on your paper.
Choose the letter that best completes the statement or answers the question.

1. The oldest rock layers lie on the bottom of a rock formation according to the principle of
a) superposition.   b) uniform processes.
c) radioactive dating.   d) peat formation.

2. Geologic processes that take place today are the same ones that have taken place throughout time according to the principle of
a) superposition.   b) uniform processes.
c) radioactive dating.   d) peat formation.

3. Most fossils that scientists find preserved are   a) hard parts of plants or animals.
b) soft parts of plants or animals.   c) entire plants or animals.   d) Precambrian animals.

4. Entire fossil insects have been found preserved in   a) trilobites.   b) peat.   c) amber.
d) all of the above.

5. Trilobites are very useful to scientists as
a) a type of land mammal.   b) index fossils.
c) a tool of radioactive dating.   d) fossils that lived in the Cenozoic.

6. The earth was formed at the beginning of the   a) Precambrian era.   b) Paleozoic era.
c) Mesozoic era.   d) Cenozoic era.

7. The Canadian Shield formed during the following era: a) Precambrian.   b) Paleozoic.
c) Mesozoic.   d) Cenozoic.

8. Most of the world's oil supply developed during the   a) Paleozoic era.   b) Mesozoic era.   c) Cenozoic era.   d) all of the above.

9. The following radioactive element is used for measuring the age of the oldest rocks:
a) uranium.   b) argon.   c) potassium.
d) carbon 14.

10. The following radioactive element is used to measure the age of fossil material that lived within the last 50,000 years: a) uranium.
b) argon.   c) potassium.   d) carbon 14.

Careers

Paleontologist

Rocks have secrets. The fossils they hold illustrate the history of the world. A paleontologist studies these fossils to trace the development of life on earth.

This expert spends a lot of time outdoors. He or she oversees a dig site, where buried fossils are uncovered. Later, the puzzle pieces are studied in the laboratory to reveal how old they are and how they formed. In this way the story of ancient forms of life unfolds.

To be a paleontologist, you must first study geology for four years in college. After that, you should specialize in paleontology and get a master's or doctor's degree.

Career Information:
American Geological Institute, 5205 Leesburg Pike, Falls Church, VA 22041

Miner

Today's mines produce everything from aluminum to zinc. There are rock mines, coal mines, metal mines, even mines that produce the salt for your table. All mines have one thing in common—the workers who remove the needed materials.

Miners may work underground, above ground in strip mines, in tunnels, or in caves. These workers use high-powered equipment. They may drive trucks, drill rock, or lay down railroad tracks in the mine. Miners also handle explosives to blast out materials in the mines.

Most miners learn from other workers on the job. Sometimes these workers take classes to teach them how to use specialized machinery.

Career Information:
United Mine Workers of America, Communications Dept., 900 15th St., NW, Washington, DC 20005

Gem cutter

A diamond does not sparkle when it is first discovered. Instead, an uncut diamond may look like a lump of white stone. A gem cutter changes that by cutting and polishing rough gems until they look like stones you see in rings and other jewelry.

A gem cutter does very detailed work. He or she must first study the structure of the uncut precious stone. In this way, the gem cutter knows the proper directions to cut the stone. If the gem is not cut carefully, it may shatter and be of little value. A gem may have a design added to it, but it is not finished until each of the cuts the gem cutter makes is polished.

This exacting work requires years of apprenticeship. This means training on the job and some technical classes.

Career Information:
Jewelers of America, 1271 Avenue of the Americas, New York, NY 10020

Cartographer

Cartographers draw maps of many kinds. Scientists and researchers may call on cartographers to draw crop maps, weather maps, geologic maps, or graphs.

Maps must be accurate to be useful. Cartographers often start with a photograph taken from an airplane. Using special instruments, they make a model of the land in the picture. Then the cartographers carefully measure the model and map it on paper.

People who like to draw can take classes in technical schools for two years to become qualified cartographers.

Career Information:
American Congress on Surveying and Mapping, 210 Little Falls Rd., Falls Church, VA 22046

Mineralogist

No one can identify each of the thousands of minerals in the crust. Mineralogists, however, are the people who know the most about what minerals are made of and where they can be found. These experts can tell you where you are most likely to find diamonds as well as where you may find copper and tin.

Mineralogists use microscopes and X-ray photographs to examine the structure and makeup of minerals. They can pinpoint the quality, durability, and uses of rocks and minerals.

These experts may travel to mines or out into the field in search of a particular mineral.

For this highly technical job, students must complete four years of college. They will study geology, chemistry, and math.

Career Information:
American Geological Institute, 5205 Leesburg Pike, Falls Church, VA 22041

Quarry worker

Quarries are large pits where rocks used for buildings, bridges, and dams are taken from the earth. People who work in a quarry cut and haul stones out to prepare them for shipping.

They handle picks, steam hoses, crowbars, and sledge hammers. The stone gets cleaned or broken into equal-sized chunks as it comes out of the ground. Quarry workers also attach the cables that lift these huge rocks out of the pit.

These workers learn many skills and the importance of teamwork. They get on-the-job training.

Career Information:
Building Stone Institute, 420 Lexington Ave., New York, NY 10170

UNIT THREE
THE CHANGING CRUST

Is this an eerie, Martian landscape? It could be a lacy coral formation seen through crystal clear ocean water. But *what* is the red feature?

This picture was taken on earth, but it is not a common sight. The photographer was standing on a rock ledge above Mount Etna, a volcano in Sicily. Delicate crystals of ice ring the crater of the volcano. Fortunately, the red-hot lava was calm long enough for the photographer to take the picture. This unit describes happenings such as this that change the crust.

Chapter 10 Earth's Crust on the Move
The surface of the earth is divided into large sections, called plates, that move slowly but constantly.

Chapter 11 Earthquakes and Volcanoes
Active volcanoes and earthquakes develop where plates meet or pull apart.

Chapter 12 The Mobile Crust
Mountains can form at plate boundaries. The crust also moves up and down, balancing the weight of sediments.

Chapter 13 Weathering of the Earth's Surface
Air, water, and acids break rocks into smaller pieces.

Chapter 14 Erosion
Running water, ice, wind, gravity, plants, and animals transport weathered materials such as rocks and soil.

Chapter 15 Mapping and Landforms
Topographic maps show the elevations and shapes of landforms.

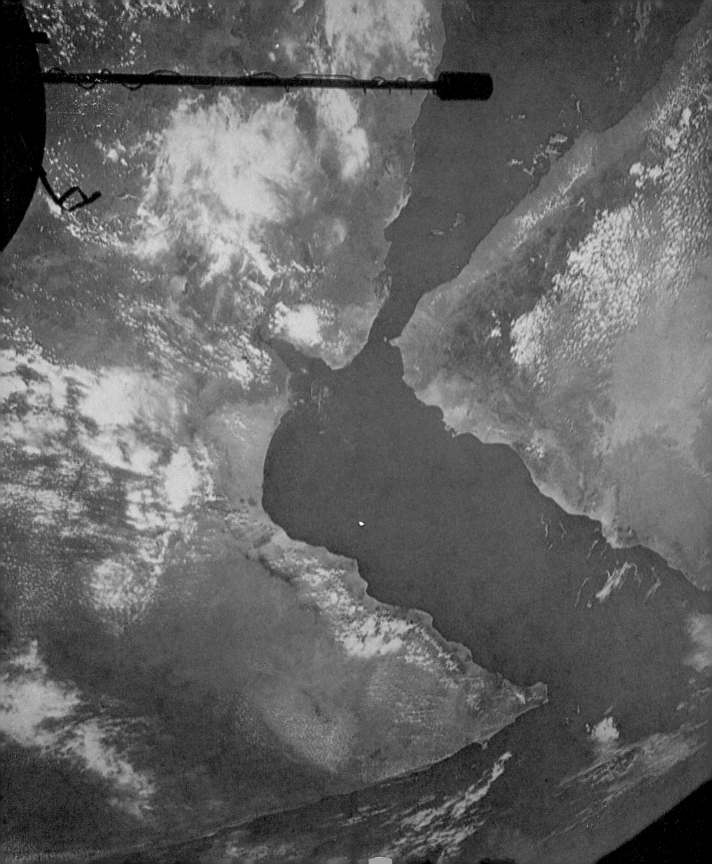

Chapter 10
Earth's Crust on the Move

This is how eastern Africa, the Red Sea, and Arabia look from a satellite circling the earth. Imagine that you could remove the Red Sea and rotate Arabia toward Africa. Surprisingly enough, these land masses would fit together rather well. By the time you finish this chapter you will know why.

This chapter explains some new theories about the earth. Changing old ideas about the nature of the earth's crust took many years. It started with the strange idea that continents might be moving or drifting over the earth. Research in the oceans revealed surprising evidence. Many questions about our earth have not yet been answered, but the new theories furnish the starting point for future research.

Chapter Objectives

1. Explain the meaning of continental drift.
2. List the evidence for sea-floor spreading.
3. Compare three types of plate boundaries.
4. Describe two forces that could cause plates to move.

10–1
The Jigsaw Puzzle of Continents

Many mysteries about our planet have stirred the curiosity of observant people. Earlier in this century, explorers were amazed to find rocks with fossil imprints of ferns in the frozen lands of the far north and the far south. How could plants that thrive in warm, moist climates exist in what is now a harsh climate? What changes had taken place? The answers to the questions below are one man's attempt to solve these mysteries:

a. What is the theory of drifting continents?
b. What was the evidence for continental drift?

Theory of Drifting Continents

The first realistic maps of Europe and America were drawn in the 1600s. Since that time many people have wondered about the jigsaw puzzle fit of the Atlantic coastlines of South America and Africa. But they could only guess why these continents looked as if they might fit together. In 1912, Alfred Wegener (Vā′gə nər), a German scientist, published a theory to explain the jigsaw fit. He stated that all the continents were once joined. The map shows the joined continents Wegener called **Pangaea** (pan jē′ə), which means "all the land" in Greek.

Wegener believed that Pangaea began breaking up and drifting apart many millions of years ago. He insisted that the jigsaw fit of the continents was not an accident, but the result of the splitting of Pangaea. He said that the continents slowly drifted over the ocean floor until they reached their present positions.

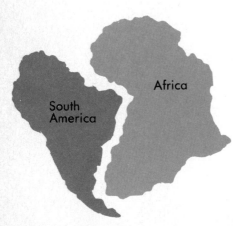

Wegener's Evidence for Continental Drift

What was Wegener's evidence for continental drift? First, explorers had found fossils and rock layers on the east coast of South America that were similar to those found on the west coast of Africa.

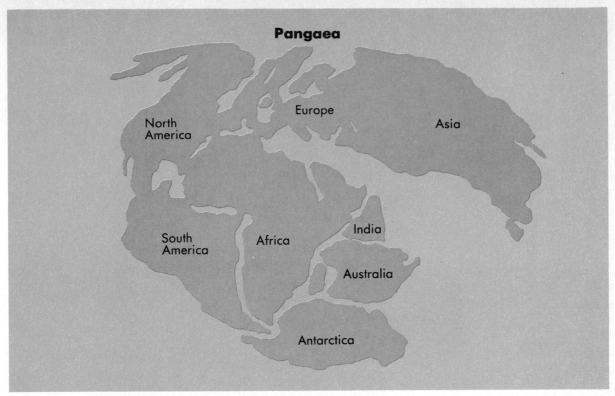

Pangaea

North America

Europe

Asia

South America

Africa

India

Australia

Antarctica

Fossils of the animal shown to the right were discovered in both South America and Africa. These findings convinced Wegener that the continents were once joined. Second, explorers found rocks made of glacial sediments at the equator where no glaciers could exist. How did Wegener explain this finding? He believed that the land mass drifted to a warmer region of the earth.

Wegener's evidence was interesting, but it did not prove that continents moved. Scientists rejected the continental drift theory because Wegener could not explain how or why continents moved. His imaginative theory is not entirely correct, but it set the stage for other bold ideas.

Review It

1. List the continents that were part of Pangaea.
2. How would Wegener account for fossil ferns found in the rocks of Antarctica?

191

Activity

Jigsaw Puzzle of Continents

Purpose
To explore how the continents might have been joined.

Materials
- scissors
- glue
- continental cut-out sheet
- notebook paper

Procedure
1. Cut out the continents from the map provided by the teacher.
2. Try to fit the Atlantic coastlines of Africa and South America together.
3. Fit all the continents together the way Wegener thought they were joined in Pangaea.
4. Find other ways to fit the continents together.
5. When you think you have found the closest match possible of the coastlines, glue the continent pieces onto notebook paper.

Analysis
1. Which continents fit together best?
2. Which continents could fit in several positions?
3. Suggest one reason why two continents that may have once fit together no longer appear to fit today.
4. Briefly describe the direction each continent moved to get from Pangaea to its present position.

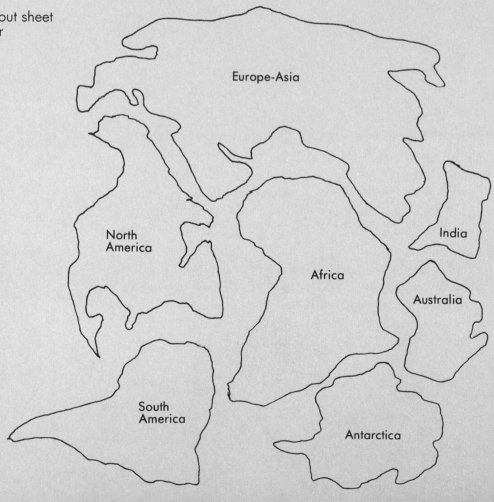

Breakthrough

Why Is Pangaea Important?

Startling scientific discoveries have convinced geologists that Pangaea really existed. Besides its curiosity value, why is Pangaea important?

For one thing, shallow seas and swampy areas surrounded the land masses when they separated from Pangaea. Coal, oil, and gas formed in these watery regions. If geologists can learn how the land masses moved, they will know where to look for these valuable deposits of fuel.

In addition, the breakup of Pangaea probably changed ancient plant and animal life. This, in turn, affected the development of life on earth.

Reptiles, such as dinosaurs, roamed freely across Pangaea. Scientists believe these reptiles became extinct about 65 million years ago at the end of the Mesozoic era. How did the breakup of Pangaea, which took place during the Mesozoic, affect the climate and the dinosaurs' food supply?

Small mammals also lived throughout Pangaea. When the supercontinent began to split, animal populations were separated by shallow seas. How did the isolation of present-day continents affect the development of mammals?

Cattle and many meat-eating animals, such as wolves and bears, developed on land masses that had once been part of northern Pangaea. Today certain kinds of bears are found only in North America and northern Europe.

Elephants' ancestors originally lived in the south half of Pangaea. These animals are now found in Africa and India.

Some unique animals emerged on the island continent of Australia. The photographs show two mammals that are found *only* in Australia.

Questions about Pangaea, our earth, and its creatures may never be answered. But curious people will keep looking for the answers. The story of Pangaea is one link in our chain of knowledge.

For Discussion
1. How can knowledge of Pangaea be helpful today?
2. On what part of Pangaea did the ancestors of modern meat-eating mammals live?

Koala bear

Kangaroo

193

10–2
Discoveries in the Ocean

Scientific breakthroughs in the 1960s sparked interest in Wegener's continental drift theory. Research data suggested that the Atlantic Ocean was growing. How can an ocean grow? Could the crust of the earth be moving? Consider the questions below as you read:

a. What are mid-ocean ridges, rifts, and trenches?
b. What is sea-floor spreading?
c. How do magnetic records in rocks prove sea-floor spreading?

Trenches, Mid-Ocean Ridges, and Rifts

Scientists knew very little about the ocean floors when Wegener first discussed continental drift. In the late 1940s, new instruments enabled scientists to map the ocean floors and record earthquakes in the ocean crust.

For many years sailors knew there were deep places in the oceans. Sea-floor mapping defined the depth and size of the ocean's deepest regions. These deep regions, called **trenches,** are long and narrow in shape. Notice the number of trenches around the borders of the Pacific Ocean on the map. Trenches in the Pacific are almost ten kilometers deep in some places.

Mapping the Atlantic Ocean floor revealed huge underwater mountains named the **Mid-Atlantic Ridge.** A ridge is a long, narrow chain of hills or mountains. The Mid-Atlantic Ridge is now known to be part of an underwater mountain chain that winds 65,000 kilometers around the earth.

The underwater ridges throughout the world vary greatly in size and shape. Many ridges in the Pacific Ocean are flat-topped mountains. In contrast, the ridges in the Atlantic Ocean are two parallel chains of mountains. A valley, 2 to 50 kilometers wide, runs between the mountains. This valley, known as a **rift,** is shown in the margin. The ridges and trenches in the oceans are shown on the map.

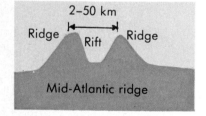

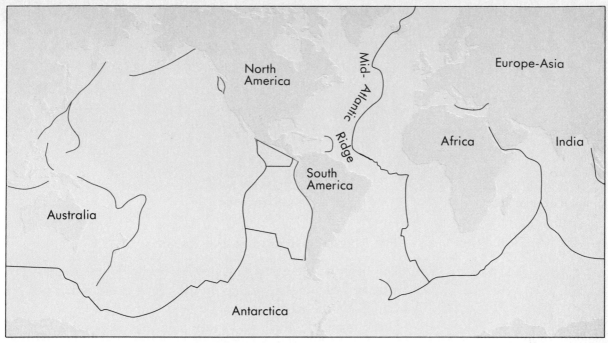

World Map of Ridges and Trenches   Mid-ocean ridge line = —— Trench = ——

Sea-Floor Spreading

In 1962 scientists dared to suggest that new crust is forming at the ocean ridges. They found evidence for this outrageous idea on the ocean floor. Scientists found cracks along the middle of mid-ocean ridges where the ocean floor was splitting. Magma, melted material from the mantle, is rising out of these cracks. It hardens and forms new crust. The new crust is piled high to form the ridges. As more magma comes up, it pushes the newly formed crust away on both sides, carrying the older crust with it. Ocean sediments, which are particles that settle from water, are thin or missing on the ridges. The sediments gradually become thicker away from the center of the ridges.

The formation of new crust on the ocean floor is called **sea-floor spreading.** New crust on the ocean bottom suggested that the whole crust is moving—not just the continents.

Have You Heard?

Sea-floor spreading is so slow that it is not noticeable. Also, because it happens on the ocean floor, we can not see it, except with special instruments. From 2 to 20 centimeters of new crust forms a year in oceans throughout the world.

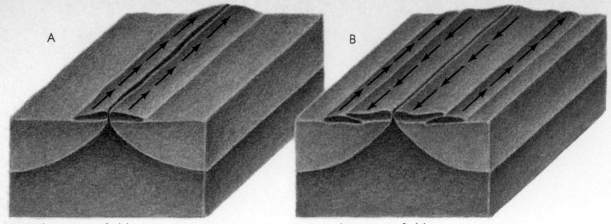

A

Normal magnetic field

B

Reversed magnetic field

The Magnetic Record in the Rocks

The study of the earth's magnetic field helps researchers interpret what is happening on the ocean floor. Scientists who study the earth's magnetic field found that the location of the magnetic north and south pole reverses over a long period of time. If there were a **magnetic reversal** today, the north-seeking needle of a compass would point to south rather than north.

The magnetic poles reverse approximately every half-million years. Scientists have constructed tables and charts that indicate when the earth's magnetic field has reversed in the past. These magnetic reversal charts can be used to determine the age of rocks.

Scientists discovered that magnetic records are frozen in rocks. In Diagram A, the crust splits and spreads apart when magma rises in the center of a mid-ocean ridge. Grains of iron and other magnetic substances in the magma tend to line up in the direction of the earth's magnetic field. When the magma hardens, the rock that is formed contains a record of the original magnetic field.

Diagram B shows what happens thousands of years later —after the magnetic field has reversed. Magma, rising through cracks at the ridge, records the changed magnetic field. The magma pushes the crust, formed in Diagram A, away from the center of the ridge and the magma hardens. Again it retains the record of the reversed magnetic field. This process is repeated time and time again.

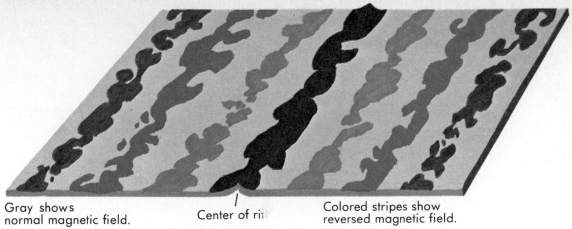

Gray shows
normal magnetic field.

Center of ri[...]

Colored stripes show
reversed magnetic field.

Ships tow instruments that measure the magnetic properties of rocks. They have recorded strange zebra-striped patterns on the ocean floor. The colored stripes in the drawing represent magnetic properties of rocks on the ocean floor. These stripes appear in matching pairs on both sides of mid-ocean ridges. The pairs of stripes increase in age away from the center of the ridge.

The evidence for sea-floor spreading is:

1. A great amount of magma is rising at the mid-ocean ridges.
2. Rocks gradually get older from the center of the ridge out on both sides.

The ocean floor was thought to be the oldest part of the crust. In fact, Atlantic Ocean crust is younger than the continents surrounding it, and the Atlantic Ocean is increasing in size.

Review It

1. Describe the Mid-Atlantic Ridge.
2. Where is the youngest rock in a mid-ocean ridge?
3. List evidence for sea-floor spreading.

10–3
Plate Tectonics, a New Theory

To increase your understanding of any subject, you must add new information to the knowledge you already have. For example, you read and understood numbers long before you learned to tell time. Similarly, earth scientists used the information from sea-floor spreading to develop a broader theory that explains why the earth looks as it does. As you read about this new theory, think about these questions:

a. How did the plate tectonic theory change our thinking about the earth's surface?

b. What are three types of plate boundaries?

The Plate Tectonic Theory

According to the **plate tectonic** (tek ton′ik) **theory,** the surface of the earth is broken into about 20 large sections called **plates.** They are about 70 kilometers thick. The diagram shows that the plates are as deep as the **lithosphere** (lith′ə sfir), which is the solid outer shell of the earth. The lithosphere contains the crust and upper mantle. The plates are rigid and they move over the softer asthenosphere of the mantle. The asthenosphere is a partly melted region in the mantle.

On the map of the plates, notice that one plate can contain both continental crust and ocean crust. The arrows show the directions the plates are moving now. The directions of movement may have been different in the past.

Have You Heard?

Plates move at a rate of 2 to 20 centimeters per year. The Pacific plate is moving about five and a half centimeters per year northward past North America. At this rate, Los Angeles, which is on the Pacific plate, will be next door to San Francisco in 10 million years.

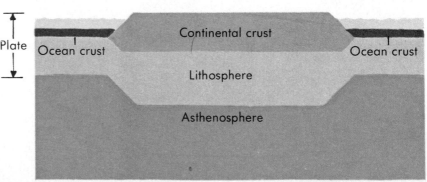

Plate

Ocean crust | Continental crust | Ocean crust

Lithosphere

Asthenosphere

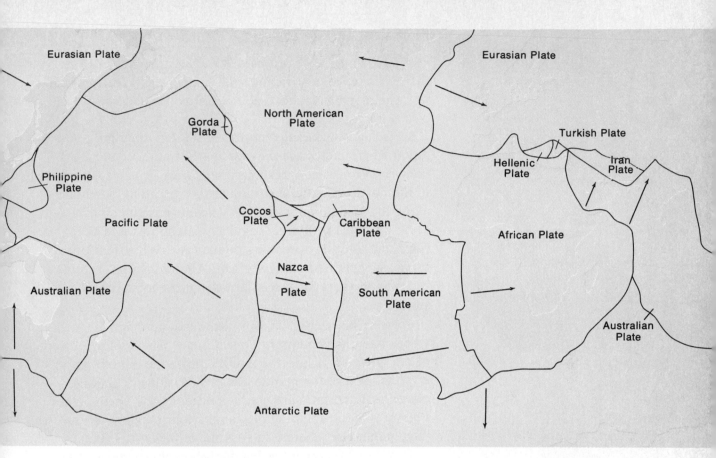

Until recently, scientists relied on magnetic records in rocks to find out about plate movements. Now, they have more precise ways to get information.

One way uses special very bright beams of light called lasers. Laser beams are sent from earth stations to a satellite. Reflectors on the satellite return the beams to the stations. Scientists at each station carefully record the time it takes for the beams to go to the satellite and return to earth. They can use this data to calculate the distance between two stations. If the stations are on different plates, any change in the distance means the plates have moved. Scientists believe they will soon be able to detect plate movements of even one centimeter per year!

Have You Heard?

The most promising places to look for untouched deposits of valuable metals are the boundaries between the plates on the map above—especially on the unexplored ocean bottoms. Today's oceanographers are also prospectors. The *Alvin* and other submersibles have found tremendous deposits of copper and other valuable ores off the coasts of Oregon and South America.

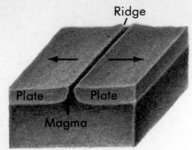

Ridge

Plate   Plate

Magma

Spreading boundary

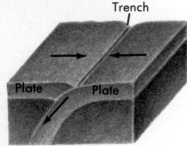

Trench

Plate   Plate

Colliding boundary

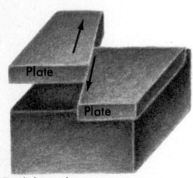

Plate

Plate

Fault boundary

Plate Boundaries

The region where plates meet is the plate boundary. How the plates move determines what happens at plate boundaries. The plates may move apart, collide, or slide past each other.

Spreading Boundaries, pictured in the top diagram, are found where plates are moving apart at mid-ocean ridges. New crust forms at spreading boundaries. Iceland, an island in the north Atlantic, emerged at the spreading boundary along the Mid-Atlantic Ridge. Volcanoes steam and the earth trembles with great regularity along this mid-ocean ridge and at other spreading boundaries. When Pangaea broke, it separated along the Mid-Atlantic Ridge. It took 200 million years for the Atlantic to grow to its present size.

Colliding Boundaries, shown in the middle diagram, form where two plates bump into each other. The leading edge of one plate sinks into the mantle under the edge of another plate. Where the mantle absorbs the edge of sinking plate, heat and pressure create volcanoes and earthquakes. Pressures along colliding plates may fold rock layers into huge mountain systems, such as the Himalayas in India.

Trenches bordering the Pacific Ocean are regions where the Pacific plate is sinking. The size of the plate slowly decreases as it sinks into the trenches. The Pacific Ocean is shrinking slowly. The loss of crust in the trenches balances the formation of new crust in the mid-ocean ridges.

Fault (fôlt) **Boundaries,** shown in the bottom diagram, occur where two plates rub past each other. Faults are cracks in the earth. Earthquakes shake the land when rocks move along a fault. The San Andreas Fault in California marks the boundary of two plates sliding past one another. People who live near the fault must expect earthquakes.

Review It

1. Describe a segment of the earth called a plate.
2. What caused the trenches around the Pacific Ocean?

Activity

Sea-Floor Spreading Model

Purpose
To better understand earth processes at ridges and trenches.

Materials
• two sheets of unlined paper
• scissors
• crayons or colored pencils
• ruler

Procedure
1. Place one sheet of unlined paper with a long side toward you. Lightly fold the sheet of paper into quarters to get three crease lines.
2. Starting 6 cm down from the top of the paper, as shown in *a*, draw a line 11 cm long in each of the three creases. Cut along the drawn lines to make three slits. Flatten the paper to remove creases.
3. Fold the second paper in half lengthwise, and cut along the fold to make two equal strips as in *b*.
4. Put the two strips together, and run them up through the middle slit as in *c*.
5. Pull the strips out 4 cm, and fold them back on opposite sides of the middle slit. Color the exposed parts of both strips the same color.

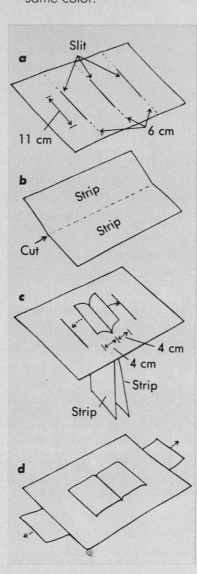

6. Continue pulling the strips up and folding back. Change colors every 4 cm, until the strips are completely colored.
7. Again, pull the strips up through the center slit so the colors show. This time, run each strip down through the outer slit nearest it, as in *d*.
8. Practice the step above, getting the matching color bands to come up and go down at the same time.

Analysis
1. What earth features do the three slits represent in your sea-floor spreading model?
2. What do the two strips represent?
3. Mark the two matched bands, which you colored first, with X's. Write "youngest" on the parts of the two strips that you think represent the youngest material on the model.
4. What kinds of boundaries are found in your model?
5. Suggest a reason why the layer of sediment is thin or missing in the rift valley.
6. Suggest one way in which your model might be different from sea-floor spreading as it really occurs.

10—4

Forces Strong Enough to Move Plates

Excitement among earth scientists grew as the plate tectonic theory developed in the late 1960s. The question of what causes the plates to move, however, is not yet known. This section presents ideas about forces strong enough to move pieces of the earth's crust. Think about these questions as you read:

a. How could convection currents move plates?
b. How might plumes cause plate movement?
c. What are hot spots?

One Possibility—Convection Currents

Convection (kon vek′shən) **currents** transfer heat through liquids or gases. The diagram of the coffee pot shows two convection currents in water. Note that the water nearest the flame rises. When it cools near the surface, it sinks.

Some scientists have suggested that convection currents flowing in the mantle may cause the plates to move. Because of the great heat in the mantle, parts of the mantle may flow like a very thick liquid. Compare the diagram of the coffee pot to the diagram of the mantle. A plate might move above a huge convection current like an object riding along on a giant conveyor belt.

Plumes in the Mantle

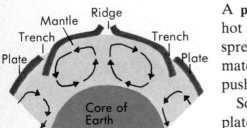

A **plume,** pictured on the right, is a narrow, jetlike flow of hot material from a great depth in the mantle. Plumes at spreading boundaries might cause plates to move by adding material to the edges of plates. The added material may push the plates apart.

Scientists do not know whether the force driving the plates is due to convection currents, plumes, a combination of the two, or other unknown factors.

Investigating Hot Spots

Volcanoes appear where magma from plumes reaches the earth's surface. Places with a great deal of volcanic activity are called **hot spots.** Hot spots are found over plumes in the mantle. Some plumes are located beneath plate boundaries. Earth scientists believe, however, that plumes also occur away from plate boundaries. For example, hot spots that occur in the middle of a plate are caused by plumes away from plate boundaries.

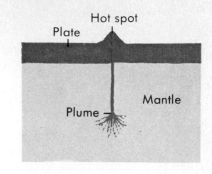

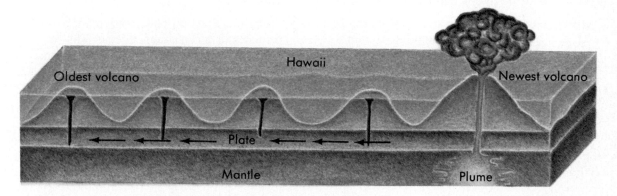

Hot spots in the middle of the Pacific plate formed the Hawaiian Islands. These volcano-islands are actually huge mountains rising from the ocean floor. Notice in the diagram that the erupting volcano is directly over the plume.

During the past 80 million years, the Pacific plate has been moving to the northwest. The volcanoes move with the plate, but the plume in the mantle does not move. Volcanoes that move away from the plume leave their source of magma. They are inactive.

As the inactive volcanoes move along, new, active volcanoes appear above the plume. Because the plate moves to the northwest, new volcanoes appear to the southeast.

Have You Heard?

Although most hot spots are found in the ocean, some hot spots are on continents. Hot spots on land might be areas where continents are starting to split. Some scientists think Yellowstone National Park is a hot spot where the continent of North America may break apart in the future.

Review It

1. What is a convection current?
2. In what layer of the earth does a plume originate?
3. If you visit a hot spot, what would you expect to see?

Chapter Summary

- Alfred Wegener proposed that the continents were once joined in a large continent called Pangaea. (10–1)

- Wegener used rock layers, fossils, and changes of climate as evidence for continental drift. (10–1)

- The mid-ocean ridge is a mountain chain 65,000 kilometers long in the oceans of the world. (10–2)

- Magma rises from the mantle creating new ocean crust at the mid-ocean ridges. (10–2)

- The plate tectonic theory states that the rigid outer part of the earth is broken into a number of pieces called plates. The plates move apart, collide, or slide past one another. (10–3)

- The flow of material in the mantle by convection and/or plumes may cause plate movement. (10–4)

- Hot spots are regions on the surface of the earth that lie directly over a plume. (10–4)

Interesting Reading

Fodor, Ronald. *Earth in Motion*. Morrow, 1978. Describes how knowledge about plate tectonics is important in locating valuable resources.

Kiefer, Irene. *A Global Jigsaw Puzzle*. Atheneum, 1978. Discusses the plate tectonic theory and its development.

Young, Patrick. *Drifting Continents, Shifting Seas*. Watts, 1976. Discusses plate tectonics and the earth's structure.

Questions/Problems

1. Compare Wegener's continental drift theory to the plate tectonic theory.

2. Imagine a reason, other than continental drift, for identical fossils in South America and Africa.

3. Why is sediment in the center of mid-ocean ridges either thin or absent?

4. What would happen to the crust if there were spreading boundaries but no colliding boundaries?

5. Using the chart on plate movement and trenches in this chapter, explain why so many earthquakes occur in the Philippine Islands.

6. What type of surface feature might occur on a plate where a convection current is sinking in the mantle?

7. An active volcano is at the south end of a north-south chain of volcanoes that are no longer active. What direction is the plate moving?

Extra Research

1. Using books in the library, describe the history of Surtsey, an island on the Mid-Atlantic Ridge. Be sure to mention the type of plate boundary and the amount of volcanic activity.

2. Draw the intersection of three imaginary plates moving at different rates and in different directions. Start by drawing a map of three imaginary plates, using the map of plates of the world as a guide. Describe surface features you might see.

3. Study sea-floor exploration in periodicals such as *Oceans, Scientific American,* or *National Geographic*. Name and describe three instruments scientists use to study plate activities on the ocean bottom.

Chapter Test

A. Vocabulary   Write the numbers 1–10 on a piece of paper.
Match the definition in Column I with the term it defines in Column II.

Column I

1. the name of Wegener's large continent *e*

2. large underwater mountain chain that winds around the earth *d*

3. a valley between parallel ridges on the ocean bottom *h*

4. a theory that the earth's surface is broken into many rigid pieces *f*

5. surface feature found where one plate moves under another plate *j*

6. hot material rises, spreads sideways, and then sinks again *a*

7. a theory that describes the formation of new crust *i*

8. region on the earth's surface that has a great many volcanoes *c*

9. a jetlike flow of hot material from deep within the mantle *g*

10. theory that land masses move over the ocean floor *b*

Column II

a. convection current

b. continental drift

c. hot spot

d. mid-ocean ridge

e. Pangaea

f. plate tectonics

g. plume

h. rift

i. sea-floor spreading

j. trench

B. Multiple Choice   Write the numbers 1–10 on your paper.
Choose the letter that best completes the statement or answers the question.

1. Scientists disagreed with Wegener's idea because he could not explain   a) similar fossils.
b) forces necessary to move continents.
c) identical rock formations.   d) climate changes.

2. Evidence of sea-floor spreading came from
a) sea life.   b) sea-floor magnetism.   c) sea water.   d) glacial deposits.

3. The magnetic stripes recorded on the ocean floor illustrate   a) magnetic field reversals.
b) the North Pole.   c) rotation of the earth.
d) the sun's radiation.

4. The Mid-Atlantic Ridge is *not*   a) located where two plates collide.   b) parallel ridges.
c) part of the world underwater mountain chain.   d) where new crust forms.

5. New ocean crust is produced at
a) trenches.   b) mid-ocean ridges.   c) faults.
d) beaches.

6. Old ocean crust is being destroyed at
a) trenches.   b) ridges.   c) faults.
d) volcanoes.

7. If many trenches surround a plate, the plate is probably   a) getting larger.   b) getting smaller.   c) remaining the same size.
d) getting thicker.

8. Fault boundaries occur where   a) one plate sinks under another.   b) plates are no longer moving.   c) two plates are spreading apart.
d) two plates are sliding past one another.

9. A possible cause of plate movements is
a) convection in the mantle.   b) the earth's rotation.   c) the pull of the moon.   d) the pull of the sun.

10. The Hawaiian Island chain was probably created as the Pacific plate passed over a
a) fault.   b) plume.   c) trench.   d) mid-ocean ridge.

Chapter 11
Earthquakes and Volcanoes

In the picture you see an eruption of Mount St. Helens in Washington State. The eruption affected the land and air for kilometers around. Earthquakes, like volcanoes, can cause a great deal of damage. Earthquakes occur every day somewhere in the world. Fortunately most of these earthquakes cause little damage. Earthquakes that cause great damage are rare.

In this chapter you will read about earthquakes and volcanoes on Earth and on other planets. This chapter also suggests some "signs" that scientists are using in an effort to predict earthquakes and volcanic eruptions.

Chapter Objectives

1. Explain the relationship between faults, earthquakes, and plate boundaries.
2. Explain how scientists use seismic waves to locate the epicenters of earthquakes.
3. Contrast the formation of intrusive and extrusive rocks.
4. Describe four types of volcanic cones.
5. Compare volcanoes on other planets and their moons with volcanoes on earth.

11–1
Earthquakes

An earthquake is a trembling or shaking of the earth. What causes an earthquake? Huge explosions can shake the earth, or magma moving up in a volcano may cause an earthquake. Most earthquakes, however, happen because rocks move along a fault. Think about these questions as you read about earthquakes:

a. How are earthquakes related to faults?
b. Where do most earthquakes occur?
c. What does the Richter scale tell you about an earthquake?
d. What are aftershocks?

Earthquakes and Faults

Imagine what happens when you bend a plastic ruler. If you bend it far enough, the ruler breaks. Both pieces snap back to a straight position. Rocks in the earth's crust that are under pressure also bend, break, and snap back. A fault is a break in rocks along which rocks have moved.

Earthquake zones

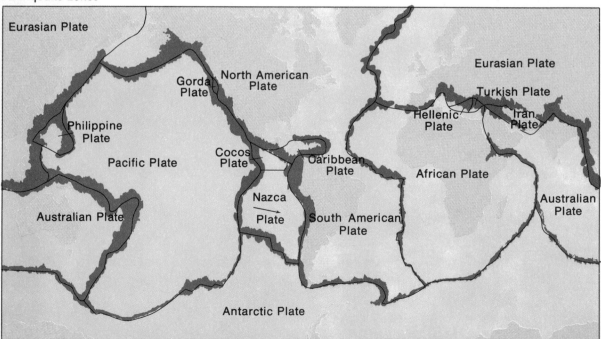

When the break occurs, energy is released. This energy makes the earth shake, and we feel an earthquake. The point inside the earth where the rock breaks or moves is the **focus** (fō′kəs) of the earthquake. The focus of most earthquakes is shallow, usually around 100 kilometers or less in depth. Deep focus earthquakes, up to 700 kilometers, generally occur at trench boundaries where one plate is moving under another.

The lines on the earthquake map to the left indicate plate boundaries. The colored zones represent recent earthquakes. Notice that most earthquakes occur near plate edges. The diagram below shows how earthquakes are related to plate boundaries.

Some earthquakes occur far from plate edges. Geologists suggest that heat and pressure develop under a plate as it drags along over the mantle. Earthquakes may be a result of this "drag" on the plates. In 1811 and 1812, three violent earthquakes struck near New Madrid, Missouri. New Madrid is in the middle of the North American plate. People felt these earthquakes as far away as Massachusetts.

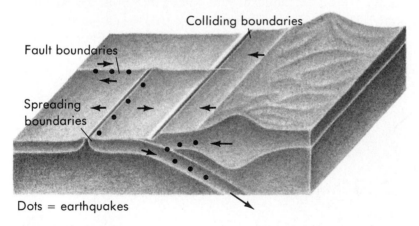

Dots = earthquakes

The Richter Scale

When you read about an earthquake in the newspaper, the description usually includes a number from 1 to 10 on the **Richter scale.** This number indicates the strength of an earthquake. An increase of one number on the Richter scale means an increase of 30 to 50 times the energy released by an earthquake.

Have You Heard?

Many people have reported seeing colored lights or a glow in the sky during earthquakes. Some scientists think that certain rocks in the earth take on an electrical charge when they are shaken violently. The charge causes lightning-like sparks that produce the strange lights.

Strong Earthquakes and Aftershocks

Challenge!
The Modified Mercalli scale is an earthquake scale based on the observations of people who were in the earthquake. Look in the encyclopedia to see how this scale differs from the Richter scale.

The strongest earthquakes recorded in history took place in 1906 off the coast of Ecuador and in 1933 near the coast of Japan. These earthquakes had values of 8.9 on the Richter scale. The Good Friday earthquake of 1964 in Alaska, rated at 8.6, caused the damage shown in the photograph of Anchorage.

Many small earthquakes, called **aftershocks,** usually follow a strong earthquake. The San Fernando, California, earthquake in 1971 registered 6.6 on the Richter scale. Within three days, more than 1,000 aftershocks followed the main earthquake. Some of the aftershocks measured up to 5 on the Richter scale.

Review It

1. How can you tell that a fault releases energy?
2. Where do most deep focus earthquakes occur?
3. What increase in energy is an increase of one number on the Richter scale?
4. Where did the strongest recorded earthquakes occur?

Did You Know?

Animals Predict Earthquakes

A government agency in China has reported that strange animal behaviors were observed just hours before an earthquake. Cattle, sheep, mules, and horses would not enter corrals. Rats fled their homes. Hibernating snakes left their burrows early. Pigeons flew continuously and did not return to their nests. Rabbits raised their ears, jumped about aimlessly, and bumped into things. Fish jumped above water surfaces.

China was not the only country to report such unusual animal behavior. Late on May 6, 1976, an earthquake shook a town in Italy. Before the earthquake, pet birds flapped their wings and shrieked. Mice and rats ran in circles. Dogs barked and howled. Perhaps the animals sensed the coming earthquake.

For many years farmers throughout the world have told stories about changes in animals' behavior just before an earthquake. Chinese scientists were among the first to believe these stories might have a scientific basis. They have even proposed that zoo animals might forewarn people of a coming earthquake.

Scientists in many countries are interested in finding the causes for the strange behavior. They have suggested that one or more of the following may be possible causes:
1. slight changes in the earth's magnetic field;
2. increased amounts of electricity in the air;
3. very small air pressure changes;
4. changes in noise level;
5. gas escaping from the ground.

When scientists find the causes of the strange animal behavior, they may be able to predict earthquakes within hours.

For Discussion
1. What are some possible causes for strange animal behavior before earthquakes?
2. Why are scientists interested in determining the causes of this behavior?

11–2

Detecting and Forecasting Earthquakes

An earthquake of 7.3 on the Richter scale shook El Asnam, Algeria, in October, 1980. For ten days, life in this town was a nightmare. This section explains what happens when rocks move inside the earth. Learn more about earthquakes, as you answer these questions:

a. What are the three types of seismic waves?
b. How do scientists find the epicenter of an earthquake?
c. What are some earthquake warning "signs"?

Seismic Waves

Energy moves away from the focus of an earthquake in the form of waves called **seismic** (sīz′mik) **waves.** These waves, pictured in the margin, travel away from the focus in all directions. The **epicenter** (ep′ə sen′tər) of an earthquake is the point on the surface of the earth that is directly above the focus. The epicenter of the Algerian earthquake was near El Asnam. The strongest seismic waves were felt at El Asnam.

P-waves are the fastest seismic waves. They can travel through any material in the earth. P-waves push and pull materials that lie along their paths in the earth. When P-waves meet with a soft or liquid substance, they slow down and lose energy. They slow down at the outer core of the earth. Scientists, therefore, assume this region is liquid. Our knowledge of the earth's layers is based on the changes in speed of seismic waves as they move through different substances.

S-waves move about half as fast as P-waves. The movement of S-waves in the earth resembles the wavelike motion that you see when you shake a rope. Since S-waves cannot travel through liquids, they are stopped at the outer core of the earth.

L-waves move along the surface of the earth. The rippling of L-waves along the ground is responsible for the destruction of property during an earthquake.

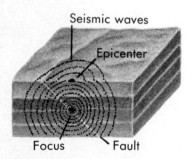

Seismic waves
Epicenter
Focus
Fault

Have You Heard?

Every year seismographs record 800,000 earth movements. We do not feel them because they register 2 or less on the Richter scale. All people living near the epicenter of an earthquake measuring 5 on the Richter scale feel it. There are about 1,400 earthquakes of this strength per year in the world.

Using Seismographs to Find the Epicenter

A **seismograph,** shown in the picture, is a sensitive instrument that measures and records seismic waves. When a seismic wave shakes the seismograph, the pen marks zigzag lines on the revolving paper roll. The lines are similar to this:

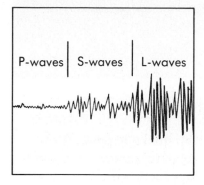

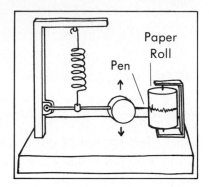

Since P-waves travel fastest, they arrive first at the seismograph, followed by S-waves. L-waves move across the surface of the earth, and arrive last.

Scientists can calculate the distance to the epicenter of an earthquake by reading charts, if they know the time difference between the arrival of the P-waves and the S-waves at a seismograph.

It takes readings from three seismograph stations to locate the epicenter of an earthquake. Assume a scientist finds that the distance from Station A to the epicenter of an earthquake is 1,000 kilometers. The epicenter, therefore, might be at any point on a circle with a radius of 1,000 kilometers around Station A. The scientist draws this circle around his station on a map. Assume that scientists at Station B and Station C have also read the charts and determined the distances to the epicenter to be 500 kilometers from Station B, and 400 kilometers from Station C. Scientists draw circles around their stations at B and C on maps, using the distance to the epicenter for the radius of each circle as before. The epicenter of the earthquake, shown to the right, is the point where the three circles intersect on a map.

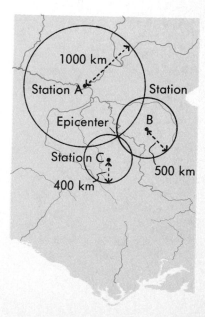

A strong earthquake on the San Andreas Fault leveled San Francisco in 1906. The photograph shows a street that collapsed during this earthquake. Scientists now believe that a strong earthquake occurs on this fault every 50 to 100 years. Therefore, they are monitoring the San Andreas Fault very closely.

Warning—Earthquake Ahead

Where and when will the next earthquake happen? How strong will it be? Scientists are trying to answer these questions.

People all over the world who watch faults find that certain "signs" often occur before earthquakes. The ground sometimes bulges or tilts near a fault before an earthquake. An increased number of small earthquakes on a fault could mean that a strong earthquake is coming. Also, changes in the water level in a well near a fault is often an earthquake sign. A sudden slowing of P-waves in a fault zone can mean trouble ahead. These changes might last for several months before small earthquakes or for years before large ones.

Using these signs and many others, scientists have been able to correctly predict some small earthquakes. Perhaps in your lifetime earthquake forecasts will become accurate enough to save lives.

Review It

1. Which two seismic waves move through the earth?
2. Why do scientists need three seismograph readings to find an earthquake?
3. What might the slowing of P-waves indicate?

Activity

Locating an Earthquake

Purpose
To find the epicenter of earth-quake X.

Materials
• one sheet of unlined paper
• compass
• metric ruler

Procedure
1. Folding on the dashed lines as in *a,* find and mark the center of your paper.
2. Mark Stations A, B, and on the paper. Start by marking a point 2.5 cm above the center point on the paper. This is Station A. Draw in B and C using diagram *a.* You are making a map to find the epicenter.
3. Scientists know how fast P- and S-waves travel. They can calculate the distance to the epicenter of an earthquake by measuring the *difference* in arrival time of P- and S-waves at their stations. The difference in arrival time of the waves is:
120 seconds at Stat. A
 80 seconds at Stat. B
 80 seconds at Stat. C
Using the Epicenter Table *b,* read and record the distance to the epicenter from each station.

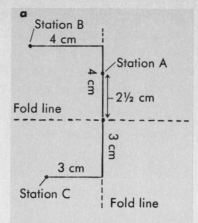

a

Station B
4 cm
Station A
4 cm
2½ cm
Fold line
3 cm
3 cm
Station C
Fold line

b

Epicenter Table

Distance to epicenter (in km)	Difference in arrival time of P- and S-waves (in sec)
200	40
300	60
400	80
500	100
600	120

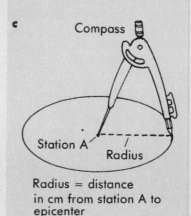

c

Compass

Station A

Radius

Radius = distance in cm from station A to epicenter

4. Convert each distance to cm, so the data can be used on your map. Use the scale 1 cm = 100 km. This data will be the radius of each circle in step 5.
5. On your map draw a circle around Stat. A, as in *c.* The radius of the circle is the distance in cm that you recorded in step 4.
6. Repeat step 5 for the other two stations.
7. The location of the epicenter of earthquake X is the point where the three circles intersect. Mark this point with an X.

Analysis
1. When do scientists need to use this method to find the epicenter?
2. Where is the focus of earthquake X?
3. Why is it necessary to draw a circle around each station with the distance to the epicenter as the radius?
4. How could someone predict the approximate location of an epicenter without a seismograph?

11–3
Magma and Lava

Like an earthquake, the eruption of a volcano means that something is happening inside the earth. When the Mexican farmer watched a volcano emerge in his cornfield, he knew that the earth was boiling and churning under his farm. Study these questions as you read:

a. What forms when magma is trapped underground?
b. Where does lava reach the surface of the earth?
c. Why is lava important at plate boundaries?
d. How can you classify volcanoes by their activity?
e. How do the shapes of volcanic cones differ?

Magma Inside the Earth

Rock formed from magma that cools and hardens underground is intrusive rock. You cannot see intrusive rock unless some geologic process exposes the hidden rock. For example, water may wear away the rocks on the surface. Five intrusive structures are illustrated together below, so that you can see the shape and relative size of each.

A **batholith** (bath′ə lith), shown in the diagram, is so large that its bottom is often unknown.

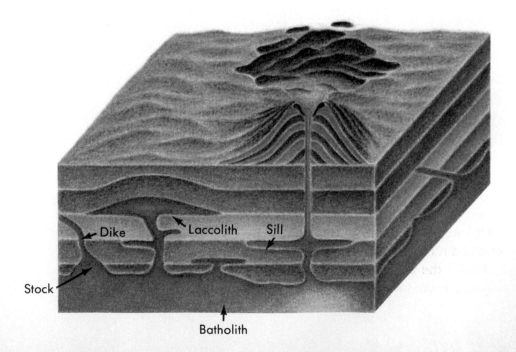

Dike

Laccolith   Sill

Stock

Batholith

In fact, the cores of many mountain chains are batholiths. The **stock** is similar to but smaller than a batholith. When magma works its way between rock layers, a **sill** forms. The mushroom-shaped **laccolith** (lak′ə lith) forms when magma pushes up on the rock above it. When magma cuts across existing rock layers at an angle, a **dike** (dīk) is the result.

Lava on the Earth's Surface

When magma comes out on the surface of the earth, it is called **lava.** Lava reaches the surface through volcanoes or through cracks in the ground. These cracks are called **fissures** (fish′ərz). Extrusive rocks are hardened lava on the earth's surface.

Lava from large fissures may flood wide areas of land. The "flood basalts" in the photo are ancient lava flows from fissures in Washington and Oregon. The fissures may have been three kilometers long. In some places the lava is one and a half kilometers thick.

Notice the layering in the flood basalts. Many separate lava flows created these thick, layered extrusive rocks.

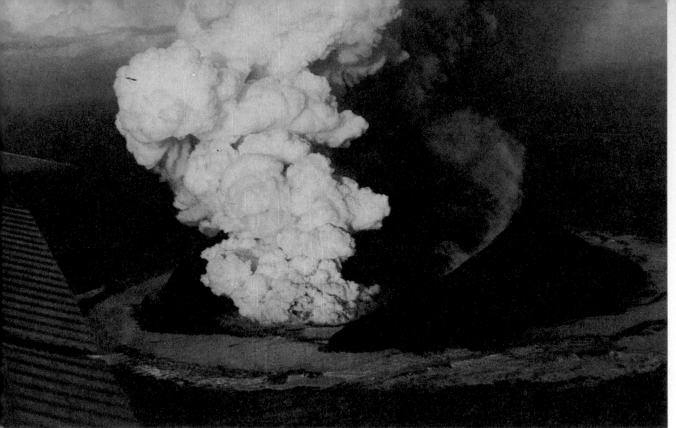

Surtsey

How an island arc forms

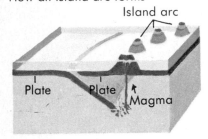

Have You Heard?

Pillow lava is a type of lava that cooled and hardened under water. It is common at spreading boundaries. The strange, rounded lumps of hot lava pop, hiss, and crackle when they meet with cold ocean water.

Lava at Plate Boundaries

Most extrusive rocks form where you cannot see them—on the ocean floor. These rocks are the new crust born at mid-ocean ridges. Vast amounts of lava rise through fissures or volcanoes at spreading boundaries. Occasionally volcanoes on the ocean floor grow large enough to become islands. In 1963, the volcano Surtsey, shown in the photograph, grew from the ocean bottom at the Mid-Atlantic Ridge.

Many volcanoes are near colliding boundaries. The diagram shows one ocean plate sinking under another ocean plate. The sinking crust melts in the asthenosphere. Then the magma that forms from the melted crust rises. This magma gives rise to volcanoes on islands called **island arcs.** The Japanese Islands are an example of an island arc.

Volcanoes may also form on land where an ocean plate sinks under a land plate.

This type of boundary produced the Cascade Mountains of Washington and Oregon—where Mount St. Helens is located. The Andes Mountains of South America were born in the same way.

Volcanic Activity

Volcanoes differ in appearance and behavior. Some volcanoes shoot water vapor and other gases, dust, ash, and rocks explosively. The 1980 eruption of Mount St. Helens followed this pattern. Other volcanoes quietly ooze lava.

Why did Mount St. Helens blow its top? Visualize the effects of shaking a warm soda pop. The bottle may explode, releasing the soda and the dissolved gas in the soda, carbon dioxide. Gases and water vapor, which are under pressure inside a volcano, may also explode.

One of the biggest volcanic explosions that ever took place was the eruption of the volcano Krakatoa (krak′ə tō′ə), a volcanic island in the strait between Java and Sumatra. In 1883 it exploded so violently that people heard the explosion 3,200 kilometers away. Most of the island disappeared. Volcanic dust remained in the air around the world for two years. A giant sea wave created by the explosion killed more than 36,000 people on nearby islands.

Volcanoes often give warnings before they erupt. These warnings include gas and smoke from the volcano. Earthquakes may signal the rise of magma inside the volcano. The ground around or on the volcano may bulge or tilt slightly. Scientists watched the bulge on the north side of Mount St. Helens for weeks before the volcano exploded.

If a volcano has erupted in the recent past, it is called an active volcano. A dormant (dor′mənt) volcano is one that erupted in the past but has been quiet for many years. Mount St. Helens was dormant for over 100 years before it erupted in 1980. An extinct (ek stingkt′) volcano is one that is not expected to erupt again. Most of the volcanoes in the Hawaiian Islands are extinct.

Mount St. Helens—before and after 1980 eruption

Have You Heard?

Many countries of the world use hot water or steam from the ground to heat their homes or make electricity. Water in the ground is heated by igneous activity. Energy from the heat of the earth is called geothermal (jē′ō thėr′məl) energy.

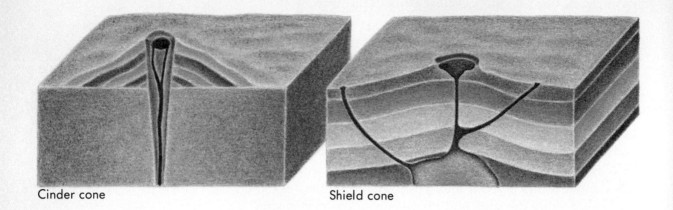

Cinder cone   Shield cone

The Volcanic Cone

The mountain built by a number of volcanic eruptions is the volcano's cone. It is made of lava, volcanic ash, and rocks. A cone usually has a central vent. The volcanic materials come up through the vent. The top of the cone ordinarily has a crater, which is a bowl-like depression. The shape of a volcano depends on the way it erupts and the type of volcanic material that leaves the cone.

A **cinder cone,** pictured above, forms when the eruptions throw out mostly rocks and ash but very little lava. Paricutin (pa′ra kōo tēn′) is a famous cinder cone volcano in Mexico. In 1943, this volcano appeared in a cornfield. In six days the cone was 150 meters high! The volcano reached 400 meters in height before it became dormant.

Non-explosive eruptions with easy flowing lavas create **shield** (shēld) **cones,** shown in the diagram. The volcanic islands of Hawaii with their gently sloping surfaces are typical shield volcanoes.

Alternating eruptions of dust, ash, and rocks followed by quiet lava flows build **composite** (kəm poz′it) **cones,** shown to the right above. Mount St. Helens and Mount Ranier are composite cones.

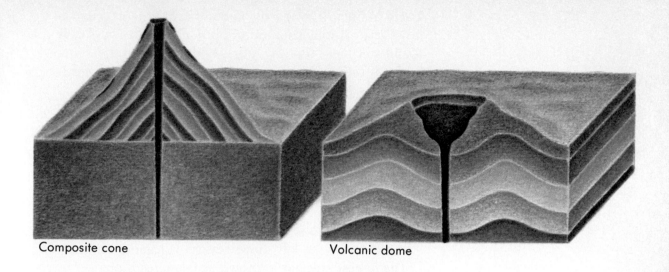

Composite cone

Volcanic dome

Volcanic domes result from violent eruptions of lava so thick that it barely flows. As you can see in the diagram, these volcanoes have sloping sides and dome-shaped tops. Mount Pelée (pə lā′) is a dome volcano on the Caribbean Sea island of Martinique. It erupted violently and with little warning in 1902. A fiery cloud of gas and ash rolled down the side of the volcano, killing most of the people in the town below.

The effects of volcanic eruptions are far-reaching. Huge amounts of volcanic dust in the air contribute to beautiful sunsets and sunrises. If dense enough, volcanic dust can change the weather. The increased cloud cover from the dust can cause rain, and even cool weather. The fertile soils of the Hawaiian Islands developed from volcanic ash and rocks. Scientists think the gases in the air and the water in the ocean came from ancient volcanic eruptions.

Review It

1. What is a batholith?
2. What is a fissure in the earth?
3. How does an island arc form?
4. What is an extinct volcano?
5. Which of the types of cones is not steep-sided?

11–4
Volcanoes in the Solar System

Earth has many volcanoes, and until recently we knew of no others. Through space exploration, however, we have found volcanoes on three other bodies in our solar system. Some of these volcanoes are more spectacular than any on Earth. As you read this lesson, consider:

a. How large is the largest volcano on Mars?
b. How do Io's volcanoes compare with Earth's?
c. How do we study the surface of Venus?

Volcanoes on Mars

Spacecraft have discovered that Mars has huge volcanoes. The picture on the left shows several volcanoes on Mars.

The largest volcano is known as Olympus Mons (ō lim′pəs monz), which is 600 kilometers across at its base. This volcano is over three times higher than the highest land mountain on Earth. The picture to the right below shows it towering over the clouds of Mars.

Why does Mars have such large volcanoes even though it is a smaller planet than Earth? One explanation could be that Mars does not have drifting plates. Once lava from inside Mars starts rising to form a volcano, the volcano does not move away.

Volcanoes on Mars

Olympus Mons

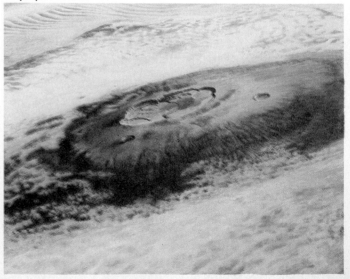

Volcanoes on Io

When the *Voyager 1* spacecraft flew by Jupiter in 1979, the biggest surprise of all was on Jupiter's moon Io (ē′ō). Over a dozen volcanoes were erupting on Io. They sent eruptions of volcanic material hundreds of kilometers into space, as shown on the right. Most of these volcanoes were still erupting four months later when the next *Voyager* spacecraft flew by. Volcanoes on Earth do not erupt for as long. Also, they do not send material up so high. The picture on the left shows a closeup of Io.

Scientists think that the other moons of Jupiter tug Io back and forth as it moves in its orbit. Io is squeezed and unsqueezed so much that its inside heats up. This pulling and heat makes the lava flow. The lava has completely covered the surface of Io. It gives the red color that you see in both photos above.

Montes Maxwell

Volcanoes on Venus

We cannot see through Venus' clouds because they are too thick. Fortunately, we can send radar waves through the clouds to find out what Venus' surface is like. The *Pioneer Venus* spacecraft that circled Venus in 1979 and 1980 made a map of Venus' surface.

The spacecraft discovered Montes Maxwell. This mountain, which may have formed by volcanic activity, is larger than Mount Everest—the largest mountain on Earth. The drawing above shows this mountain. Scientists have not spotted any active volcanoes. But craters and shield cones on Venus indicate that volcanoes exist.

The radar map shows signs, other than volcanoes, that plate tectonics may have taken place on Venus in the past. For example, Venus has a huge valley or rift, much larger than the Grand Canyon on Earth. Plate movement in Venus' crust may have stopped because the crust became too thick to allow plates to move.

Review It

1. What bodies in the solar system have active volcanoes?
2. What kind of maps do we have of Venus?

Activity

Earthquakes and Volcanoes

Purpose
To compare the locations of earthquakes and volcanoes around the Pacific.

Materials
- pencil
- outline map of Pacific and countries surrounding it
- globe or map of the world

Procedure
1. Using a globe or world map, locate on your outline map the earthquake areas named in *a*. Notice that the area names include cities, states, islands, and countries.
2. On your outline map mark with a Q the locations that you found in the step above.
3. Draw a line from one Q to the next nearest Q until all Qs are joined.
4. Using a globe or world map, locate the volcano sites listed on this page. You will probably not be able to find the volcanoes themselves, but you can find the islands, states, countries, or areas where the volcanoes are located.
5. Mark these locations with a V on your outline map.
6. Repeat step 3 above for all of the Vs.

Analysis
1. Describe the figures that resulted from joined Qs and the joined Vs.
2. What relationship exists between earthquake zones and volcano zones on your map?
3. How do the earthquake and volcano zones compare with plate boundaries shown on the map in Chapter 10?
4. At which of the three types of plate boundaries are all of the volcanoes and earthquakes located?
5. What other surface feature is likely to be near the volcanoes on your map?
6. Why do you think the area around the Pacific is called ''The Ring of Fire''?

a

Areas of Frequent Earthquakes	Volcanoes
Acapulco, Mexico	Iraziu, Costa Rica
Aleutian Islands,	Koryakskaya, Pacific
Anchorage, Alaska	Coast, USSR
Concepción, Chile	Lassen Peak, California
Costa Rica	Misti, Peru
Ecuador	Mt. St. Helens, Washington
Fiji Islands	Osorno, Chile
Hokkaido, Japan	Paracutín, Mexico
Indonesia	Pogromni, Aleutian Islands
Los Angeles, California	Sangay, Ecuador
New Guinea	Santa Maria, Guatamala
Nicaragua	Ruapehu, New Zealand
New Zealand	Taal, Philippines
Portland, Oregon	Wrangell, Alaska
San Francisco, California	
Santiago, Chile	
Yokohama, Japan	

Chapter Summary

- Most earthquakes are a result of the movement of rocks along a fault.   (11–1)

- Most earthquakes occur near plate boundaries.   (11–1)

- Numbers on the Richter scale indicate the strength of an earthquake.   (11–2)

- P-waves, S-waves, and L-waves carry energy away from the focus of an earthquake.   (11–2)

- Seismographs detect and record seismic waves.   (11–2)

- Rocks form inside the earth and on the surface of the earth because of volcanic activity.   (11–3)

- Most volcanic activity on the earth's surface is near plate boundaries.   (11–3)

- Depending upon the amount of volcanic activity, a volcano is called active, dormant, or extinct.   (11–3)

- Cinder cones, shield cones, composite cones, and volcanic domes are different types of volcanoes.   (11–3)

- Volcanoes exist on Mars, Venus, and Io, a moon of Jupiter.   (11–4)

Interesting Reading

Aylesworth, Thomas G. *Geological Disasters: Earthquakes and Volcanoes.* Watts, 1979. Describes recent earthquake and volcanic activity and what caused it.

Mercer, Charles. *Monsters in the Earth: The Story of Earthquakes.* Putnam's, 1978. Tells about some of the earth's most disastrous earthquakes.

Simon, Seymour. *Danger from Below.* Four Winds, 1979. Discusses why and where earthquakes occur and how they might be predicted.

Questions/Problems

1. What causes earthquakes in the middle of a plate?

2. Explain what is meant by a deep focus earthquake.

3. Why do scientists think that the outer core of the earth is liquid?

4. What causes volcanoes to occur on island arcs?

5. Scientists checked weather conditions for months after the eruption of Mount St. Helens. Explain this statement.

6. List four signs that might help scientists predict an earthquake.

Extra Research

1. Using an encyclopedia or other library resource, describe and draw two kinds of seismographs.

2. Find five interesting or unusual facts about famous earthquakes. An almanac is a good place to start. Check the index for the listings under earthquakes.

3. Read and report to the class about the progress in earthquake prediction. Consult the *Readers' Guide* in the library for recent magazine articles.

4. Gather as many volcanic rock samples as you can find in your school or home rock collection. Mount the rocks on poster board and label them. Beside the sample, write an explanation of how each rock formed. Illustrate your poster with photographs or drawings.

Chapter Test

A. Vocabulary   Write the numbers 1–10 on a piece of paper.
Match the definition in Column I with the term it defines in Column II.

Column I

1. a volcano that has not erupted recently

2. a series of small earthquakes that follow a larger one

3. a volcano that is not expected to erupt again

4. location of volcano that shoots material hundreds of kilometers into space

5. the way in which energy travels through the earth

6. the point on the earth's surface which is above the focus of an earthquake

7. an instrument that detects seismic waves from distant earthquakes

8. the point in the earth where an earthquake is centered

9. volcanic activity that takes place at the surface of the earth

10. the largest intrusive rock mass

Column II

a. aftershock

b. batholith

c. dormant

d. epicenter

e. extinct

f. extrusive

g. focus

h. Io

i. seismic waves

j. seismograph

B. Multiple Choice   Write the numbers 1–10 on your paper.
Choose the letter that best completes the statement or answers the question.

1. Most earthquakes occur near   a) large cities.   b) plate edges.   c) rivers.   d) inland seas.

2. Only by radar maps can we observe the surface of   a) Earth.   b) Mars.   c) Venus.   d) our moon.

3. To locate the epicenter of an earthquake, scientists need at least   a) one seismograph report.   b) two seismograph reports.   c) three seismograph reports.   d) four seismograph reports.

4. A mushroomed-shaped intrusive rock mass is a   a) laccolith.   b) stock.   c) sill.   d) volcanic dome.

5. A seismic wave that travels only across the surface of the earth is   a) P-wave.   b) L-wave.   c) S-wave.   d) B-wave.

6. Most magma reaches the surface at a) trenches.   b) mid-ocean ridges.   c) faults.   d) island arcs.

7. When old ocean crust moves under younger ocean crust, the resulting volcanoes are a) flood basalts.   b) continental volcano chains.   c) new ocean floors.   d) on island arcs.

8. Scientists use the difference in time between the arrival of the P-waves and the S-waves to find the location of the   a) fault.   b) focus.   c) epicenter.   d) earth tremors.

9. Volcanoes composed of alternating layers of volcanic ash and lava are   a) composite cones.   b) cinder cones.   c) shield volcanoes.   d) volcanic domes.

10. A crack in the ground through which lava oozes is a   a) trench.   b) fissure.   c) stock.   d) sill.

Chapter 12
The Mobile Crust

It was not an accident that the ancient Greeks selected Mount Olympus for the home of their gods. People have long admired, loved, and even worshipped mountains. Mountains offer beauty and adventure to people fortunate enough to see or visit them. Mountains also offer riches to those lucky enough to find precious metals, created when mountains are born.

This chapter is about slow, but constant, changes in the earth's crust. In the first section you will read what scientists think happens after a huge ice sheet retreats. Later, you will read about landforms that develop when forces push up the crust. The descriptions of the crumpling and breaking of the crust will give you some insights into the way mountains develop. When you are done with the chapter, you should have a good idea why the crust is said to be "mobile" or moving.

Chapter Objectives

1. Explain how isostasy causes some up and down movements of the crust.

2. Describe two large land features caused by uplift.

3. Compare normal, thrust, and lateral faults.

4. Explain the relationship between plates and folded mountains.

12–1
The Earth's Crust Moves Up and Down

A small boat floats lower in water when it is loaded with passengers than when it is empty. As the passengers get out, the boat rises. Like the boat, the earth's crust slowly rises or sinks in the mantle. Consider the questions below:

a. How does isostasy explain some up and down movements of the crust?

b. Where can you see evidence of isostasy?

Isostasy: A State of Balance

Isostasy (ī sos′tə sē) means the crust floats on the mantle in a state of balance. How can this statement be explained? The crust of the earth floats on the mantle because the crust is less dense than the mantle. Any volume of crust weighs less than an equal volume of mantle.

Heavy parts of the crust sink farther into the mantle than light parts. For example, the crust under mountains is thicker and denser than the crust under lowlands. The ice cubes in the diagram float in water just as the crust floats on the mantle. Notice that when a weight is added to one ice cube, the weighted cube sinks deeper into the water. Similarly, thick, dense mountain crust sinks deeper into the mantle than the thinner, lighter parts of the crust.

The **root** of a **mountain** is the thickened part that sinks deep into the mantle. The diagram shows that the higher the mountain, the deeper the root.

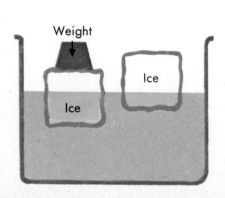

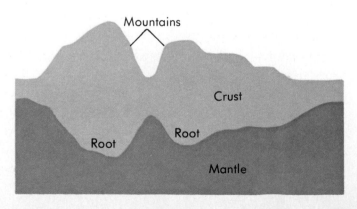

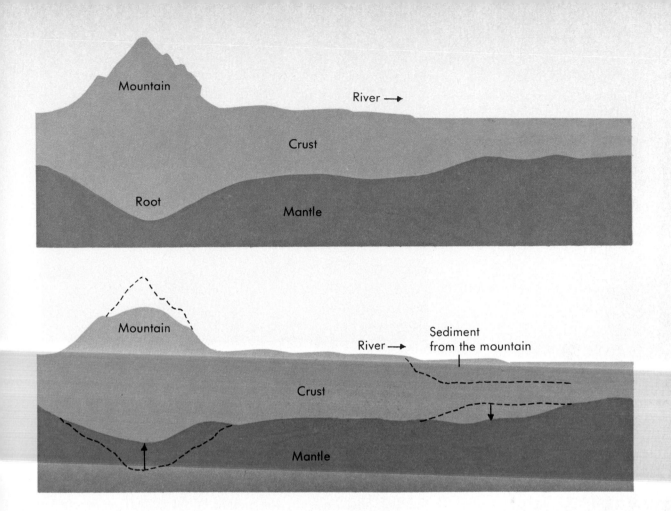

As time passes, water washes sediment away from the surface of a mountain. Therefore, the mountain loses both height and weight. Because the mountain weighs less, it floats higher in the mantle. The root rises as the weight of the mountain becomes less.

The dashed lines in the diagram show the crust before water removed the sediment from the mountain. The sediment does not disappear. It is carried away by the water and dropped somewhere else. The crust gets heavier and sinks where the sediment is deposited. The arrows in the diagram show how the crust moves. When one part of the crust sinks, another part of the crust rises. This balance is called isostasy.

231

Have You Heard?

Removing groundwater speeded the natural sinking in Venice. High water is a constant threat to the beautiful buildings in this city. The outlook for Venice has improved since industry has stopped removing groundwater near Venice.

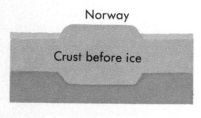

Norway

Crust before ice

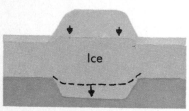

Ice

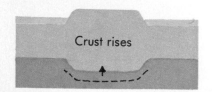

Crust rises

Evidence of Isostasy

Land that was once covered by ice is a good place to observe the effects of isostasy. During the last ice age, an ice sheet nearly three kilometers thick covered parts of Norway and Sweden. The huge weight of this ice caused the crust to sink deeper into the mantle, as illustrated in the diagram. Since the ice melted about 10,000 years ago, the crust has been rising about two meters a century in some places. Scientists suggest that the crust of Norway and Sweden is rising because the weight of the ice is gone. They believe the land will continue to rise slowly until it is as high as it was before the ice covered it, as the diagram shows.

You can see an example of the effects of isostasy in the photograph above. A section of the crust under Venice, Italy, is slowly sinking into the Adriatic Sea. As the coastline sinks, the water level rises in Venice. Eventually, the water will probably destroy the city.

Review It

1. Relate isostasy to the depth of a mountain root.
2. Why is the crust of Norway and Sweden rising?

Activity

Models of Isostasy

Purpose
To understand the process of isostasy.

Materials
- 1 birthday candle
- 1 straight pin
- 1 tall glass or beaker
- matches
- test tube holder
- 3 wooden blocks of different sizes
- 10 to 15 large washers
- large transparent container with water
- marking pen or pencil

Procedure

Part A
1. Fill the tall glass or beaker three-fourths full with water.
2. Insert the straight pin *carefully* into the bottom of the candle as in *a*. The pin should go through the center of the candle. Push it inside the candle until the head of the pin touches the bottom of the candle.
3. Holding the candle by its wick, lower it into the water carefully. Do not let the wick get wet. The candle should float upright in the water as shown in *b*.
4. On the side of the glass, mark the position of the bottom of the candle.
5. Carefully light the wick of the candle, using the test tube holder to secure the match. Every two minutes, mark the position of the bottom of the candle on the side of the container.

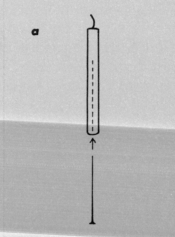

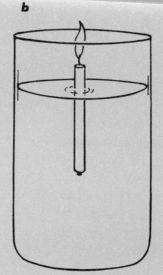

Part B
1. Place a block of wood in the large container of water.
2. Slowly add washers to the block of wood. Observe the block as you add the washers.
3. Add washers until the wood is just floating above the surface of the water. Slowly remove the washers, and observe what happens to the block.
4. Place three wooden blocks in the water at the same time.
5. Observe the blocks as they float.
6. Sketch the way the blocks are floating in the water.

Analysis
1. What happened to the candle's position in the water as it burned?
2. Why do you think this happened?
3. Compare the floating candle to a mountain that wears away.
4. Why did the block of wood sink as you added washers and then rise as you removed washers?
5. Look at your sketch of the floating blocks. How does this experiment show that roots would be deeper under high parts of earth's crust than under lowlands?

12-2
Uplift of the Land

The land under your home may be rising or sinking. You do not notice any change because it is too slow. Consider the question below as you read:

What are two large features caused by uplift of the crust?

Land Features Caused by Uplift

The term uplift means just what it says—the crust is lifted up. You read that the shifting of weight in the crust can cause up and down movements. But there are types of uplift other than those caused by isostasy. Scientists believe that huge movements in the mantle cause large areas of the crust to rise or sink.

A **plateau** (pla tō′) is a large area of flat, uplifted land. Plateaus are usually flat layers of sedimentary rocks. The ragged edges of the plateaus shown in the photograph are part of the Colorado Plateau. This plateau covers thousands of square kilometers in the southwestern United States.

In a moist climate, rivers and running water can carve mountains from plateaus.

Mesas and buttes

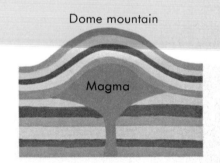

Remains of a dome mountain

For example, the Catskill Mountains of New York and the Pocono Mountains of Pennsylvania formed because water cut channels through the Allegheny Plateau.

Mesas (mā′səz) are small plateaus. They may be what is left behind when water or wind wear away a plateau in a dry climate. When you look at the picture of the flat-topped structures, you can understand why the Spaniards named them mesas, the Spanish word for table. **Buttes** (byüts) are very small mesas. Mesas and buttes are common in the West and Southwest.

Dome mountains are another large feature caused by uplift. They form when magma pushes up rocks at the surface of the earth, as shown in the marginal diagram. The Black Hills in South Dakota probably formed in this way. The core of the Black Hills dome may be a batholith, the largest intrusive rock structure. The picture on the right above shows the remains of a small dome mountain in Wyoming. The rocks at the surface wore away, exposing the buried rock layers.

Dome mountain

Magma

Review It

1. What is a plateau?
2. How do dome mountains form?

12–3
Faults and Mountains

The next time you walk along a sidewalk, look for a section that is tilted along a crack. Sections of the earth's crust also uplift along cracks, but they are on a much larger scale. Consider these questions as you read:

a. What are three types of faults?
b. How do fault-block mountains form?

Types of Faults

The crust and mantle contain a great number of faults. Most large faults are located at plate boundaries. Regardless of where the faults are located, rocks along a fault can move up and down, side to side, or in a combination of both directions.

Faults are named by the direction that the rocks move. Notice the **thrust fault** in the diagram. Rocks above the fault line moved up compared to rocks below the fault line. The diagram of the **normal fault** shows that rocks above the fault line moved down compared to those below the fault line. The movement along a **lateral** (lat′ər əl) **fault,** shown in the diagram, is from side to side.

Sometimes there is visible evidence of a fault. Lakes, rivers, or waterfalls may be present along a fault line. A chain of lakes follows the San Andreas fault line in northern California. A ridge or cliff might also occur along a fault line.

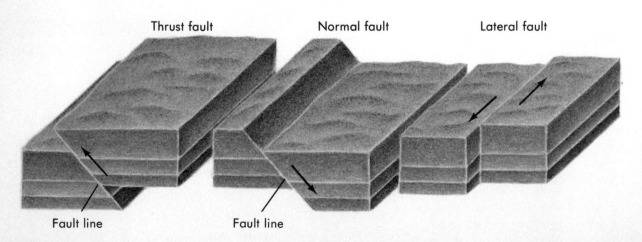

Thrust fault   Normal fault   Lateral fault

Fault line   Fault line

Rocks along most faults have not moved for hundreds, thousands, or even millions of years. If rocks along a fault are not expected to move again, it is called an inactive fault. On the other hand, rocks along an active fault may move at any time. In a strong earthquake, rocks along a fault line can move as far as 10 to 15 meters in a few seconds. Most active faults are near plate edges.

Fault-Block Mountains

The picture below shows the Grand Teton Mountains in Wyoming. Notice how the mountains rise sharply from the level land at their base. The Grand Teton Mountains formed when the movement of rocks along faults raised large blocks of land. Mountains formed in this way are called **fault-block mountains.** The diagram shows the typical steep front and sloping backside of fault-block mountains.

Fault-block mountain

Review It

1. How is a lateral fault different from a normal or thrust fault?
2. What is an active fault?
3. Describe the shape of a typical fault-block mountain.

12–4
The Folding Crust

You can bend a paper clip without much effort. Just as easily, great forces inside the earth slowly bend rock layers into folds of different sizes. If the rock layers are thick enough, mountains result. Think about the questions below as you read:

a. What is a geosyncline?
b. How do many large folded mountains form?

Upfold, Downfolds, and Geosynclines

Rock layers in the earth's crust often bend and fold rather than break when forces act on them. This process usually takes millions of years. The diagram shows rock layers that have bent to form two upfolds, or **anticlines** (an′ti klīnz). The **syncline** (sin′klīn) in the same diagram is a downfold of rock layers. These folds may be a few centimeters long or may extend for many kilometers.

A **geosyncline** (jē ō sin′klīn) is a very large trough that often forms in shallow water along the edge of a continent. This trough may be thousands of kilometers long and hundreds of kilometers wide. Rivers along the coast can drop layers of sediments up to ten kilometers thick into the geosyncline. Oil and gas are often found in the thick sediments of geosyncline. The diagram shows a geosyncline that extends from Texas across the Gulf of Mexico. Notice how thick the sediments are. Drilling for oil and gas has been very successful in the geosyncline along the Gulf Coast.

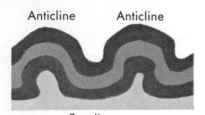

Anticline   Anticline

Syncline

Have You Heard?

Many large mountain systems of the world developed from former geosynclines. The rock layers of the geosyncline fold, and magma in the mantle rises into the crumpled layers. Scientists do not know what causes this process.

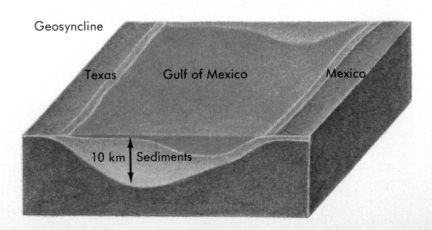

Geosyncline

Texas   Gulf of Mexico   Mexico

10 km Sediments

Folded Mountains and Colliding Plates

Rock layers squeezed between colliding plates crumple, much as cars traveling at high speeds crumple when they meet head on. However, it takes millions of years for two colliding plates to create mountains. Most large **folded mountain** systems are present where plates collide. The diagram in the margin shows a simplified cross-section of folded mountains. Both the Alps in Europe and the Himalayas in Asia are growing in height, because they are on colliding plates.

Folded mountains

The Appalachian Mountains in Eastern United States are very old folded mountains. They formed at colliding plate boundaries about 300 to 400 million years ago. This happened even before Pangaea broke up. The picture, taken in the Appalachian Mountains, illustrates the parallel ridges that are commonly seen in folded mountain systems.

You have read about mountain building processes that create volcanoes, dome, fault-block, and folded mountains. Mountain building, however, is very complex. A mountain range, such as the Rocky Mountains, may be built from a combination of these processes.

Review It

1. Compare synclines with anticlines.
2. Why are the Himalayas increasing in elevation?

Activity

Investigating Models of Faults and Folds

Purpose

To observe models of faults and folds.

Materials

- wooden blocks: A and B
- soap or candle
- centimeter ruler
- two pieces of paper
- one large paper clip
- strip of paper, 4 cm by 22 cm
- hardcover book

Procedure

Part A

1. Place blocks A and B together as shown in *a*. These blocks represent pieces of the earth's crust.
2. Use these blocks to demonstrate a normal fault.
3. Sketch how you arranged the blocks to make a normal fault. Use arrows to show how the blocks move along a normal fault.
4. Place the two blocks together again. Soap or wax the sloping ends of the blocks to reduce friction.

5. Apply a small, steady pressure to the ends of the blocks until the blocks move.
6. Sketch the blocks in this position and use arrows to show how they moved.
7. Place blocks A and B together again. Use the blocks to show the type of motion that takes place along lateral faults.
8. Sketch your lateral fault. Use arrows to show the direction of block motion.

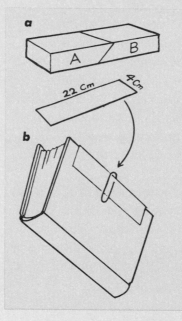

Part B

1. Place the paper strip on the long edge of the hardcover of the book.
2. Place the paper clip halfway down the strip of paper and fasten it to the book cover, as shown in *b*.
3. Slowly push the ends of the paper strip toward the middle, causing the paper to fold.
4. Sketch the folds. Label with "syncline" or "anticline" the parts of the sketch that resemble these earth features.

Analysis

1. Describe the direction of movement on both sides of a normal fault.
2. What type of fault did you make in Part A, step 5?
3. At which type of plate boundary would you expect to find this type fault?
4. In Part B you made a model of a folded rock layer. Draw arrows on your sketch to show the direction of forces necessary to fold rocks in this way.

Breakthrough

J. Tuzo Wilson: Geophysicist

What happens when someone has an exciting new idea in science? New ideas must be tested and retested . J. Tuzo Wilson, shown below, is a scientist with new ideas. He has proved to many people that the new ideas are valid.

Dr. Wilson, a Canadian geophysicist, was one of the people who made the theory of plate tectonics as well known as it is today. Dr. Wilson and many other scientists took Wegener's theory of drifting continents off the shelf and adapted it. It became the theory of plate tectonics.

Dr. Wilson has spent much of his time writing and talking about the new theory. He convinced a number of scientists that the theory of plate tectonics answers many questions about the earth. It answers questions about the location of mineral deposits, mountain ranges, earthquakes, and volcanoes.

But the new theory also leaves many questions unanswered or presents new questions. Dr. Wilson has helped fill in a few of the many missing pieces in the plate tectonic theory with his imaginative ideas. For example, he described and named a type of fault found at plate boundaries—the transform fault. He suggested that volcanoes in the middle of the plates were caused by hot spots. He proposed that large continents contained "patched on" pieces from other continents. Part of Florida, Dr. Wilson said, came from Africa, and part of the New England states was once attached to Europe!

Dr. Wilson has had a long and successful career. He was the first Canadian to be elected president of the American Geophysical Union (AGU). Dr. Wilson is at an age when most people slow down. But he continues to work and produce still more fresh ideas.

For Discussion
1. Was plate tectonics accepted immediately by all scientists?
2. What were two of Dr. Wilson's contributions to the new theory?

Chapter Summary

- The thick parts of the crust float deeper in the mantle than the thin parts. (12–1)

- The crust constantly adjusts to large changes or shifts in weight by moving up and down. This balance of the crust is called isostasy. (12–1)

- Plateaus form because of an uplift of the crust. (12–2)

- Dome mountains sometimes form where magma pushes up surface rocks. (12–2)

- Lateral, normal, and thrust faults are three kinds of faults. At these faults, rocks move up and down or sideways. (12–3)

- Fault-block mountains result from the uplift of large sections of crust along faults. (12–3)

- Synclines and anticlines form where forces squeeze and bend the rock layers into folds. (12–4)

- Geosynclines near continental coasts can be thousands of kilometers long. The deposits in geosynclines are up to 10 kilometers thick. (12–4)

- Folded mountains may develop where plates meet. (12–4)

Interesting Reading

Shimer, John A. *Field Guide to Landforms in the United States*. MacMillan, 1972. Discusses plateaus and mountains of the United States.

Shurkin, Joel N. *Update-Report on the Planet Earth*. Westminster, 1976. Discusses forces from inside the earth or forces from space that shape the earth.

Wyckoff, Jerome. *The Story of Geology*. Golden Press, 1976. Describes faults and mountain-building processes.

Questions/Problems

1. Suggest where you should drill a hole through the crust in order to study the mantle.

2. Why should the crust uplift after very thick sheets of ice melt from it?

3. Tell how geosynclines develop.

4. How does the plate tectonic theory explain folded mountain ranges?

5. How are plateaus, mesas, and buttes alike?

6. Describe four types of mountains that you read about in chapters 11 and 12. Make diagrams to go with your description.

Extra Research

1. The Rocky Mountains formed by a combination of several of the methods discussed in the last three chapters. Using an encyclopedia or a geology book from the library, write a report about the development of this mountain chain.

2. Write your state geologic survey for information regarding outstanding surface features in your state. Your teacher will tell you how to find the address of your state survey. Report to the class any unusual surface features located in your state.

3. If the region where you live is rising or sinking, find the average rate and the reason for the change. You might begin your search by looking up the geology of your state in the card catalogue in your public library.

Chapter Test

A. Vocabulary   Write the numbers 1–10 on a piece of paper.
Match the definition in Column I with the term it defines in Column II.

Column I

1. a downfold of rock layers

2. one section of crust moves up and over another section

3. a large raised area of crust with flat-lying rock layers

4. flat-topped feature that may be the remnant of a plateau

5. a long trough that forms along continental coasts

6. mountains formed when intrusive rock pushes up the surface of the earth

7. an upfold of rock layers

8. heavy parts of the crust sink farther into the mantle than light parts

9. the fault along which sideways motion of crust takes place

10. mountains formed by collision of plates

Column II

a. anticline

b. dome mountains

c. folded mountains

d. geosyncline

e. isostasy

f. lateral fault

g. mesa

h. plateau

i. syncline

j. thrust fault

B. Multiple Choice   Write the numbers 1–10 on your paper.
Choose the letter that best completes the statement or answers the question.

1. The earth's crust is thickest under
a) lowlands.   b) faults.   c) mountains.
d) buttes.

2. Most active faults are located near   a) large cities.   b) plate edges.   c) plateaus.
d) rivers.

3. Rocks above the fault line move down compared to rocks below the fault line in a
a) reverse fault.   b) normal fault.   c) thrust fault.   d) lateral fault.

4. Fault-block mountains usually   a) are not high.   b) are worn-down plateaus.   c) have steep faces.   d) have no roots.

5. A trough on the earth's surface that can be thousands of kilometers long is a   a) fault.
b) mesa.   c) butte.   d) geosyncline.

6. Parallel ridges are a characteristic of
a) folded mountains.   b) volcanoes.
c) domes.   d) fault-block mountains.

7. The gradual elevation of land after thick ice melts is evidence of   a) volcanism.
b) isostasy.   c) plate movement.   d) faults.

8. Large folded mountain systems form at
a) spreading boundaries.   b) colliding boundaries.   c) fault boundaries.   d) continental interiors.

9. If one part of the crust rises because of great shifts of weight, another section of the crust will   a) rise.   b) sink.   c) remain the same.   d) none of the above.

10. The Pocono Mountains were created when water cut down through   a) a plateau.
b) dome.   c) an anticline.   d) a geosyncline.

Chapter 13
Weathering of the Earth's Surface

The boulders in the picture are broken and tossed about like marbles in a giants' game. The giants are water and freezing weather. It took hundreds of thousands of years to crack and shatter these rocks.

This chapter tells how weather affects rocks. Then it explains how plants, people, animals, water, acids, and air also destroy or change rocks. The chapter ends by describing soils and how they form from the weathering of rocks on the earth's surface.

Chapter Objectives

1. Describe the causes of physical weathering.
2. Explain how water, oxygen, and acids affect rocks in chemical weathering.
3. Describe soil textures and zones.
4. Compare three major soil types.

13–1
Physical Weathering

Hiking or backpacking in the mountains can be difficult. At times the trail winds near the base of steep slopes. Hikers must climb over large boulders or scramble across fields of sharp rocks. This section explains where these rocks and boulders come from. Consider the questions below as you read:

a. What is weathering?
b. How does freezing water break rocks?
c. How do plants and animals cause physical weathering?

Little Rocks from Big Ones—Weathering

Rocks on the earth's surface are exposed to conditions in the environment that cause them to break down. **Weathering** is a process that changes rocks or breaks large rocks into smaller and smaller pieces.

There are two types of weathering. **Physical weathering** breaks rocks apart without changing their minerals. Freezing and thawing, plants, and animals bring about physical weathering. **Chemical weathering** changes the minerals that make up the rock.

Freezing and Thawing Cause Physical Weathering

Rock surfaces often develop cracks, which are called **joints.** Water seeps into joints in rocks. When water in a joint freezes, it expands. The ice pushes against the sides of the rock. It acts like a wedge driven into wood. Freezing and thawing in joints split the rock, as shown in the picture.

Potholes in streets and roads also begin when water freezes in cracks in the pavement. Car wheels plunging into a pothole make it bigger. Road crews often pour tar into cracks in the road to prevent water from getting into the pavement and freezing.

The effect of physical weathering is often seen near the tops of mountains where rock is exposed to great changes of temperature. Over long periods of time, very high and low daily temperatures combined with moisture will weaken rocks.

Joints in rocks

Have You Heard?

Sudden temperature changes can shatter or crack some rocks. Campers sometimes hear shale pop and crack from the heat of their campfires.

Physical Weathering Caused by Plants and Animals

Have you seen a sidewalk that is split or buckled by a tree root? Trees can weather rock too. Trees and small plants grow in the soil that collects in the cracks of rocks. The picture shows a small tree growing out of a rock. As the tree grows larger, the roots and trunk get larger. They push against the sides of the joint in the rock. In time, the rock will split apart along this crack. Even small plants can split rocks. Rocks in high mountain meadows often support tiny flower gardens in their joints.

People cause some of the physical weathering of rocks on the earth. They expose and break rock when they clear land for farms and homes and build roads. The picture shows how people can change the land when they remove stone from the ground. Even small animals, such as worms, burrow in the ground and add to the breakdown of rock.

People cause weathering

Review It

1. How are rocks changed as a result of physical weathering?
2. Why does freezing water break rocks?
3. How do plants contribute to physical weathering?

Have You Heard?

You can snap a mushroom in half with one finger. But growing mushrooms exert enough force to push through 15 centimeters of asphalt paving.

13–2
Chemical Weathering

The copper statue in the picture below turned green when the copper combined with water and carbon dioxide in the air. A wet, steel-wool scrubbing pad that is left out overnight may be rusty the next day. The iron in the pad rusts when oxygen and water are added. Similar changes occur in minerals or rocks. As you read about these changes, think about the following questions:

a. What effect does water have on minerals?
b. How do oxygen and acids aid chemical weathering?
c. Why do rocks resist chemical weathering?

Water and Chemical Weathering

Chemical weathering changes the minerals in rocks. Minerals react with water, oxygen, and acids to form new substances during chemical weathering. The products of chemical weathering are often softer and smaller than the original rock.

Water is an important agent of chemical weathering. Water that seeps into rocks may dissolve minerals and wash them away. This process is named **leaching** (lēch′ing). Also, minerals may absorb water. Feldspar, for example, eventually breaks into clay minerals and other substances when it absorbs water.

What acid rain does to rock

Minerals Combine with Oxygen and Acid

Minerals can "rust" like the steel-wool pad. Certain minerals in rocks combine with oxygen from the air to form new substances, **oxides** (ok′sīdz). Iron combines easily with oxygen to form iron oxides. They are most often rust-colored or yellow. Red soil, shown above, gets its color from iron oxide. Soft oxides crumble away from the rock and can be carried away by water.

Rain and water in the ground combine with carbon dioxide to form **carbonic** (kär bon′ik) **acid.** As this weak acid trickles through the ground, it leaches away many minerals.

Limestone is easily dissolved by carbonic acid. Water containing carbonic acid seeps through tiny holes in the limestone and makes them larger. In time, these holes in rocks may become large enough to be called caves. The picture shows a cave in limestone.

Limestone cave

Smokestack particles added to rain or snow also form acids. These acids, diluted by water, fall as acid rain. Rain and snow are acidic enough in some areas to damage plants, animals, and rocks. The picture shows what can happen to stone that is weathered by air and acid rain.

Plants and animals also provide acids for the chemical weathering of rocks. Small plants, such as lichens (lī′kənz), grow on rocks. They give off acids that can cause the outer surface of rocks to weaken and crumble into a thin soil.

Some Minerals Resist Chemical Weathering

Chemical weathering attacks some minerals more easily than others. Quartz resists chemical weathering. Since granite has a high quartz content, it resists chemical weathering.

Scientists studied the different types of rock used for tombstones in a Connecticut cemetery. Sandstone and marble tombstones weathered the most rapidly. Slate and granite weathered very slowly. The picture shows two tombstones that are about 150 years old. The lighter tombstone is made of limestone. It shows the effects of weathering. The other tombstone, made of slate, is almost unchanged.

Chemical weathering is most effective in a moist climate. The Sphinx and the Pyramids in Egypt are made of sandstone, which would weather quickly in a moist climate. But in the dry deserts of Egypt, these monuments have lasted for thousands of years.

Review It

1. Name two ways that water is involved in chemical weathering.
2. What is an oxide?
3. Why does a building made of granite outlast a limestone building?

Activity

Models of Chemical Weathering

Purpose
To study chemical weathering.

Materials
- one large funnel
- ring stand or other support
- paper towels or filter paper
- sugar and sand mixture
- two jars or beakers
- graduated cylinder
- limestone chips or pieces of chalk
- dilute hydrochloric acid
- safety glasses

Procedure

Part A
1. Set up the funnel and support stand as shown in *a*.
2. Cover the small opening of the funnel with a piece of paper towel or filter paper.
3. Put about 100 mL of the sand and sugar mixture on the paper towel covering the funnel.
4. Add about 100 mL of water to the funnel and let the water drip into another container, as shown in *a*.

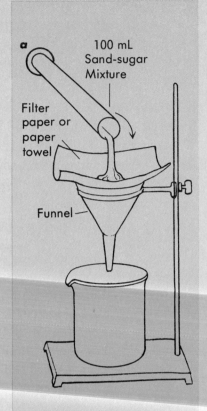

a

100 mL Sand-sugar Mixture

Filter paper or paper towel

Funnel

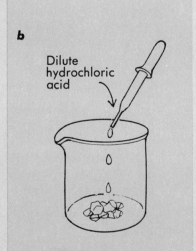

b

Dilute hydrochloric acid

Part B
1. Put a small piece of limestone in a jar or beaker.
2. CAUTION: *wear safety glasses for this step.* Drop dilute hydrochloric acid on this piece of limestone as shown in *b*. Observe and record what you see.
3. Put another small piece of limestone in the second jar.
4. On this limestone chip, put about the same amount of water as the acid you used in step 2.

Analysis
1. What happened to the sugar in Part A?
2. What process in chemical weathering does Part A represent?
3. Would sand or sugar remain in topsoil longest? Why?
4. Describe the difference in appearance between the limestone chip in water and the one in the acid.

13-3
How Soils Form

When the earth's crust first formed, there was no soil on our planet. A visitor at that time would have seen only bare rock. But things changed. Because of the weathering of exposed rock, a thin layer of soil appeared. Think of these questions as you read:

a. Where does soil come from?
b. What are the three soil zones?
c. What are three soil textures?
d. How does climate affect the development of three types of soil?

Bedrock Weathers into Soil

Soil comes from weathered bedrock. **Bedrock** is the solid rock under the earth's loose surface material. First, bedrock splits into large boulders. In time, the boulders weather into smaller and smaller pieces. These small pieces—plus air, water, and the remains of life—form soil.

The illustration shows two weathering products of granite. Other rocks yield different minerals. This variety of weathered material gives us the many kinds of soil found in the world.

Rivers, lakes, glaciers, and the wind move soil from one area to another. A great deal of the soil where you live probably came from bedrock that is far from your home.

How granite weathers

Quartz

Granite

Feldspar

Sand

Clay

Forest

Soil zones

A   Humus
      Sand
      Clay

B   Roots
      Clay
      Iron oxides

C   Partly
      weathered rock

Granite

Soil Zones

The part of the soil you see most often is **topsoil.** Topsoil is actually one of three layers, or zones, of soil. The illustration shows these three zones. The **A-zone** is sand and clay mixed with bits of decayed plants and animals. This decaying material is known as **humus** (hyü′məs). It gives topsoil its dark color and helps soil hold moisture. Humus contains acids that leach minerals from the topsoil.

Many minerals that can be dissolved by acids and water are washed out of the topsoil. They trickle into the middle soil layer, or **B-zone.** This zone contains the roots of large plants, clay, iron oxides, and other minerals leached from the A-zone. Iron oxides give the B-zone a reddish-brown or yellow color. The B-zone has little or no humus in it.

Where soil is well-developed, the **C-zone** extends down many meters to the bedrock. This zone includes solid bedrock and partly weathered bedrock.

In some places, one soil zone may be missing. In mountains, it is common to find a few inches of soil lying on solid rock. The three zones have not yet developed.

Have You Heard?

About 100 years ago, Iowa had 40 centimeters of rich topsoil. About half of this soil has washed away. Much of Iowa's topsoil is now in the Gulf of Mexico.

Clay soil

Sandy soil

Particle Size and Soil Texture

The size of the particles in the soil affects the texture of the soil. The three main soil textures are clay, sand, and loam.

Clay soil, which appears in the top photograph, feels slippery or greasy. Because a clay particle is very small, you cannot see it unless it is magnified. This type of soil is fertile and holds water very well, but it drains poorly. Clay soils contain more than 30 percent clay.

Sandy soil, shown in the lower photograph, is mostly grains of sand. It feels gritty when it is rubbed between your fingers. Sand grains are much larger than clay particles. Sandy soils tend to dry out, because water drains away from them quickly.

Loam soil is a mixture of clay, sand, and silt. The term *silt* means a particular size of particle. Silt is larger than clay particles, but smaller than grains of sand. Loam is good for farming, because it holds some water but drains away excess water. It is usually easy to plow.

What makes a soil good for growing crops? The soil should hold water long enough for the roots of plants to absorb moisture. Soil that does not pack and clump requires less energy to plow. Dark soil often indicates the presence of a great deal of humus, which enriches the soil. Dark soil also absorbs more heat than light-colored soil. Many young plants thrive in warm, dark soil.

Farming uses minerals from the soil faster than they can be replaced by weathering. Even good loam soils need to have minerals replaced. Farmers use fertilizers to add minerals to the soil.

How Climate Affects Soil

The climate of an area affects how soils are formed. Chemical weathering that turns rocks into soil takes place more quickly in climates with high temperatures and heavy rainfalls. However, it can take up to 100,000 years for good topsoil to develop.

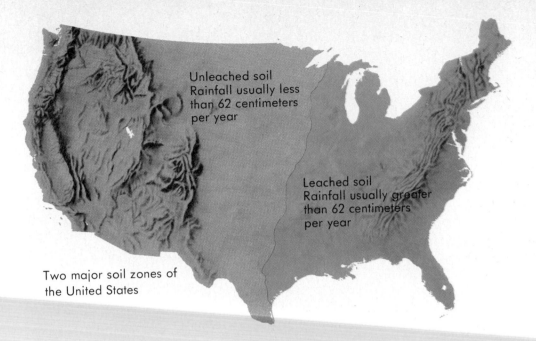

Unleached soil
Rainfall usually less
than 62 centimeters
per year

Leached soil
Rainfall usually greater
than 62 centimeters
per year

Two major soil zones of
the United States

The location of the two major types of soil found in the United States is shown on the diagram. They are largely determined by the amount of rainfall. In the eastern part of the country, heavy rainfalls leach the elements calcium and magnesium out of the soil and into the ground water. This fertile soil is good for farming. In the drier west, the calcium is not leached out. It remains in the soil. Much of this soil is not as good for farming because of the dry climate.

A third major type of soil is common in tropical climates. Because chemical weathering is so rapid in tropical climates, the soil is rich in iron and aluminum but poor in humus. This deep red soil, called **laterite** (lat′ə rīt) soil, is very poor for farming. Laterite soils in Jamaica, however, are so rich in aluminum that aluminum compounds can be taken directly from the soil.

Have You Heard?

Most of the heavily populated, undeveloped nations of the tropics have laterite soils. Even though these soils support rich rain forests, they are very poor for growing food crops.

Review It

1. Compare the materials in soil zone-A with those in zone-C.
2. What determines soil texture?
3. How does climate affect soil formation?

Activity

Investigating Soil

Purpose

To observe and identify the particles that make up the soil.

Materials

- samples of soils from home or school
- several sheets of paper
- hand lens or magnifying glass
- cloth, 15 cm x 15 cm
- water
- two test tubes or large baby food jars with lids
- flashlight
- rubber band or string

Procedure

Part A

1. Spread a small amount of your soil sample onto a piece of notebook paper.
2. Observe the soil through a magnifying glass. Look for particles with different shapes, sizes, and colors. Estimate the percentage of each in your sample. Record your observations in a labeled drawing.
3. Rub a small amount of your soil between your thumb and fingers. Describe and record the texture of the soil.

Part B

1. Fill a test tube or jar one-third full with soil.
2. Carefully add water until the container is almost full. Record what you see.
3. Cover the container and shake the water and soil mixture.
4. Allow the container to sit for a few minutes. Compare the appearance of the soil now with your observations from step 2, Part B.

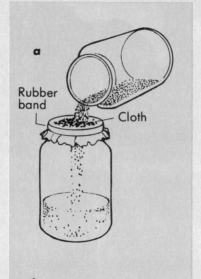

Rubber band

Cloth

a

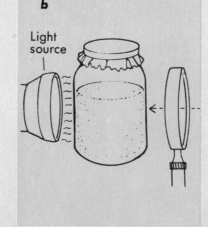

Light source

b

Part C

1. Shake the soil and water mixture from Part B once more.
2. Use a rubber band or string to attach the cloth to the top of the second container as pictured in *a*.
3. Slowly pour the soil and water mixture through the cloth into the second container.
4. Feel the texture of the material on the cloth. Record your observations.
5. Place a light between you and the second container. Look at the liquid, as shown in *b*. Record your observations.
6. Clean up your materials according to your teacher's instructions.

Analysis

1. When you did Part B, what size particles settled first? Why?
2. Compare the size of the particles left on the cloth in Part C to those that passed through the cloth.
3. Predict what size particles would wash out of the soil most easily.

Issues in Earth Science

Save the Topsoil

Free farmland! All you want! Yours for the taking! All you have to do is stand at the mouth of any large river and scoop it up as the river flows by you.

The United States is losing its best farmlands at an alarming rate. Wind and water are carrying away an astounding four billion tons of good topsoil each year. This process is called erosion.

A dust storm in New Mexico

The photograph, taken in the 1930s, shows a dust storm in New Mexico. That was the time of the Great Dust Bowl disasters. The best topsoil was washed or blown away. Because of poor farming techniques, thousands of families lost their farms.

Soon after these dust storms, people began looking for ways to cut erosion. Since then, our country has spent more than fifteen billion dollars to conserve our soils.

Farmers worked successfully to combat erosion. They planted trees and shrubs around fields. They plowed following the slope of the land. Unused fields were planted with clover or other ground covers. Many people, including farmers, thought the erosion problem was solved.

But the situation has changed in the last ten years. Farmers are under pressure to produce larger crops. They

have spent large amounts of money on new equipment, seeds, fertilizers, and pesticides. A single bad season can ruin a modern farmer. To survive, many farmers are concerned about this year's profits, not the condition of the soil in twenty years.

As a result, many farmers neglect soil conservation. They know how to use fertilizers and pesticides to produce good crops even in poor soil.

Erosion is a natural process. Too much soil erosion, however, is a national disaster. Practicing good farming methods now is vital to saving our topsoil for the future.

For Discussion
1. What caused the Great Dust Bowl storms of the 1930s?
2. Why should someone who lives in a city worry about soil erosion?

Chapter Summary

- Weathering is a process that breaks down rocks at the earth's surface. (13–1)

- Physical weathering breaks rocks into smaller pieces. Agents of physical weathering are water, temperature change, plants, and animals. (13–1)

- Chemical weathering alters the minerals in a rock. Agents of chemical weathering are water, oxygen, and acids. (13–2)

- Soil is a product of weathering. A well-developed soil can be divided into three zones. (13–3)

- Soils are divided by particle size into three textures: sand, clay, and loam. (13–3)

- The amount of rainfall and the climate are important factors in soil formation. (13–3)

- Two major soil types are present in the United States. The soils in the eastern half of the country are well-leached by rainfall. Most soils in the west, where the rainfall is generally less, are unleached. A third major soil type exists mainly in tropical countries. This soil is rich in aluminum, but poor in decayed plant and animal matter. (13–3)

Interesting Reading

Keen, Martin L. *The World Beneath Our Feet: The Story of Soil.* Messner, 1974. Describes how soil forms and its importance.

Matthews, William H. *Soil.* Watts, 1970. Describes soils and how they develop.

Risser, James. "A Renewed Threat of Soil Erosion: It's Worse Than the Dust Bowl." *Smithsonian,* March 1981, pages 122–130. Tells how farmers can reduce erosion.

Questions/Problems

1. How are physical weathering and chemical weathering different?

2. How can water cause physical weathering of rocks?

3. Give at least two examples of how plants and animals cause weathering.

4. Describe a good soil for crops, using what you have learned about soils.

5. Give the characteristics of each of the three zones of soil.

6. Explain how climate affects soil formation.

Extra Research

1. Look for a place where you can observe the materials beneath the topsoil. You might look at an excavation for a road or building, or the side of a gully or stream bank. Draw and describe it. Indicate soil zones on your drawing.

2. Observe, describe, and record any evidence of weathering you see during a walk near your home or school.

3. Locate the branch of local government that repairs your streets and roads. Write a one-page report on how potholes are repaired, how long the repairs last, and how much the repair work costs the taxpayers yearly.

Chapter Test

A. Vocabulary Write the numbers 1–10 on a piece of paper.
Match the definition in Column I with the term it defines in Column II.

Column I

1. product of chemical weathering on feldspar

2. what forms when water and carbon dioxide combine

3. a part of soil formed from decaying plants and animals

4. a process in which a rock breaks into pieces, but its minerals are unchanged

5. minerals dissolve and are carried away in this process

6. dark red soil found in the tropics

7. iron rust

8. condition in which chemical weathering is rapid

9. good soil for farming

10. a crack in a rock

Column II

a. carbonic acid

b. clay mineral

c. humus

d. joint

e. laterite

f. leaching

g. loam

h. oxide

i. physical weathering

j. tropical climate

B. Multiple Choice Write the numbers 1–10 on your paper.
Choose the letter that best completes the statement or answers the question.

1. The expansion of water as it freezes in joints of rocks causes   a) leaching.
b) physical weathering.   c) chemical weathering.   d) silt formation.

2. All of the following cause chemical weathering *except* a) water.   b) acids.   c) oxygen.
d) calcium.

3. Granite resists weathering because it
a) formed underground.   b) contains limestone.   c) is very old rock.   d) contains quartz.

4. Rainwater combined with carbon dioxide forms   a) carbonic acid.   b) limestone.
c) clay.   d) humus.

5. Bedrock is   a) always visible.   b) never visible.   c) the major source of soil.   d) an oxide.

6. The particles formed from the weathering of quartz are a) silt.   b) sand.   c) clay.
d) humus.

7. The least weathered rocks in the soil are in a) humus.   b) zone-A.   c) zone-B.   d) zone-C.

8. Humus is the name given to   a) sandy soil.
b) small rocks.   c) wet and damp climates.
d) decayed plant and animal material.

9. The presence of iron makes soil   a) black.
b) red.   c) sandy.   d) silt.

10. The weathering of granite produces   a) all oxides.   b) sand.   c) clay.   d) sand and clay.

Chapter 14
Erosion

In May 1980, the people who live in Wintergreen, Florida, were stunned when a depression in the earth suddenly appeared. It grew to the size you see in the picture. The hole swallowed a home, some buildings, a truck, five sports cars, and even the local swimming pool. After you read this chapter, you will understand what caused the land to sink.

This chapter tells you what forces shape the surface of the earth. You will find out what causes landslides. You will learn how water or ice changes the appearance of the countryside. Even the wind brings about changes that you may have seen.

Chapter Objectives

1. List the agents of erosion.
2. Explain how gravity alters the landscape.
3. Describe river erosion and deposits.
4. Explain how groundwater causes erosion.
5. Compare the two types of glaciers.
6. Explain the role of wind in eroding the land.

14–1
Erosion Moves Rocks

How does soil from Missouri end up in the Gulf of Mexico? Or why is a piece of granite from Canada resting in Cape Cod many kilometers away? Find out how soil and rocks move by answering these questions:

a. What causes erosion?
b. What happens when gravity acts on rocks and soil?

Who or What Causes Erosion?

Erosion (i rō′zhən) is the movement of weathered rock and soil from one place to another. This process is powerful enough to level hills and mountains. Why isn't the world as flat as a pancake by now? Because forces inside the earth build mountains and lift the land after erosion has flattened it. More erosion follows the uplift, and the cycle continues.

The "agents of erosion" are gravity, running water, ice, wind, and people. Running water plays the biggest part. For instance, it was the Mississippi River that carried the soil from Missouri into the Gulf of Mexico. For the last 100 years, however, people have played big roles as agents of erosion. The photograph below shows one way people cause erosion by moving rocks and soil.

Climate has a great effect on erosion. For example, glaciers moved into North America when the climate was colder than it is today. A glacier carried the piece of granite from Canada to Cape Cod.

People cause erosion

Gravity Moves Rocks and Soil

Loose soil and rocks on hills and mountains move very slowly down the slope because of gravity. Sometimes loose soil, like that in the picture, **creeps** down the slope. Notice how the tree is bent. The tree is rooted in deeper soil that is not moving as much as the soil near the surface.

Soil creep

Heavy rainfall soaks into loose soil on slopes. Water makes loose soil move more easily. Enough water causes soil to move almost like a liquid. This moving soil is called a **mudflow.**

Sometimes water, steep slopes, and gravity work together to make rocks and soil move very quickly. A **landslide** is a fast movement of rocks and soil down a slope. The house pictured in the margin was destroyed by a landslide on a hill in California. The **talus** (tā′ləs), in the marginal picture, is a sloping mass of loose and broken rocks at the foot of a slope. Talus builds up when rocks fall or slide down from a cliff or mountainside. The picture below shows how loose soil **slumps** on a hillside. Millions of dollars are lost every year when homes on cliffs slump into lakes and oceans.

Result of a landslide

Review It

1. What is erosion?
2. What causes rocks to move quickly down a slope?

Soil slump

Talus

263

14-2
Rivers and Streams Cause Erosion

The water in most rivers does not look clean and clear. The water looks muddy, because it is full of silt and clay. This is erosion in action. Think about the following questions as you read about rivers:

a. What happens to rainwater that runs off the land?
b. What are the erosional stages of rivers?
c. Where do rivers deposit sediments?

Rainwater Runs off the Land

The movement of rainwater into rivers is also the path of erosion. Runoff is rainwater that drains off the land into streams. Runoff carries sediments into the streams. Streams join to become part of a **river system.** The diagram that looks like a leaf shows a river system. The "veins" are streams and rivers. All the land covered by the leaf is drained by the streams and rivers in this system. The mouth of the largest river is at the bottom of the diagram. Sediments and water flow into a lake or ocean at the mouth of the largest river in the river system.

Erosion and the River Valley

The river valley is the land on either side of a river. The shape of the valley tells us how much erosion has taken place along a river.

Young River Valley   If very little erosion has taken place, the river has a V-shaped valley. The young river valley is typical of mountain streams.

A river system

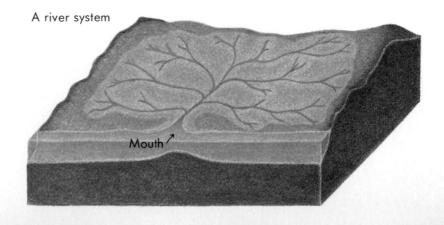

Mouth

Flathead River in Montana

A river that runs through a V-shaped valley is usually narrow and fast. The river cuts downward, making the valley deeper. Waterfalls and rapids are common. The diagram shows a young river valley.

Young river valley

Mature River Valley As erosion continues, a mature river valley develops. At this stage the river cuts the sides of its channel, or bed, as well as the bottom. The valley is wider than the channel, as shown in the diagram. During floods the river rises out of its channel and overflows. A flat region called a **floodplain** develops on both sides of the river.

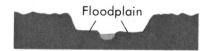

Mature river valley

Old River Valley As erosion progresses, an old river valley appears. The floodplain, shown in the diagram, becomes several times wider than the channel. The river cuts sideways, eating at its banks. Many large, looping curves called **meanders** (mē an′dərz) mark the course of the river. The picture shows meanders in a river. The small lakes in the same picture are oxbow lakes. These lakes formed when the river took a straighter course, cutting off the meanders. If the land uplifts, the river returns to a younger erosional stage. The river again cuts deeply, creating a V-shaped valley.

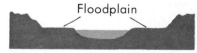

Old river valley

265

Alluvial fan

Have You Heard?

The turbulent water at the bottom of Niagara Falls erodes the soft shale more than the limestone above. From time to time, pieces of the unsupported limestone fall into the river below. In this way, the falls move upstream at the rate of one meter a year.

Limestone

Shale

The River Carries and Drops Sediments

The material a stream or river carries is called its load. The size of the load depends on the size and weight of the particles and on the water speed. A stream flowing one kilometer per hour can carry large sand grains and very small pebbles. A stream flowing about five kilometers per hour can roll stones the size of eggs. Rushing mountain streams move even huge boulders.

A mountain stream slows down as it moves into flat lands. Its channel becomes wider and more shallow. The stream deposits some of its load when the channel changes shape. Often in dry climates the deposits form a fan-shaped feature called an **alluvial** (ə lü′vē əl) **fan.** The picture shows an alluvial fan building up at the base of the mountains.

When river water slows down, large pieces of sediment drop fairly quickly. But fine sediment, like silt and clay, may be carried for hundreds of kilometers. The Mississippi River has a mud bottom because of sediment dropped from the water.

Obstructions, such as trees and boulders in the stream bed, slow the flow of water too. Sediment settles at such places and forms sand- or mudbars. Some of these bars become large enough and high enough to be islands on which plants grow.

266

A river drops a great deal of sediment along its course. But at the same time, it picks up sediment on its journey to the sea. Notice the difference in color between the river water and sea water in the photograph. The sediment that the river is carrying gives the water its milky color. The river water slows down when it empties into a lake or ocean. The stream's load of sand, silt, and mud then settles to the bottom of the ocean or lake. Unless strong currents remove this sediment, it forms a fan-shaped **delta** of land sticking out into the lake or ocean.

New Orleans and other towns in Louisiana grew up near the mouth of the Mississippi River. These cities grew up on the soil of the Mississippi delta. It is a constant battle to save sinking buildings, homes, and concrete structures built on soft delta soil.

In the satellite photograph of the Nile River in Egypt, farmlands show up red. Egypt's best farmlands are on the floodplain and delta of the Nile River.

Review It

1. What is meant by a river system?
2. Contrast a young river valley with an old one.
3. How does an alluvial fan differ from a delta?

The Nile delta

The river empties into the ocean

Activity

Rivers

Purpose

To use a stream table to see how rivers erode their banks and deposit sediments.

Materials

- paint tray
- coarse sand
- water
- 2 blocks of wood
- bucket or large coffee can
- 2 or 3 small stones
- empty plastic detergent bottle, 946 mL or larger
- pointed tool
- rubber or plastic tubing (optional)

Procedure

1. Examine *a* as you set up your stream table. Use the pointed tool to punch a water-drain hole in the paint tray. Push the tubing into the hole. Position the bucket and tray so that water can drain from the tubing or hole into the bucket.
2. Raise the end of the tray with one block of wood.
3. Put sand into the tray. Dampen the sand and pat it smooth.
4. With your finger, make a straight, deep, and narrow groove in the sand, as shown in *b*. This represents a straight river. Fill the plastic detergent bottle with water. Squeeze a stream of water along the groove, as shown in *b*. Record what happens.
5. Raise the end of the tray higher, using 2 blocks of wood. Smooth the sand and repeat step 4.

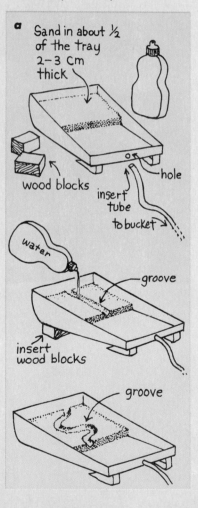

6. Remove both of the blocks. Smooth the sand. Make an S-shaped groove in the sand, as shown in *c*. Squeeze water into the groove as you did before. Record what happens.
7. Repeat step 6, raising the tray with first one then both blocks. Record your results.
8. Once again make one straight groove in the sand. This time place stones or other obstacles in the groove to *partly* block the movement of the water. Raise the end of the tray with one block and run water down the groove. Repeat this using two blocks. Record both results.

Analysis

1. Draw and name the deposit that forms at the mouth of the river.
2. Make a drawing to show how the river cuts into its banks along curves.
3. What eventually happens to curves in a river?
4. Explain how islands develop in rivers.
5. How does the steepness of the slope affect the way a river cuts the land?

Did You Know?

The Disappearing Lake

"Where is our lake?" Residents of Iberia Parish, Louisiana, may have asked that question on November 20, 1980. At 7:30 A.M., things seemed normal at Lake Peigneur—a large but shallow lake. A few hours later, nothing was left but a muddy hole in the ground. Where did the water go?

It is a strange story. For some time, an oil company had been drilling for natural gas from a platform in the lake. On November 20, without warning the drilling rig began to tip. The crew escaped unharmed, but the rig fell over and disappeared into the bottom of the lake.

About 50 miners were also starting the day's work on the morning of the 20th. They were mining salt from deep beneath Lake Peigneur. Suddenly water began pouring through the ceiling of the mine. The workers escaped, but Lake Peigneur's water, land, the drilling rig, barges, and several buildings were sucked into the mine.

Within a few hours, the lake was empty and the salt mine was flooded.

But that was not the end of the strange events. Several streams and a canal that flowed away from the lake reversed their courses. They began to flow into the drained lake. Within three days, the lake was full again!

Why did the lake disappear? The huge, underground salt mine was 460 meters directly beneath the lake. Through the years, enough salt was removed to enlarge the mine into an enormous cavern. People think the drill from the oil rig pierced the ceiling of the mine. The water drained into the mine just as if someone had pulled the plug of a bathtub.

Stories like this are not unusual. From time to time, land collapses into mines or caverns below. Except for the fish, this episode at Lake Peigneur ended without tragedy.

For Discussion
1. What caused Lake Peigneur to disappear?
2. How did the lake refill?

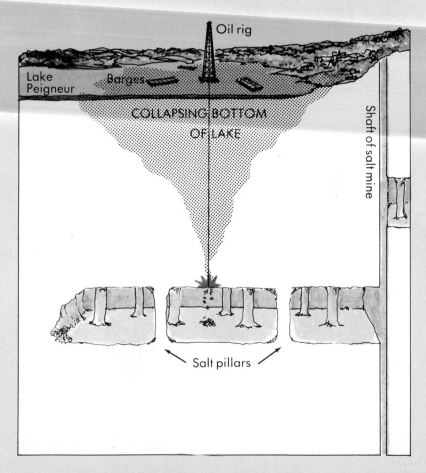

Oil rig

Lake Peigneur

Barges

COLLAPSING BOTTOM OF LAKE

Shaft of salt mine

Salt pillars

14-3
Water in the Ground

If you have had a cool drink of spring water, toured an underground cave, or visited Old Faithful geyser, you have had experience with water in the ground. Answer these questions as you read:

a. What is the water table?
b. What causes geysers and hot springs?
c. What are three features found in caves?

Groundwater and the Water Table

Groundwater is water in the ground near the earth's surface. Since groundwater shapes the land as it moves through the earth, it is an agent of erosion. The slow-moving water constantly leaches minerals from the soil and dissolves rocks.

When groundwater seeps through limestone, it dissolves calcium carbonate. The groundwater becomes **hard water.** Water is said to be hard when it contains minerals dissolved from rocks. **Soft water,** such as rainwater, has few or no dissolved minerals.

Groundwater would dry up without rain and snow. Notice in the diagram what happens to rainwater in the soil. Plants use some of the moisture. The rest of the groundwater moves downward through soil and rock until it comes to a rock layer through which water cannot pass. Here water stops moving down, as shown on the diagram. Water gathers in the spaces of the soil or rocks above this line. Where these spaces arc filled with water, the soil or rock is saturated. The *top* of the saturated soil or rock is the **water table.**

Challenge!

Some wells have been dug which require no pumps. The water rises naturally to the surface. These are called artesian (är tē′zhən) wells. Find out more about artesian wells. Are there any in your area?

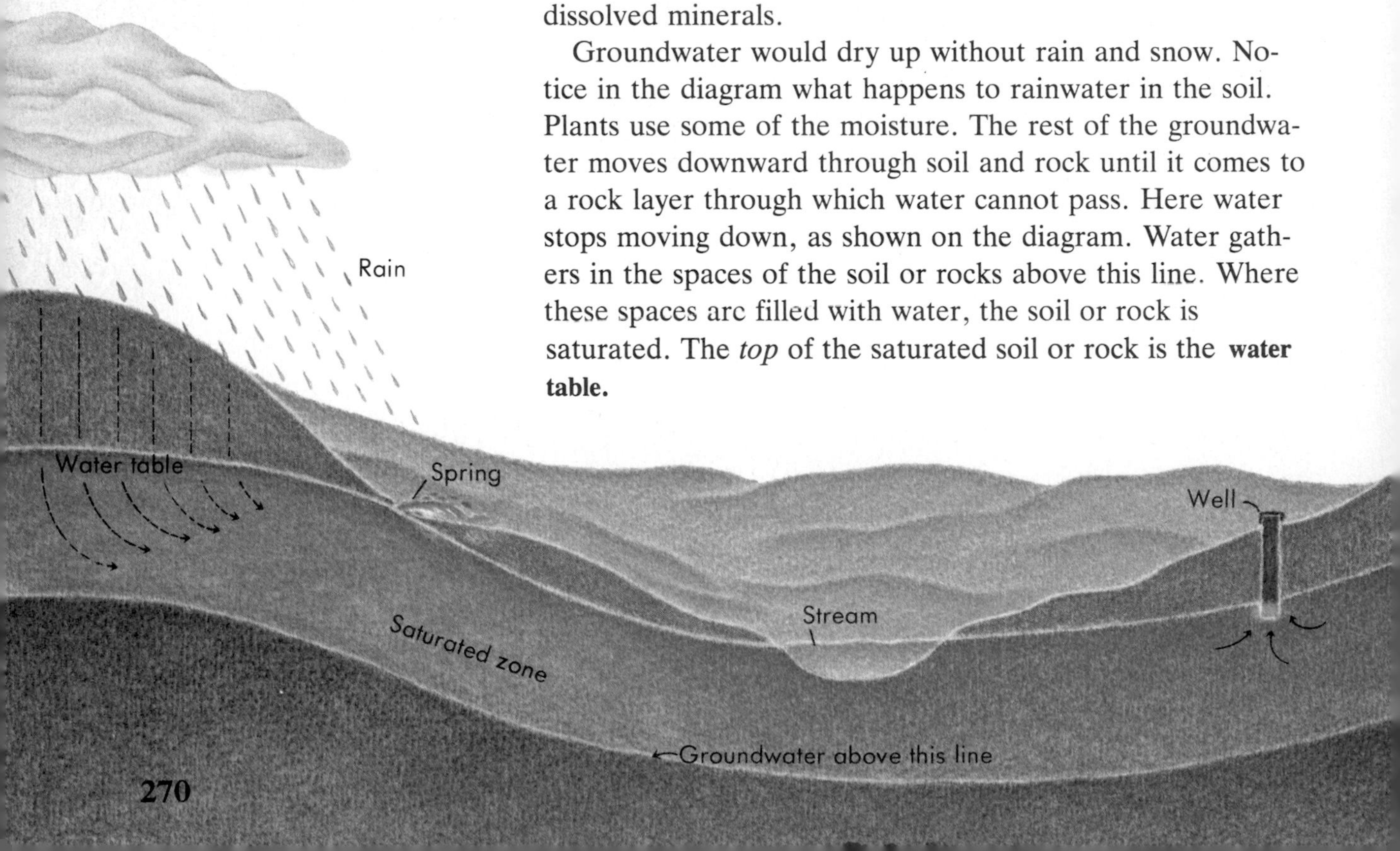

Rain

Water table

Spring

Well

Stream

Saturated zone

←Groundwater above this line

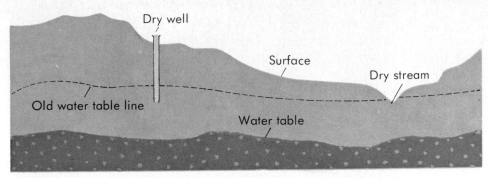

Dry well

Surface

Dry stream

Old water table line

Water table

When the water table drops

Notice how the water table roughly follows the shape of the land. It rises under hills and sinks under valleys. Where the water table comes to the surface, groundwater may flow out as a spring. The water table also reaches the surface at natural lakes and streams that flow throughout the year.

You can get water from the ground by drilling a well below the water table, as in the diagram. Groundwater runs into the well from the saturated rock and soil around it. Water can then be pumped to the surface.

Often groundwater is used faster than it is replaced by rain or snow. As a result, the water table sinks farther from the surface, as shown in the drawing above. A lower water table means that many springs, wells, and rivers go dry. It may take years for the water table to rise again.

Geysers and Hot Springs

In some places groundwater is close to hot volcanic rock or magma in the crust. The water is heated and rises toward the surface. Hot water and steam may erupt almost explosively at the surface as a **geyser.** Yellowstone's famous Old Faithful, a geyser, is pictured in the margin.

Hot springs are similar to geysers. But they flow to the surface rather than erupt. There are about 1,000 hot springs in the U.S. alone. Homes in Iceland are heated by steam from hot springs. Many places, including northern California, use hot springs to generate electricity.

Old Faithful

Sinkhole ponds in Indiana

Groundwater Creates Unusual Features

Chemical weathering and erosion by groundwater create limestone caves. Unusual deposits, such as those in the picture of Carlsbad Caverns in New Mexico, grow from the ceiling and floors of caves. Water with dissolved calcium carbonate may drip from the ceiling of a cave. When the water evaporates, a calcium carbonate deposit is left on the ceiling. This deposit is a **stalactite** (stə lak'tīt). If the drops of water from the ceiling fall to the floor, another deposit builds up. **Stalagmites** (stə lag'mīts) are the calcium carbonate deposits that build up from the floor. Sometimes the stalagmites and stalactites grow until they meet and form a pillar of calcium carbonate.

Many caves formed in the layers of limestone in Florida. The picture at the beginning of the chapter shows what can happen when the roof of an underground cave sinks or collapses. The depression in the Wintergreen, Florida picture is called a **sinkhole.**

Water may fill a sinkhole and form a small round pond. The rolling landscape of southern Indiana, shown in the picture, is dotted with sinkhole ponds.

Carlsbad Caverns

Review It

1. What is hard water?
2. How do hot springs and geysers differ?
3. Contrast the way stalactites and sinkholes form.

Activity

Hard and Soft Water

Purpose
To see how hard and soft water react with soap.

Materials
- pure soap flakes or bar of soap
- borax
- epsom salts
- distilled water or rainwater (soft)
- tap water
- four 100 mL test tubes
- stoppers for test tubes
- test tube rack
- one 100 mL beaker
- graduated cylinder
- medicine dropper
- tape for labeling
- cm ruler
- teaspoon

Procedure
1. Put 50 mL of distilled water in a test tube and label it Distilled water (soft).
2. Put 50 mL of warm tap water in another test tube and add a pinch of borax. Cap the test tube and shake it to dissolve the borax. Label the tube Borax (soft).
3. Add a pinch of epsom salts to 50 mL of warm tap water in the third test tube. Cap and shake as before. Label it Epsom salts (hard).
4. Put 50 mL of tap water in the fourth test tube. Label it Tap water.
5. Add about 1 rounded teaspoon of soap flakes or shavings from a bar of soap to 50 mL of *hot* tap water in the beaker.
6. Copy Table *a* on your paper.
7. Use the medicine dropper to put two or three drops of the soap solution into the test tube of distilled water. NOTE: Count the number of drops you add. Cap the tube and shake it well. Set the test tube in the rack for about 10 seconds. Measure the height of the suds on top of the water.
8. Repeat this procedure until the suds are 1 cm high.
9. Complete the proper column on the Table.
10. Repeat steps 7, 8, and 9 for the other three test tubes.
11. Record the appearance of the glass inside each test tube. Empty the test tubes. Rinse them and return them to the racks.

Analysis
1. Give two reasons why soft water is better for home use than hard water.
2. Is your tap water hard or soft? Explain.
3. Which of the four samples is the best for home use? Explain.
4. Would borax be useful to soften water at home? Explain.

a Table . . . Testing water for hardness

	Borax Solution in water	Epsom salts in water	Distilled water	Tap water
Number of soap drops to make 1 cm of suds				
Hard or soft water	soft	hard	soft	
How water looks after shaking examples: clear cloudy, milky, scum, particles, etc.				
Appearance of glass inside the test tube (step 11)				

14—4
Glaciers and Erosion

Glaciers are the most powerful agents of erosion. They sculpture mountain peaks in the Alps and other mountains. They have left deep scratches on rocks in Iowa and other places covered by glaciers. Think about these questions as you read:

a. Where and how do glaciers form?
b. What is a valley glacier?
c. How can a continental ice sheet be described?
d. What are some land features created by glaciers?

Glaciers: Moving Ice

A glacier is a moving body of ice. About 10 percent of the land on earth is covered by glaciers. Glaciers form on high mountains and in cold parts of the world. In places where winter snow is abundant and summer temperatures cool, more snow falls than melts. Each winter, more snow is added. The snow at the bottom is packed together by the weight of later snows. Over a period of years, the packed snow gradually changes to solid ice.

Gravity causes a glacier to move down a mountainside. On level land, the weight of the ice causes the glacier to move or spread out from its thickest part. Ice at the bottom of a glacier melts where it rubs across the ground. The melted ice "oils" or greases the glacier's movement.

There are two types of glaciers. First, **continental glaciers** are sheets of ice that spread over large areas of land. Over 96 percent of glacial ice in the world is of this type. Most of Greenland and Antarctica are covered by huge ice sheets. **Valley glaciers,** the second type, develop in mountain valleys. They are like rivers of ice that move down mountainsides. Less than 4 percent of the world's glaciers are valley glaciers.

Valley Glaciers—Rivers of Ice

Valley glaciers begin when snow and ice gather in a hollow or depression in the mountains. In time, the hollow fills with ice and overflows. The glacier starts its journey down

Have You Heard?

Where is the world's water? Ninety-seven percent is in the oceans of the world. Two percent is tied up in glaciers and polar ice. The remaining water is in the air, rivers, lakes, groundwater, plants, and animals.

the mountainside. The picture shows a **cirque** (sėrk) in the mountains in Utah. A cirque is a large bowl-shaped depression where a valley glacier got its start.

Valley glaciers may be as much as 90 kilometers long. The speed of a glacier can vary from a centimeter to thirty meters a day. Sometimes a glacier stops moving for several years. Later, it may surge as fast as six kilometers in one year. Glaciers' movements are unpredictable.

Like rivers, glaciers join with other glaciers along their paths. Glaciers cut U-shaped valleys. Notice the dark bands in the joined glaciers in the picture below. These dark bands are rock and soil ripped from the sides of the mountains as the ice passed. The dark bands show that the ice of the two glaciers does not mix.

The hanging valleys in the upper drawing are similar to the famous Hanging Valley of Bridal Veil Creek in Yosemite. A hanging valley appears when two joining glaciers, which are at different elevations, melt. The drawing below shows the same area before the ice melted.

Ocean-filled valleys along the coast of Norway and Sweden are called **fiords** (fyôrdz). Glaciers cut the fiords as they moved from mountains into the sea. Glaciers also created the fiords along the west coast of Canada, as they flowed from the mountains into the Pacific Ocean.

A cirque

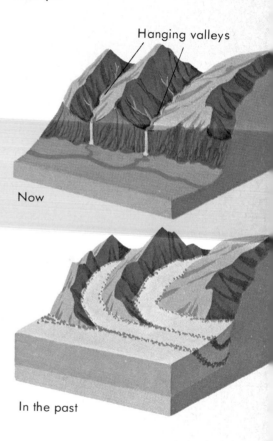
Hanging valleys

Now

In the past

Where glaciers meet

Greenland's ice sheet

Ross Ice Shelf

Antarctica

Glacier

Land (90% covered by ice)

Continental Glaciers

Continental glaciers are thick in the middle and thinner around the edges. The diagram shows the tremendous Greenland ice sheet, which is over three kilometers thick in some places.

Pieces of ice sometimes break away from an ice sheet where the land meets the sea. These pieces, called icebergs, often break away from the Greenland ice sheet. Icebergs— sometimes as big as islands—drift into the North Atlantic. They are a year-round hazard to ships.

The huge Ross Ice Shelf, shown in the diagram, covers the ocean near Antarctica. It is attached to the Antarctic ice sheet. This floating ice sheet is as large as the state of Texas.

Great ice sheets have advanced and retreated many times throughout the history of the earth. Only about 15,000 years ago ice covered much of the United States. No one knows when, if ever, the glaciers will advance again.

After the Glaciers Retreated

Thousands of years ago the glaciers advanced almost as far south as the Ohio River in the United States. They gouged out the five Great Lakes between the United States and Canada. These lakes and many other land features are evidence that the glaciers passed over North America, Europe, and Asia.

The land changed because glaciers lift and move soil and rocks. **Drift** is the name given to any material deposited by glaciers. There are two kinds of drift. First, sediments that simply dropped when the glaciers melted are unlayered and unsorted by particle size. Soil, pebbles, and rocks are mixed at random. This kind of drift is called **till.** Another kind of drift is found in deposits laid down by the rivers of water that flowed out from the melting glacier. Sediments in these deposits are layered and sorted by size, like river deposits. They are called **outwash.**

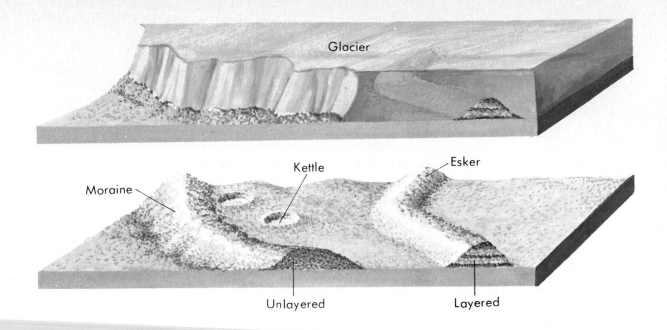

Glacier

Esker

Kettle

Moraine

Unlayered

Layered

The picture shows several kinds of glacial deposits. Long, thin **moraines** (mə rānz′) are deposits that mark the sides and front of a glacier. A scientist searches for moraines in order to find the boundaries of glaciers that melted long ago. When the last ice sheets melted, large, isolated blocks of ice remained buried in glacial tills. When these blocks melted, depressions, called **kettles,** were left in the land. Many of these kettles filled with water and became lakes. **Eskers** (es′kərz) are long, narrow ridges. They may be deposits from streams of melted ice that ran through tunnels in glaciers. Unlike moraines, the outwash deposits of eskers are sorted by size, like those of river deposits. Sand and gravel from eskers are a valuable product of glaciers.

Review It

1. Why do glaciers move?
2. Where does a valley glacier originate and travel?
3. Describe the general shape of a continental ice sheet.
4. How do we know that much of the United States was covered by glaciers?

14–5
Erosion by the Wind

Did you ever get "stung" on the face by pieces of wind-blown dirt or sand? The wind can change the earth's surface by moving sand and dust. In this section you will read how the wind causes erosion. As you read about wind erosion, think about the questions below:

a. How does the speed of the wind affect erosion?
b. What are two types of wind deposits?

The Wind and Erosion

The wind, an agent of erosion, transports soil and pieces of rock. The effects of wind erosion are very striking, especially in dry areas of the world. When the wind blows over dry, bare soil, it causes terrible dust storms. In the 1930s dust storms were common over the drought-stricken southwestern United States. Soil from Kansas, Oklahoma, and Colorado was carried as far as New England in one dust storm.

The amount of soil and sand carried depends on the size of the pieces and on the wind speed. Light winds can lift only fine dust. The same wind will roll and bounce sand grains along the ground. Rocks and pebbles are too heavy to be moved by ordinary winds. However, strong winds can move heavy particles. The picture shows how pebbles carried by a 200-kilometer per hour wind in Boulder, Colorado, wrecked an automobile windshield.

If you look at a grain of sand through a magnifying glass, you can see that it has sharp, hard edges. Given enough time, windblown sand grains can pit and destroy a rock. They "sandblast" the rock, just as a building is sandblasted to remove the dark outer layer of rock.

Loess and Dunes

When the wind slows down, it drops some of the material it is carrying. The heavier particles drop first. Over long periods of time, deposits of windblown silt and clay particles or dust called **loess** (lō′is) may build up in one place.

Sand dunes in Colorado

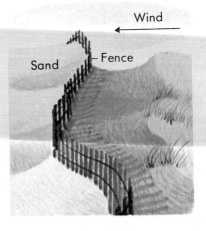

Wind

Sand — Fence

They reach depths of hundreds of meters. The loess deposits of the Mississippi and Missouri River valleys were deposited many thousands of years ago. Soils that develop on loess often make excellent farmlands.

Dunes are hills of windblown sand. The photo shows sand dunes in Colorado. When rolling sand grains meet an obstacle, such as a rock or tree, they stop. Dunes grow to be hundreds of meters high in the deserts of Saudi Arabia.

The wind not only builds dunes, but it also moves them. Sand dunes along the shoreline of Lake Michigan move as much as five to seven meters a year. Moving dunes have been known to cover entire forests.

We cannot stop erosion by the wind. Once weathering breaks rocks into small pieces, the wind will act on them. The drier the climate, the greater is the power of the wind. Wherever it is possible, the land should be covered by grass, plants, and trees. Vegetation holds the soil together and protects it from the wind.

Challenge!

Explain why the sand is stacked up this way in front of the fence.

Review It

1. What factor determines how much the wind can carry?
2. What can you do to stop wind erosion in your yard?

279

Chapter Summary

- Erosion is the removal of weathered material from the land. The agents of erosion are gravity, moving water, ice, wind, and people. (14–1)

- Mudflows and landslides result when gravity acts on loose soil and rocks on a slope. (14–1)

- Rivers form valleys by eroding their beds, carrying away rock and soil. (14–2)

- When rivers slow down, they deposit some of their load as sandbars, alluvial fans, and deltas. (14–2)

- The top of rock and soil that is saturated with groundwater is called the water table. (14–3)

- Heated groundwater rises as geysers and hot springs. (14–3)

- Continental glaciers are large ice sheets. Valley glaciers are mountain glaciers. (14–4)

- Glaciers cut U-shaped valleys. They deposit till, which is unsorted glacial material. (14–4)

- Loess and dunes are two deposits of wind-blown sediments. (14–5)

Interesting Reading

America's Majestic Canyons. National Geographic Society, 1979. Describes famous valleys and canyons in the U.S.

Brucker, Roger and Watson, Richard. *The Longest Cave.* Knopf, 1976. Tells about the exploration of Mammoth Cave.

Deming, H. G. *Water: The Fountain of Opportunity.* Oxford University Press, 1975. Discusses water pollution and water purification.

Questions/Problems

1. Define the terms *weathering* and *erosion*. Give an example of each.

2. Why are studies of creep or slump of soil important to the construction of buildings and homes?

3. Compare alluvial fans and deltas.

4. Explain two factors that cause the water table to drop.

5. Relate leaching by groundwater to erosion.

6. Compare the sorting by particle size and layering of stream deposits to that of glacial deposits.

7. Relate the speed of wind and running water to the carrying power of each.

Extra Research

1. Write your state geologic survey to find out what is being done to control erosion in your state.

2. List examples of weathering and erosion you have observed in your yard or schoolgrounds. Describe and draw or photograph each example. Suggest ways that the processes can be stopped or slowed down.

3. List the agents of erosion down the lefthand side of a piece of paper. Divide the page into two columns. Entitle one column "Benefits of Erosion" and the other "Harmful Effects of Erosion." Complete the chart using the chapter and outside readings for information.

Chapter Test

A. Vocabulary Write the numbers 1–10 on a piece of paper.
Match the definition in Column I with the term it defines in Column II.

Column I

1. deposit that marks the boundary of a glacier

2. deposit that grows from the roof of a cave

3. heated groundwater forced to the surface

4. river deposit

5. glacial sediment, unsorted by size and unlayered

6. possible result of a landslide

7. glacial sediment, sorted by size and layered

8. a large, looping curve in a river

9. the removal of rock by wind, ice, or water

10. windblown silt deposit

Column II

a. alluvial fan

b. erosion

c. geyser

d. loess

e. meander

f. moraine

g. outwash

h. stalactite

i. talus

j. till

B. Multiple Choice Write the numbers 1–10 on your paper.
Choose the letter that best completes the statement or answers the question.

1. Erosion by gravity progresses fast   a) on a hillside.   b) in dry climates.   c) in the presence of water and loose soil.   d) a and c.

2. As the speed of water in a stream increases, the size of the stream's load will   a) decrease.   b) remain unchanged.   c) increase.   d) none of the above.

3. A river deposit at the mouth of a river in a lake or ocean is called a(n)   a) alluvial fan.   b) delta.   c) sandbar.   d) island.

4. Oxbow lakes were once   a) inland seas.   b) cirques.   c) till.   d) meanders.

5. A young river valley may have   a) a U-shaped valley.   b) rapids and waterfalls.   c) wide floodplains.   d) a and b.

6. When spaces between soil or rock particles fill with groundwater, the soil or rock is said to be   a) eroded.   b) weathered.   c) saturated.   d) evaporated.

7. Groundwater creates   a) caves.   b) creep.   c) deltas.   d) kettles.

8. The bowl-shaped depressions at the head of glaciers are called   a) horns.   b) cirques.   c) grooves.   d) moraines.

9. Eskers are   a) not the result of glaciation.   b) probably deposited by running water within a glacier.   c) made of till.   d) depressions in the ground.

10. Wind erosion is most effective in   a) grasslands.   b) humid areas.   c) dry areas.   d) mountain ranges.

Chapter 15
Mapping and Landforms

The boaters in the photograph are weaving their way through Glen Canyon in Utah. It is easy to see the depth and shape of the canyon walls in this picture. But from the river it is not easy to see what lies ahead. It may be a waterfall, rapids, or a sharp bend. To explore the river, the boaters can use a special map. The map shows not only what lies ahead but also the depth and shape of the canyon.

This chapter shows you how to use a map to visualize landforms. In the first two sections, you will learn the symbols used on these maps and how to interpret them. Then, you will read about the major landforms in the United States from east to west.

Chapter Objectives

1. Explain the functions of a topographic map.
2. Describe the major features of USGS topographic maps.
3. Describe the major landforms found in the eastern, central, and western United States.

15-1
Topographic Maps

A map is a representation of how objects, such as the earth's features, are arranged. You look at one kind of map when you watch a weather report and another kind when you give directions to a lost motorist. As you read about a special kind of map you may not have used yet, keep these questions in mind:

a. How are topographic maps different from other maps?
b. How do contour lines show elevation?
c. How are landforms shown on a topographic map?

Topographic Maps Are Different from Other Maps

One of the most helpful tools that an earth scientist has is a **topographic** (top′ə graf′ik) **map.** A topographic map shows the shape and elevation of the land surface. It also shows features, such as mountains or structures made by people, that are not shown on other maps. For example, a road map might mark the location of a mountain with an X. But a topographic map shows you not only the location but also the shape and elevation of that mountain.

A topographic map has some features that are also on other kinds of maps. It contains a legend that explains the symbols on the map. The legend usually appears at the bottom of the map or somewhere in the margin. The legend also shows the scale used on the map and the date that the map was made.

A map scale relates distance on the map to distance on the ground. Suppose the scale is 1 to 240,000 (1:240,000). This ratio means one unit on the map equals 240,000 of the same units on the earth's surface. If there is one centimeter between two points on the map, there are 240,000 centimeters, or 2.4 kilometers, between the same two points on the earth's surface.

Contour Lines Show Shape and Elevation

The key to understanding topographic maps is understanding contour lines. A **contour** (kon′tür) **line** on a map connects all points of equal elevation.

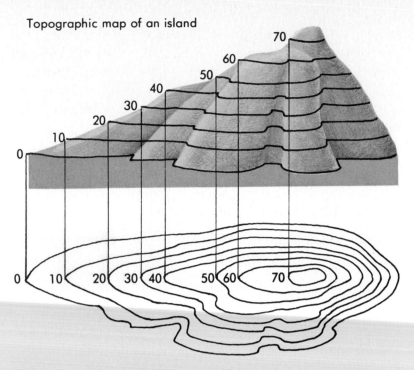

Topographic map of an island

The top of the diagram shows imaginary contour lines wrapped around an island. At the bottom of the diagram, you can see how these contour lines appear on a map. Notice that every point located on the zero contour line is at sea level. The elevation is zero feet above sea level. Every point located on the 10-foot contour line is ten feet above sea level. Every point on the 20-foot contour line is 20 feet above sea level, and so on.

The vertical, or up-and-down, distance between each contour line on this map is ten feet. This vertical distance between contour lines is the **contour interval.** Every map has a specific contour interval. The contour interval may be 5, 10, or 20 feet if the map shows mostly flat land. The interval may be 50, 100, or 200 feet if the map shows mostly steep slopes.

You can tell if a slope is gentle or steep by the closeness of the contour lines. The island in the diagram has one gentle and one steep slope. Notice the wide spaces between contour lines on the gentle slope. The contour lines are much closer together on the steep slope. Contour lines are very close together or even on top of one another at a cliff.

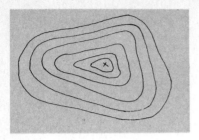

Hill or mountain

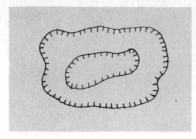

Depression contours

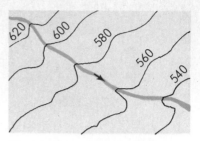

River valley; arrow indicates direction of water flow

Contour Lines Show Land Features

A series of small closed contour lines—one inside another—shows a hill. The smallest loop is the highest contour on the hill. The top of the hill is actually higher than the highest contour line. On high mountains, the peak is marked by an X, as shown in the diagram.

A pit or depression is also shown by closed contour lines. But the loops have little marks on the inside of the closed contour lines. The drawing shows that these marks—called **hachures** (hash′ŭrz)—point downslope into the depression. Depression contours are used to show sinkholes and the craters of volcanoes.

Contour lines that cross a river valley form a V on a map. The base of the V always points upstream, the direction from which the water is coming. Since rivers flow from higher to lower elevations, the base of the V points toward the higher elevation. You can tell which way the land slopes by examining the contour lines.

All contour lines eventually close somewhere—either on the map or beyond the map's margin. Contour lines do not cross or intersect each other. They can, however, be on top of one another at a cliff.

Review It

1. What advantage does a topographic map have over a road map?
2. How do contour lines show steep slopes?
3. Name three landforms that can be shown by contour lines on a topographic map.

Activity

Contour Lines

Purpose
To construct contour lines on a model mountain.

Materials
- modeling clay
- sharp pencil
- centimeter ruler
- 2 rubber bands
- 1 paper clip
- sheet of paper

Procedure
1. Use about .25 kilogram of modeling clay to make a small mountain. Mold the mountain on a sheet of paper to keep your desk clean. Make one side of the mountain steeper than the other side, as in *a*.
2. Use the paper clip to gouge out a river valley on the model, as in *a*.
3. Use the rubber bands to attach a sharp pencil 1 cm from the end of the ruler, as in *b*.
4. Hold the ruler straight up and down on the desk. Carve a line around the mountain 1 cm from the bottom, as shown in *c*.

5. Move the pencil to the 2 cm mark on the ruler. Repeat step 4 to cut a second contour line that is 2 cm from the bottom of the mountain.
6. Carve contour lines around the mountain every centimeter until you reach the top.

Analysis
1. Look at the model mountain from the side (at eye level). Describe the appearance of the lines.
2. What is the contour interval used on your model?
3. Look down on the model from above. Describe the appearance of the lines.
4. Tell which contour line has the highest elevation.
5. How does the distance between the contour lines show whether the slope is steep or gentle?
6. How do the contour lines show a valley down the side of the mountain?
7. Using the contour lines, give the elevation of your model to the nearest 0.5 cm.

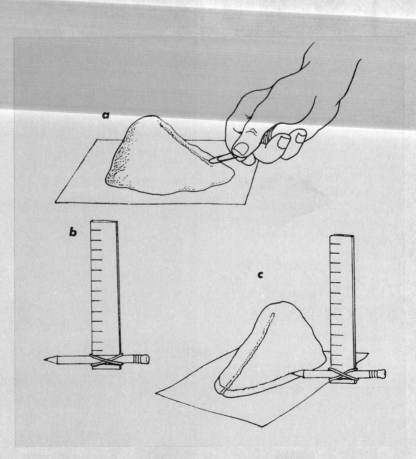

15–2
Using Topographic Maps

Once you understand how to read topographic maps, you can use them in a variety of ways. For example, if you go hiking, a detailed topographic map will show you trails, steep cliffs, rivers, rest stations, and other features you can expect to find along the way. Using this tool requires practice. Become familiar with topographic maps as you answer these questions:

a. How are topographic maps used?
b. What colors and symbols are used on USGS maps?
c. What are townships?

Uses of Topographic Maps

Topographic maps are extremely important to many people. They are used to plan highways, dams, pipelines, and other types of construction. They are important tools for soil and water conservation and geologic research.

Topographic maps are also popular with people who enjoy outdoor activities and recreation. Maps showing slopes, trails, clearings, streams, and other features are valuable to hikers, skiers, snowmobilers, and explorers. In a new sport, called orienteering, people use topographic maps to find the quickest route through unfamiliar countrysides. Vacationers, like the girl below, use topographic maps to find campgrounds and fishing spots.

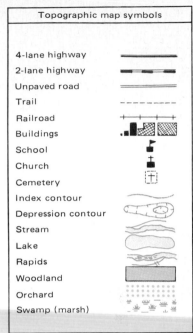

Topographic map symbols	
4-lane highway	
2-lane highway	
Unpaved road	
Trail	
Railroad	
Buildings	
School	
Church	
Cemetery	
Index contour	
Depression contour	
Stream	
Lake	
Rapids	
Woodland	
Orchard	
Swamp (marsh)	

Reading USGS Topographic Maps

You can order topographic maps from the United States Geological Survey (USGS). This government group makes most of the topographic maps in our country. Each USGS map covers an area called a **quadrangle** (kwod′rang′gəl). A quadrangle is a rectangular area with latitude and longitude lines for boundaries. A typical USGS map covers about 540 square kilometers, which is one-fourth of a degree of latitude and longitude. Other USGS maps cover about 270 square kilometers. They show about one-eighth of a degree of latitude and longitude on each side. The map above shows part of a USGS topographic map.

The USGS uses several colors and many symbols to represent different land features. Some of the more common symbols are listed in the table above.

All contour lines are brown. Every fifth contour line is heavily colored to make the map easier to read. Also, the elevation of every fifth line is marked. This line is called the **index contour.**

The USGS measures exact elevations at thousands of places across the United States. These spots are marked with metal plates known as **bench marks.** The picture shows what a bench mark looks like. You can see the letters BMX on the map above. BMX means there is a bench mark at that spot. BMX475 means that the elevation at X is 475 feet above sea level.

USGS bench mark

Township boundary (6 miles)

6	5	4	3	2	1
7	8	9	10	11	12
18	17	16	15	14	13
19	20	21	22	23	24
30	29	28	27	26	25
31	32	33	34	35	36

← → Section boundary
(1 mile)

Checkerboard patterns
of fields and roads

Many Maps Use Townships

When our nation was organized in the 1780s, the old boundaries of the thirteen colonies were fairly well set. Roads followed cow paths that had once been wildlife trails. Border lines were often along or in rivers. Sometimes borders were marked by tall trees and piles of rocks. But people decided that boundaries in the new lands to the west should be established in a more organized way.

Surveying teams went first into the territory around the Great Lakes, which was known then as the Northwest Territory. The teams divided the Northwest Territory into squares that were six miles on each side. These areas were named **townships.** Each township was divided into 36 sections. Each section was a square that was one mile on each side. The diagram shows how sections were numbered. Sections can be divided into smaller and smaller units. People built roads along the section boundaries.

Before counties were established, townships were the seats of local governments. One section in each township was set aside for schools. Many school districts still have township boundaries, and many schools are called "township schools."

Today, you can see the results of the surveyors' efforts in many states. For example, if you fly over the central United States, you will see the checkerboard pattern of the fields and roads. The photograph shows how the roads follow township and section lines.

Review It

1. List three activities for which topographic maps are useful.
2. What does BMX270 mean on a topographic map?
3. What are townships and sections?

Activity

Topographic Maps

Purpose
To construct a topographic map.

Materials
• unlined paper
• centimeter ruler
• colored pencils or fine-point markers (red, blue, brown, black, green)

Procedure
1. On the paper, construct a square that is 18 cm on each side to represent a township. Divide the township into 36 sections of equal size, as shown in *a*.
2. Lightly pencil in the section numbers as shown.

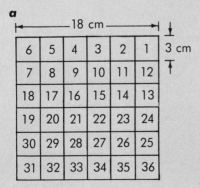

a

	18 cm						
6	5	4	3	2	1	3 cm
7	8	9	10	11	12	
18	17	16	15	14	13	
19	20	21	22	23	24	
30	29	28	27	26	25	
31	32	33	34	35	36	

3. With a blue pencil, draw a river winding through sections 4, 9, 15, 23, and 24.
4. Draw and label all contour lines. Three of the contour lines have been drawn and labeled for you in *b*. Add the necessary contour lines, using the following information:
   • The highest part of the map is 700 feet above sea level in 6.
   • The contour interval is 20 feet.
   • The land slopes gently down to the southeast with the lowest elevation at 500 feet in 36.

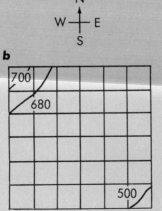

b

5. Using the correct symbols and colors (shown in the table on page 289) draw the following on your map:
   • a four-lane highway running north and south across the map from 5 through 32
   • a two-lane highway running west from the four-lane highway across 30
   • another two-lane highway running east from the four-lane highway across 20 and 21 and to the center of 22
   • this two-lane highway turning northeast through 14 and 12
   • an unpaved road running south from the two-lane highway in 22 down through 27 and 34
   • a railroad running diagonally across the map from 19 to 12
   • three houses along the west side of the highway in 8
   • a cemetery on the east side of the highway in 17
   • a small lake in 31
   • two houses with a trail between them in 23
   • a woodland covering most of 1, 2, and 3
   • a school along the east side of the road in 27
   • two sinkholes, one in 35 and one in 36

Analysis
1. If this were a map of an actual place, where else might you expect to find roads?
2. How should you draw the contour lines at the river?

15–3
Landforms Across the United States

What are some of the things you do because of the climate or landforms in your area? Someone who lives on the rocky coast of Maine may work and play differently from someone on the Great Plains. Answer these questions as you read about the landforms across our nation:

a. Where are the oldest mountains in the United States?
b. How can you describe the central United States?
c. How do we know many features in the western United States are geologically young?
d. What major features are found in Alaska and Hawaii?

Old Mountains and New Plains—Eastern United States

The map shows some major landforms in the United States. The eastern United States is characterized by some of the oldest mountains that exist on the earth. The East also has a large, relatively young coastal plain that borders the Atlantic Ocean.

The Coastal Plain starts in Massachusetts and sweeps around to the Gulf Coast of Texas. It is a young plain that formed mostly in the Cenozoic era. Sandy beaches and marshes are common. The picture shows marshes of the Florida Everglades, one of our largest national parks.

Florida Everglades

A good deal of the Plain is less than 30 meters above sea level. Much of the Coastal Plain extends into the Atlantic Ocean. In fact, Chesapeake Bay and Delaware Bay are actually sunken river valleys of this plain.

West of the Coastal Plain, the Appalachian highlands rise sharply. Part of these highlands are plateaus deeply cut by streams. The highlands also include folded mountain ranges, such as the Appalachian and Blue Ridge Mountains, that are parallel to the coast. Most of the highlands formed in the Paleozoic era when the North American plate collided with several other plates to form Pangaea. The highlands were much higher than the Rocky Mountains are now. Since then, the highlands have eroded into smooth, rolling hills.

Lowlands and Plains—Central United States

The map shows large areas of plains and lowlands in the central part of the country. Much of the central United States is flat fields or gently rolling land. But the Black Hills of South Dakota and the Ozark Mountains in Arkansas and Missouri are in the central United States too. This section of the country also includes the limestone plateaus of Kentucky and Tennessee. Many caves exist in the limestone bedrock in this region. Mammoth Cave in Kentucky is the largest of these caves.

Glaciation is responsible for some of the flatness of the northern part of the Central Lowlands. However, glaciers also deposited moraines, eskers, and other rolling features.

The photograph taken in the Wisconsin Dells shows a typical river scene in the Midwest. The thick deposits of sedimentary rock were gouged out by water. Notice how flat-lying the layered beds of shale are.

The Great Plains lie west of the Central Lowlands. The Plains start beyond the Mississippi River at an elevation of 600 meters above sea level. They rise gradually to the "mile-high" city of Denver, Colorado. Much of the rich soil of the Great Plains developed in sediments eroded from the Rocky Mountains.

Flat-lying rocks in Wisconsin

The Restless Land—Western United States

The West has many landforms that are young and growing. You can see this youthful terrain in the Rocky Mountains that rise sharply west of the Great Plains. These mountains were uplifted toward the end of the Mesozoic era. The Rocky Mountain peaks are sharper and higher than the eroded Appalachian Mountains. Geysers and hot springs in Yellowstone National Park in Wyoming are additional evidence of youth and change.

The Colorado Plateau along the south end of the Rockies is a truly colorful region. Note the bare rock stained red by iron oxides in the picture of the Painted Desert in Arizona. This is a region of steep-walled canyons. The rocks of these canyons reveal much about our geologic past.

The Painted Desert

The Bonneville Salt Flats

Utah and Nevada are mostly desert basins and dry mountain ranges. Many of the basins are ancient glacial lake beds. The lake water evaporated long ago. Death Valley and the Bonneville Salt Flats are located on two glacial lake beds. The Bonneville Salt Flats are ideal for racing rocket-powered cars like the one shown in the picture.

West of the Rockies, in Washington and Oregon, ancient lava flows built the basalt plateaus along the Columbia and Snake Rivers. The lava oozed out of fissures in all directions and hardened.

The West Coast is the most geologically active region of the United States. Here, the Coast Ranges, the Sierra Nevada, and the Cascade Range formed near plate boundaries. The eruption of Mount St. Helens indicates that these mountains are young and growing. Earthquakes have been detected beneath Mount Hood and Mount Shasta south of Mount St. Helens. These activities may be signs that more volcanic eruptions are coming. In recent years, California has had many small and a few large earthquakes. Some scientists have suggested that the volcanic activity in the Coast Ranges may be related to earthquake activity farther south in California.

Before the earthquake

After the earthquake

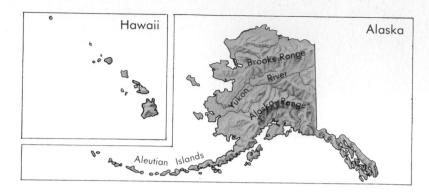

Alaska and Hawaii

The Coast Ranges of the United States do not stop at the state of Washington. They extend through western Canada and into Alaska. Alaska is a land of geologic extremes. It has fiery volcanoes, thousands of mountain glaciers, and a vast frozen plain—the Yukon Basin. The Yukon is bordered on the north and south by mountain ranges, as shown on the map. The Alaska Range in the south includes Mount McKinley. It is the highest peak in North America. The Brooks Range lies north of the Yukon.

Most of Alaska was built from several small plates that joined. Alaska and the rest of the American West Coast lie on the volcanic Ring of Fire. Alaska's volcanic and earthquake activity is concentrated along a trench boundary in the Aleutian Islands, which is an island arc. In 1964, an earthquake near the coast raised some areas of the ocean floor above sea level. The photographs show the coast before and after the earthquake.

There is also great volcanic activity in Hawaii. The Hawaiian Islands are the tops of some of the world's highest mountains. They are volcanoes that rise as far as 9.6 kilometers above the ocean floor.

Have You Heard?

Much of the Alaskan soil is permanently frozen. The layer of frozen soil is called permafrost. North of the Brooks Range, the permafrost is 300 meters thick. South of the Brooks Range, the first few meters of soil thaw in the summer. This thawing creates muddy ground that makes walking or driving difficult.

Review It

1. Describe the landforms of the eastern United States.
2. How did glaciers affect the Central Lowlands?
3. Why do scientists believe that the Rockies are young?
4. What do Hawaii and parts of Alaska have in common?

Did You Know?

The United States Geological Survey (USGS)

In 1879, Frank Woolworth opened a 5-cent store; Thomas Edison invented the light bulb; and President Rutherford B. Hayes signed an act that created the U.S. Geological Survey. The United States Geological Survey is one of the oldest government agencies. At first, the job of its 39 employees was simply to learn more about the land west of the Mississippi River. Millions of acres of land were still unexplored and unknown. Prospectors, railroad companies, farmers, and government officials were eager to know what the land was like. Where were the mountains? Where did the rivers go? What were the best places for railroad lines and roads? What were the most likely places to look for gold, silver, iron, copper, and other minerals?

The Survey was very successful in answering these questions. Within three years, Congress included the eastern states in the Survey's responsibilities. The USGS became the mapmaker, mineral-locater, fossil-researcher, water resources expert, and conservationist for the nation.

Now, a hundred years later, over 9,000 people work for the Geological Survey. They perform the functions listed above as well as many others. One of the Survey's most important tasks is to make topographic maps. The USGS has mapped about three-quarters of the United States. USGS mapmakers also update the existing maps to show changes in the landscape.

Now the Survey works with our space agencies. Using pictures taken by spacecraft, USGS made maps for lunar exploration. In addition the Survey mapped Mars, Venus, and the moons of Jupiter and Saturn. The USGS also taught geology to the Apollo astronauts.

USGS often does research for individual states, counties, or cities. It also works with other countries to find natural resources.

All information collected by the people of the USGS is available to the public in pamphlets and maps.

For Discussion
1. What are some jobs performed by the USGS?
2. What locations have been mapped by the USGS?

USGS at work

Chapter Summary

- Topographic maps show the shape and elevation of the land. (15–1)

- A contour line connects all points of equal elevation to show features such as hills, depressions, cliffs, and valleys. (15–1)

- USGS maps have standard symbols and colors to identify the features on topographic maps. (15–2)

- Many states are divided into units called townships and sections. Township and section boundaries are shown on topographic maps. (15–2)

- The eastern United States has a wide coastal plain and folded mountains to the west of the plain. (15–3)

- The central United States is primarily lowlands and plains. Evidence of glaciers is common in the northern part of this region. (15–3)

- Much of the West, including Alaska and Hawaii, is geologically active with earthquakes and volcanoes. (15–3)

Interesting Reading

Sigford, Ann E. *Tall Grass and Trouble.* Dillon, 1978. Describes environmental problems facing the Great Plains and suggests solutions.

Stewart, Anne. *What's a Wilderness Worth?* Dillon, 1979. Discusses the Boundary Waters Canoe Area Wilderness of northern Minnesota.

Wood, Elizabeth A. *Science from Your Airplane Window.* Dover, 1975. Suggests some investigations that you can try during an airplane flight.

Questions/Problems

1. Suggest a reason for the volcanic activity in the Aleutian Islands.

2. Assume you are given two points on a river. Using a topographic map, how could you tell which point has the higher elevation?

3. Would a contour interval of 200 feet be useful on a map of flat land? Explain your answer.

4. Assume that you have a topographic map of a mountain whose highest contour line is 4,300 feet above sea level. Inside this contour line, there is an X that marks the peak. If the contour interval is 100 feet, what is the highest possible elevation of the mountain peak?

Extra Research

1. Draw a map of your neighborhood or the area around your school using topographic map symbols.

2. Construct a clay model of an area of the earth's surface. The model may represent a real or an imaginary area.

3. Use magazine photographs to make a posterboard collage that represents changes in landforms from east to west across the United States.

4. Write for information on orienteering. Your teacher will provide you with the proper address.

Chapter Test

A. Vocabulary Write the numbers 1–10 on a piece of paper.
Match the definition in Column I with the term it defines in Column II.

Column I

1. series of closed contour lines

2. vertical distance between each contour line on a map

3. every fifth contour line

4. used to show depressions in the land

5. organization that makes topographic maps

6. represented on a map by BMX

7. division of land that is 36 square miles in area

8. dry desert basin

9. shown by contour lines very close to, or on top of, one another

10. region of volcanic and earthquake activity

Column II

a. Aleutian Islands

b. bench mark

c. Bonneville Salt Flats

d. cliff

e. contour interval

f. hachures

g. index contour

h. mountain or hill

i. township

j. USGS

B. Multiple Choice Write the numbers 1–10 on your paper.
Choose the letter that best completes the statement or answers the question.

1. Large regions of swamps are found on
a) the Coastal Plain.   b) the Fall Line.
c) Lake Bonneville.   d) the Colorado Plateau.

2. Much of the central United States shows
evidence of   a) faulting.   b) glaciers.
c) landslides.   d) earthquakes.

3. A contour line that crosses a stream resembles a   a) circle.   b) V pointing downstream.
c) V pointing upstream.   d) none of the
above.

4. Typical landforms in the Central United
States include   a) flat-lying rocks.   b) glacial
moraines.   c) limestone caves.   d) a, b, and c.

5. Salt beds in Utah and Nevada formed by
a) the erosion of rocks.   b) volcanic activity.
c) the evaporation of lakes.   d) none of the
above.

6. Some of the world's highest mountains are
a) volcanoes.   b) in the eastern United States.
c) islands.   d) a and c.

7. On a topographic map, brown is used to
show   a) canals.   b) roads.   c) contour lines.
d) woodlands.

8. If the scale of a map is 1:36,000, one centimeter on the map equals what distance on the
earth's surface?   a) 1 cm   b) 36,000 inches
c) 36,000 cm   d) 3,600 cm

9. The area of a section is   a) 6 square miles.
b) 36 square miles.   c) 1 square mile.   d) 60
square miles.

10. Every fifth line on a topographic map is
a) brown.   b) red.   c) at a known elevation.
d) a and c.

Careers

Surveyor's assistant

Assistants help surveyors measure land to make boundary lines, check construction sites, and collect map data.

A surveyor looks through an instrument called an alidade to see a surveying rod held by an assistant. Surveying rods are marked like rulers. In this way, a surveyor can determine the elevation of a location.

Surveying teams may have to clear their way through thick underbrush or survey along a busy street or road. Surveyors even wade along shorelines to map the effects of erosion.

Anyone who graduates from high school can become a surveyor's assistant. They get on-the-job training to learn the necessary skills.
Career Information:
American Congress on Surveying and Mapping, 210 Little Falls Rd., Falls Church, VA 22046

Bulldozer operator

Who works at almost every construction site? Bulldozer operators are present wherever people build roads, schools, and supermarkets.

Bulldozer operators use tractor equipment that has shovels or blades attached to the front. With these attachments, a bulldozer operator can clear land, scoop out ditches, or build hills. Some bulldozer drivers also work in rock quarries moving huge boulders.

People learn to use the levers and pedals that maneuver bulldozers by working as helpers at construction sites. Experienced drivers train new employees while they are working.
Career Information:
International Union of Operating Engineers, 1125 17th St., NW, Washington, DC 20036

Volcanologist

When Mount St. Helens erupted in 1980, many scientists went to the volcano to make tests and to report on the activity within the mountain. Many of these people were volcanologists.

These specialized geologists study both active and inactive volcanoes. They examine lava flows, rock formations, and even geysers and hot springs. Volcanologists can sometimes spot the weakest part of an active volcano's cone and tell in what direction lava may flow in the next eruption. These experts use highly specialized instruments and equipment.

Students who want to become volcanologists graduate from college with a geology degree. They need advanced degrees, however, to become experts in volcanology.
Career Information:
American Geological Institute, 5205 Leesburg Pike, Falls Church, VA 22041

Seismologist

Earthquakes cause great damage to buildings, roads, and living things. Seismologists study the conditions of the ground before, during, and after an earthquake. They are now trying to learn how to predict earthquakes. Builders and city planners can use seismologists' information before they decide where to construct houses, buildings, and cities.

To become an earthquake detective, you need geology, physics, and math in college. You learn to read maps and instruments that record seismic waves in the earth.

Career Information:
American Geological Institute,
5205 Leesburg Pike, Falls Church,
VA 22041

Coal inspector

At the supermarket, you buy eggs marked A, B, or C. These grades indicate the quality of the eggs. At coal mines, coal is graded too. A coal inspector tests mining products to see if they meet government standards.

Before a mine can sell coal to anyone, someone must inspect the coal. The inspector takes samples of the coal when it is loaded onto train cars. Tests that are run on a small coal sample in a laboratory point out any impurities or color changes. The inspector then reports the quality of the coal to mine owners and coal buyers.

Inspectors must have a high school diploma. They learn special testing and grading techniques in a technical school.

Career Information:
United Mine Workers of America,
Communications Dept., 900 15th
St., NW, Washington, DC 20005

Geology technician

Geology technicians join geologists on field explorations. They take data, and later they help in laboratory analyses.

A geology technician often runs equipment, makes maps, or takes rock samples and surveys. This worker takes notes and keeps records in the field for the geologist to study later.

Technicians can study earth science and learn laboratory and mapping skills in two years at a junior college. All technicians get on-the-job training.

Career Information:
American Geological Institute,
5205 Leesburg Pike, Falls Church,
VA 22041

UNIT FOUR
AIR AND WATER

Most people identify the photograph of the funnel that is churning the water as a tornado.

The picture was taken from a small plane flying near Key West, Florida, in 1969. The photograph shows a waterspout, which is similar to a tornado. Waterspouts are generally less powerful than tornadoes, but they can destroy small ships. The waterspout's funnel acts like a huge suction tube, pulling water up into the sky. This ocean feature illustrates how closely the air and oceans are linked. Unit Four deals with air, weather, and oceans.

Chapter 16
The Blanket of Air

In the satellite picture, a hazy blue blanket covers the world. The blanket clearly marks the presence of the air that surrounds the earth. Notice how thin and fragile the layer of air is compared to the earth.

In this chapter you will find out that the air is made of many gases. You will learn that the ocean of air has more than one layer. In one section you will read how the air is heated and warms the earth. Finally, you will see how our air differs from the gases surrounding other planets.

Chapter Objectives

1. List the major gases present in the earth's atmosphere.
2. Describe four layers of the atmosphere.
3. Explain the difference between heat and temperature.
4. Describe three ways that heat is transferred.
5. Briefly explain how the earth is heated by the sun's radiation and the greenhouse effect.
6. Compare the earth's atmosphere with the atmospheres of other planets in the solar system.

16–1
The Atmosphere–A Blanket of Air

We tend to take for granted the air around us. But it is air that makes our life possible. Gases in the air support plant and animal life. Some gases even block deadly rays from the sun. As you read about the gases in the air, try to answer these questions:

a. What are some important gases in the atmosphere?
b. What are the four layers of the atmosphere?

Gases in the Atmosphere

Many of the gases in the air were once trapped inside the earth. How did they get into the atmosphere? Most of the gases probably escaped from volcanoes billions of years ago. Erupting volcanoes release water vapor, carbon dioxide, nitrogen, hydrogen, and other gases. These are the main gases in our atmosphere.

Our atmosphere contains about a dozen different gases—many in small amounts. About 80% of the volume of the air is nitrogen. The diagram shows how nitrogen moves between the air and ground. This movement is called the **nitrogen cycle.** Living things use nitrogen for growth and repair of cells. But most living things can not directly use the nitrogen in the air. Bacteria in the soil change nitrogen into compounds useable by living things. Certain bacteria cause animal wastes, dead plants, and dead animals to decay. These bacteria return much of the nitrogen to the atmosphere. Lightning also changes a small amount of nitrogen into useable compounds.

Nitrogen cycle

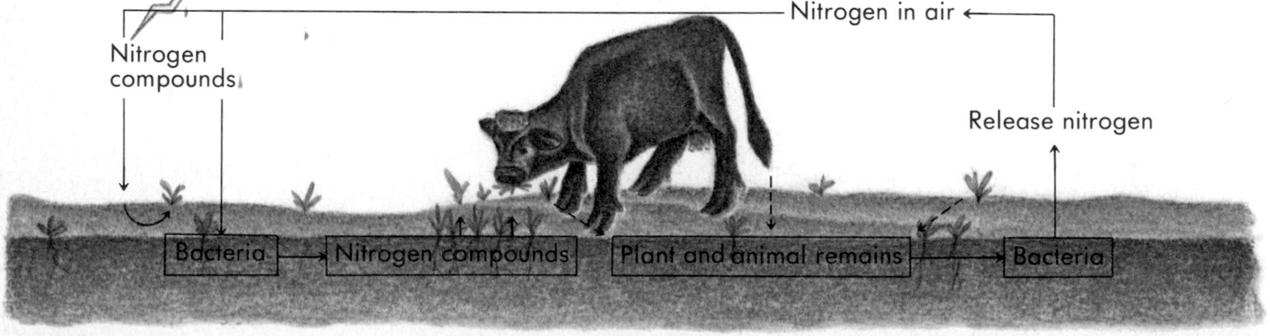

Nitrogen in air

Release nitrogen

Nitrogen compounds

Bacteria → Nitrogen compounds → Plant and animal remains → Bacteria

About 20% of the air is oxygen. Scientists believe that plants are responsible for most of the oxygen in the air. Why? Green plants give off oxygen while making food in the process of photosynthesis (fō′tō sin′thə sis). Plants and animals use oxygen to release energy from their food. Oxygen, thus, circulates between living things and the atmosphere just as nitrogen does.

The atmosphere contains very small amounts of many other gases. Among these is carbon dioxide. When animals and plants use oxygen to turn food into energy, they release carbon dioxide to the atmosphere. The diagram shows the exchange of carbon dioxide and oxygen between the earth and the atmosphere.

Ozone (ō′zōn) is a type of oxygen molecule. It is present in small amounts high in the atmosphere. If all the ozone in the atmosphere could be brought down to the earth's surface, the layer of ozone would be only 2.5 millimeters thick. This small amount of ozone protects life on earth by absorbing some harmful ultraviolet radiation from the sun.

The lower part of the atmosphere contains water vapor, which is water in the form of a gas. The lower atmosphere also contains particles of dust, soil, and salt. When water drops collect around these particles, clouds form.

Have You Heard?

Ozone—we cannot live with too much of it, yet we cannot live without it. Sunlight reacts with gases coming out of auto exhausts and factory smokestacks. This reaction can produce ozone. Ozone formed in this way causes the burning eyes and breathing problems noticed during "ozone alerts."

Carbon and oxygen cycles

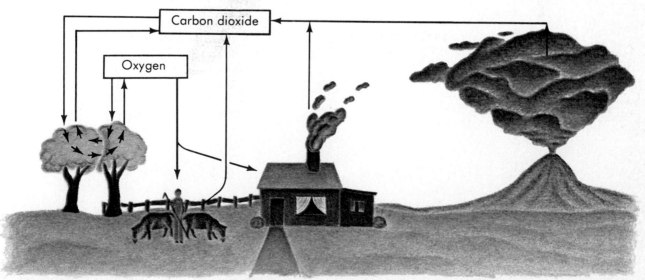

The Layers of the Atmosphere

The major gases of the atmosphere are fairly well mixed as far up as 80 kilometers. But the blanket of air has four separate layers. The line on the small graph shows how the temperature changes in the four layers.

You live in the bottom layer, the **troposphere** (trop⁄ə sfir). This layer extends from the earth's surface upward 8 to 16 kilometers. Up and down air movements and water vapor are present in the troposphere. They cause the weather and storms in this layer. The air is densest near the bottom of the troposphere. Air molecules here are packed close together by the weight of the air above. As a result, three-quarters of the atmosphere is within 11 kilometers of the ground. The air temperature drops as you go higher in the troposphere.

400 km —

300 km —

200 km —

100 km — Thermosphere and Ionosphere

50 km — Mesosphere

10 km — Stratosphere

Troposphere

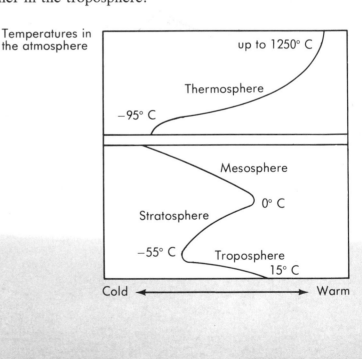

Temperatures in the atmosphere

up to 1250° C

Thermosphere

−95° C

Mesosphere

0° C

Stratosphere

−55° C

Troposphere

15° C

Cold ←————→ Warm

The second layer of the atmosphere, the **stratosphere** (strat′ə sfir), extends to about 30 kilometers above the earth. Air flow here is mainly horizontal. The temperature remains about the same in the lower stratosphere, then rises. Large jet airplanes fly in the stratosphere to avoid the "weather" in the troposphere. Most of the ozone is in a layer in the stratosphere.

Above the stratosphere lies the **mesosphere** (mes′ə sfir), where the temperature begins to drop again. The mesosphere reaches to about 80 kilometers above the ground. Notice that the lowest temperatures in the atmosphere occur near the top of the mesosphere.

The **thermosphere** (ther′mə sfir) begins about 80 kilometers above the earth. Air is very thin in this layer. The thermosphere is very hot because the nitrogen and oxygen atoms absorb unshielded energy from the sun. The sun's energy strips electrons from these atoms. Ions (ī′ənz) are atoms that have lost or gained electrons. Therefore, the thermosphere is also called the **ionosphere** (ī on′ə sfir). It reaches more than 1,000 kilometers above the earth. You can tune in distant radio broadcasts when radio waves from earth bounce off the ionosphere.

Review It

1. What are the two most abundant gases in the air?
2. In which layer does our weather occur?

Have You Heard?

Radio waves move in straight lines, unless the waves are bent or reflected. They can be bounced from the ground to the ionosphere and back again, as shown. This reflection of radio waves makes around-the-world radio communication possible even without satellites or cables.

Radio waves

16–2
Heat for the Earth

The atmosphere does more than provide the gases needed for life on earth. It also helps warm the earth. To understand how both the sun and atmosphere keep the earth warm, you need to know more about heat and how heat is transferred. Try to find answers to these questions as you read about heat:

a. What is heat?
b. How is heat transferred?

Heat Is the Energy of Moving Molecules

Everything, including the atmosphere, is made up of moving atoms and molecules. **Heat** is the energy in moving molecules. Heat moves from warm things to cooler things.

Temperature indicates how fast the molecules of an object are moving. The molecules in a hot object move more quickly than the molecules in a cold object. But temperature is not the same thing as heat. Even when only a very few molecules are present, the temperature is high if the molecules are moving very rapidly. But there is not much energy present because there are not many molecules. So there will not be much heat, even though the temperature is high. For example, you would not feel the high temperature in the thermosphere, because there are few gas molecules present in the thin air of this layer.

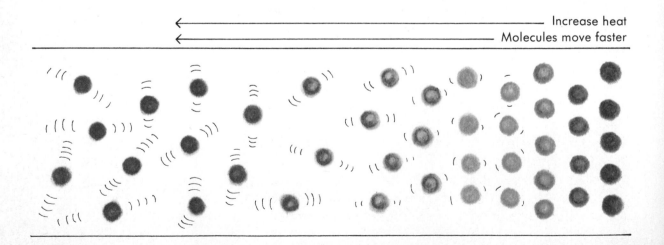

← Increase heat
← Molecules move faster

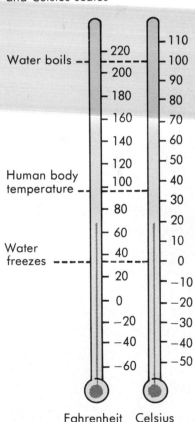

Comparing Fahrenheit and Celsius scales

Consider the burning match in the first picture and the room radiator in the second picture. Both have rapidly moving molecules. The burning match has the higher temperature, but the room radiator has more heat because it contains more molecules. The match can burn your finger, but it does not have enough energy to heat a room.

You use a thermometer to measure temperature. Scientists usually measure temperature on the **Celsius** (sel′sē əs) scale. It is also used in most of the countries of the world. In the United States we are gradually changing from the Fahrenheit scale to the Celsius scale.

We measure temperature in degrees Celsius. On the Celsius scale, water normally freezes at 0°C and boils at 100°C. On the Fahrenheit scale, water freezes at 32°F and boils at 212°F. The diagram compares the Fahrenheit and Celsius scales. Notice that each Fahrenheit degree is smaller than the Celsius degree.

Heat can also be measured. The unit used for measuring heat is the calorie. A calorie is the quantity of heat needed to raise the temperature of a gram of water one degree Celsius.

Challenge!

Use a thermometer to compare the temperature of the air near the ceiling with the air near the floor in each room of your home. Explain your observations.

Conduction, Convection, and Radiation

Heat energy travels from warm things to cooler things. The pictures show the three ways that heat is transferred.

Conduction (kən duk′shən) is the movement of heat energy from one molecule to the next molecule. Metals are good conductors of heat. For example, the handle of a metal pan gets hot soon after the pan is heated. The rapidly moving molecules at the bottom of the pan bump into and speed up the pan's other molecules. The heat energy moves from the bottom of the pan to the handle, molecule by molecule.

Gases are poor conductors of heat. As a result, conduction is not very important as a means of moving heat through the atmosphere. However, when any part of the ground is warmer or colder than the air above it, conduction carries heat between the ground and the air.

The movement of heat by **convection** is more important in the atmosphere. Convection carries heat in rising and sinking currents of gas or liquid. For example, heat moves through the air in a room by convection. A room heater, shown below, heats the air near it. Since heated air is less dense than cold air, the heated air rises. A cycle begins with hot air rising and cooler air sinking. This circular flow of air heats the room.

Conduction

Convection

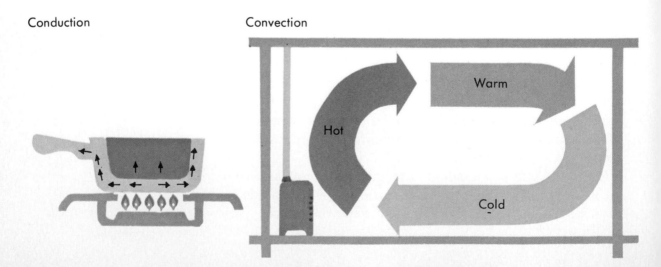

Radiation is energy that can travel through empty space. Fireplaces, heat lamps, and space heaters give off a type of radiation called infrared radiation. The diagram shows infrared radiation coming from a fireplace. When an object absorbs infrared radiation, the object gets warmer. If you are facing a warm fireplace, your front gets very warm, but your back is cool. Infrared radiation hits only the side facing the fireplace, because radiation travels in a straight line.

Challenge!

Think of two examples each that you have seen of conduction, convection, and radiation. Draw or describe them. Do not list those already mentioned in the text.

Radiation

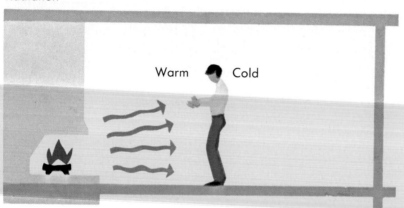

Warm   Cold

You are familiar with many kinds of radiation other than infrared radiation. Light from a lamp is radiation that you can see called visible light. Sunbathers are tanned by the sun's ultraviolet radiation. X rays, another kind of radiation, are used to examine your bones and teeth. Radio waves are also a type of radiation. They bring us radio and television broadcasts.

Most of the energy coming to and leaving the earth is in the form of radiation. The incoming radiation is mainly visible light from the sun. Energy leaving the earth is mainly infrared radiation.

Review It

1. How are heat and temperature different?
2. In what three ways is heat transferred?

Activity

Temperature and Heat

Purpose
To investigate heat, temperature, and how heat moves.

Materials
- 1 marble
- 1 metal object about the same mass as the marble
- small slab of paraffin
- tongs
- clock or timer
- 1 Celsius thermometer
- 1 Fahrenheit thermometer
- 1 large beaker
- sawdust
- Bunsen burner or heat source
- tripod and wire gauze
- water and ice
- safety glasses
- hot pad

Procedure

Part A
1. Find the mass of the marble and the mass of the metal object on the balance.
2. Set up your burner and beaker of water as shown in *a.* Carefully place the marble and metal object into the water. Heat the water to 100°C, the boiling point of water. *CAUTION: Use safety glasses for this activity. Be careful when working with fire and hot water.* Let the water boil for 5 minutes so that the marble and metal object will each be about the same temperature.
3. Using the tongs, *carefully* remove the metal object. *CAUTION: Do not touch the hot object.* Quickly place the object on the paraffin, as shown in *b* and *c.* Repeat this step with the marble.
4. Record what happened when the two hot objects were placed on the paraffin.

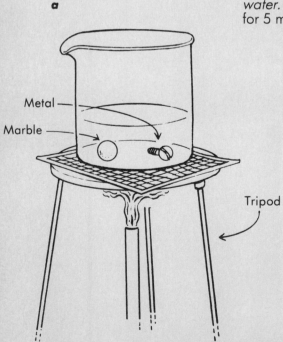

a

Metal
Marble
Tripod

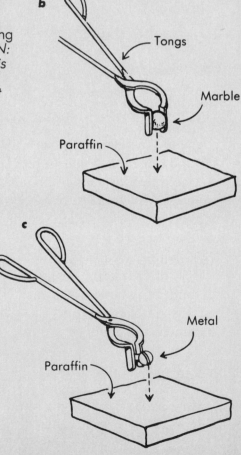

b

Tongs
Marble
Paraffin

c

Metal
Paraffin

5. Turn off the fire and empty the beaker of hot water. *CAUTION: Use the hot pad to handle the beaker of water.*

Part B
1. Read and record the temperature of your room on both the Celsius and Fahrenheit thermometers.
2. Put enough water and ice in a beaker to cover the bulbs of the two thermometers, as in *d*. Place them in the ice water for at least 2 minutes. Read and record the temperatures.

3. The boiling point of water is 100° Celsius or 212° Fahrenheit. Subtract the freezing point temperature from the boiling point temperature of both Celsius and Fahrenheit to find the number of degrees between the freezing and boiling points of water on each scale. Record your results.

Part C
1. *CAUTION: Use the safety glasses for Part C.* Fill a beaker two-thirds full with water. Drop a *small* handful of sawdust into the water and wait for it to settle. Set up the burner as in *a*. Light the burner and bring the water to a full boil. Draw and record what happens to the sawdust. Turn the fire off. *CAUTION: Use a hot pad to empty the hot water as before.*

Analysis
1. Although the marble and the metal object were at the same temperature, which contained more heat? Explain your answer.
2. Estimate the temperature of the marble and metal object after 5 minutes in boiling water.
3. List some advantages and disadvantages of using the Celsius scale. Do the same for the Fahrenheit scale.
4. What is a normal room temperature in degrees Celsius?
5. How many Fahrenheit degrees are there in one Celsius degree? Hint: Divide the number of degrees between the freezing and boiling point of Fahrenheit by those of Celsius.
6. Describe the process that caused the sawdust to move as it did.

d

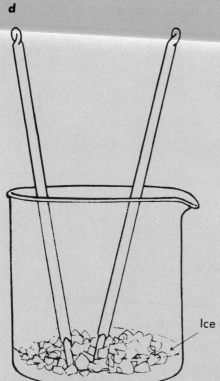

Ice and water

16–3
Energy from the Sun

The earth gets its heat from the sun. The movement of this heat back and forth between the earth's surface and atmosphere makes our planet a suitable place for life. Think about these questions as you read:

a. How does sunlight heat the earth?
b. What is the "greenhouse effect"?

Sunlight Heats the Ground

The sun is very hot and it gives off energy as radiation. The diagram in the margin shows the kinds of radiation from the sun. Notice, however, that most of the sun's radiation is visible light, called sunlight.

The diagram illustrates what happens to sunlight as it nears the earth. Part of the sun's radiation is reflected back into space by the atmosphere and the earth. A small amount of the sun's radiation is absorbed by the atmosphere. Most of the remaining radiation, however, is absorbed by the ground. The hotter the ground becomes, the more radiation it gives off as infrared waves.

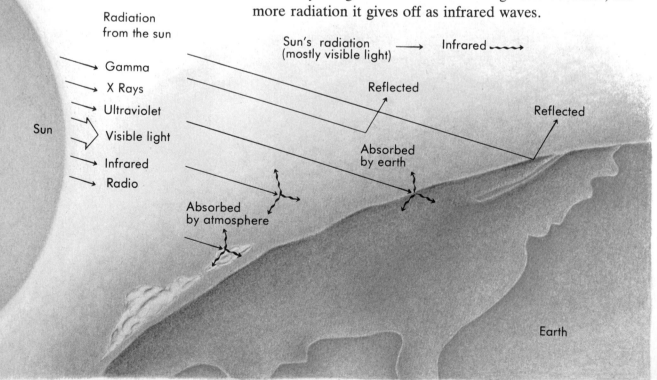

Radiation from the sun

Sun

Gamma
X Rays
Ultraviolet
Visible light
Infrared
Radio

Sun's radiation (mostly visible light) — Infrared

Reflected

Reflected

Absorbed by earth

Absorbed by atmosphere

Earth

The Greenhouse Effect Keeps the Earth Warm

Light from the sun travels right through the atmosphere on its way to the earth. Most of the infrared waves radiated by the earth, however, do not pass straight through the atmosphere and into space. Instead, water vapor and carbon dioxide, two of the gases in the lower atmosphere, trap the infrared radiation from the earth.

The trapping of heat by carbon dioxide and water vapor in the atmosphere is called the **greenhouse effect.** The picture shows how the lower atmosphere blocks infrared radiation and returns the heat to the earth.

Without the greenhouse effect, the temperature at night would be very low. Sunlight would warm the ground to only about −10°C. But because we have carbon dioxide and water vapor in the air, the earth remains warm enough for life.

Clouds are also very important in keeping the earth's surface warm, especially at night. On cloudy nights, the ground cools off much less than on clear nights.

Challenge!

Predict at least two effects that might result from a warmer climate on the earth.

Have You Heard?

Increasing the amount of carbon dioxide in the atmosphere by burning fossil fuels may increase the greenhouse effect and, therefore, may make the earth even warmer.

Review It

1. What is the main kind of radiation that the earth gives off?
2. What gases in the air are responsible for the greenhouse effect?

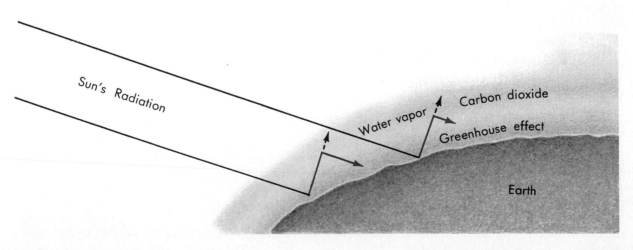

Sun's Radiation

Water vapor

Carbon dioxide

Greenhouse effect

Earth

16—4
The Atmospheres of the Planets and Their Moons

Have You Heard?

Sunlight coming through the atmosphere bounces off dust and other particles in the air. These particles act as obstacles to the sunlight. They are said to "scatter" the sunlight. The scattering of sunlight makes the sky look blue. Also, the sun appears red when it is rising or setting because the blue light has all scattered out, which leaves more red light.

The moon's black sky

Observations from spacecraft have shown us examples of other atmospheres close up. As you read, keep in mind:

a. What determines whether a planet has an atmosphere?
b. What does the mass of a planet have to do with the kinds of gases in its atmosphere?

Why Planets Have Atmospheres

Gas molecules of a planet's or moon's atmosphere are always in motion. The hotter the planet, the faster the molecules move. If gravity did not hold them back, they would fly off into space. It takes more gravity to hold the molecules on a hotter planet.

Venus, Earth, and Mars have enough mass to keep an atmosphere. But our Earth's moon and the planet Mercury are both small bodies with little mass. Therefore, they have too little gravity to keep an atmosphere. The picture, taken on the moon, shows how black the sky looks when there is no atmosphere. The other picture, taken on Mars, shows that planet's sky. Sunlight bounces off reddish dust particles in the sky and makes it look pink.

The large outer planets—Jupiter, Saturn, Uranus, and Neptune—have very thick atmospheres. Tiny Pluto, the outermost planet, is so cold that it may have an atmosphere even though the planet has little gravity.

Mars

Some moons of planets have enough mass and are cold enough to keep gases in their atmospheres. Saturn's moon Titan is larger than the planet Mercury and is much colder. It has an atmosphere of its own.

The Mass of a Planet and Its Atmospheric Gases

Venus, Earth, and Mars are small compared with giant planets such as Jupiter. They do not contain enough mass to hold in *all* the gases. The lightest gases, hydrogen and helium, have escaped.

Earth's atmosphere is mostly nitrogen and oxygen. Venus' and Mars' atmospheres are mostly carbon dioxide, another heavy gas. We would not be able to breathe on either of these planets.

Jupiter, Saturn, Uranus, and Neptune are giant planets. All the giant planets have so much gravity that they kept most of the gases with which they formed. They contain about 90% hydrogen and almost 10% helium, the lightest gases. They have only traces of other gases. The atmosphere of Jupiter has almost the same composition as the sun.

Have You Heard?

Venus' atmosphere contains so much carbon dioxide, water vapor, and sulfuric acid that the greenhouse effect works especially well. It heats Venus' atmosphere up to 475°C, much hotter than boiling water.

Review It

1. Why do Mercury and our moon not have atmospheres?
2. What kinds of gases are in Jupiter's atmosphere?

Activity

Heating an Atmosphere

Purpose
To understand why the planets have atmospheres of different temperatures.

Materials
• heat lamp
• 2 Celsius thermometers
• meter stick
• one white can and one black can
• clock or timer
• tape

Procedure

Part A
1. Set up the heat lamp at one end of the meter stick as in a.
2. Tape one thermometer half way down the meter stick and the other thermometer at the end of the meter stick, as shown. Place the thermometers so that you can read them easily. Do not touch the bulbs of the thermometers at any time. Read and record the temperature on each thermometer.
3. Turn on the heat lamp. Do not block the heat with your head or hands while the lamp is on.
4. In about 8 minutes, or when the temperatures stop rising, read and record the temperatures. Turn the lamp off.

Part B
1. Bring the thermometers back to room temperature with cool water.
2. Place one of the thermometers inside the white can and the other inside the black can.
3. Place both of the cans 30 cm from the heat lamp, as shown in b. Check and record both temperatures.
4. Turn on the heat lamp. After 5 minutes, read and record both temperatures.
5. Read and record both temperatures once a minute for 3 minutes.
6. On the side facing the lamp, touch the outside of each can. Note and record which container is warmer.
7. Turn the heat lamp off.

Analysis
1. Find the temperature change shown on each thermometer in Part A. Do this by subtracting the temperature before the heat lamp was turned on from the final temperature.
2. Estimate how much more radiation one thermometer received than the other.
3. Planet A is half as far from the sun as planet B. Estimate how much warmer planet A is than planet B.
4. In Part B, which of the cans got hotter?
5. What effect would the following conditions have on the temperature of a planet: a) covered by snow; b) all desert; c) covered by trees and green plants? (Hint: consider how surfaces reflect sunlight and the results of Part B.)

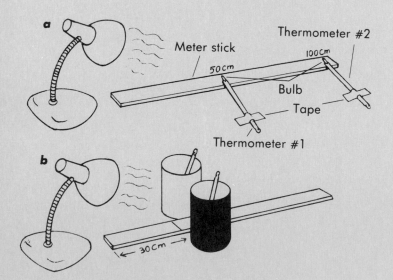

Issues in Earth Science

Is the Earth's Climate Heating Up or Cooling Down?

Scientists around the world are studying weather patterns of the past to determine what may happen to our weather in the future. They find their data in ancient soil layers, tree rings, glacial deposits, and samples from glacial ice and from the bottoms of the earth's oceans.

Why all the concern about the future of the earth's climate? Producing enough food to feed the world population depends on a favorable climate. Suppose the earth's climate cools down an average of one or two degrees, or the amount of rainfall decreases. Many people would probably starve. On the other hand, if the earth's climate heats up, the ice caps might melt. Sea level would rise about 60 meters, and coastal cities, like New York, would be under water. Only the tops of the tallest build-ings would remain above sea level.

What puzzles scientists most is that there is evidence for both a warming trend and a cooling trend! Since 1940, the Northern Hemisphere has been cooling. But the Southern Hemisphere shows signs of a warming trend.

Scientists do not know why climates change. Also, they do not know how people's activities affect the climate.

When people burn fossil fuels, great amounts of carbon dioxide are released into the air. An increase in carbon dioxide strengthens the greenhouse effect. Some scientists believe that worldwide temperatures will rise. Other scientists think that a stronger greenhouse effect will increase the moisture in the air, and more clouds will form.

The increased cloud cover will reflect incoming sunlight back to space. Thus the earth's temperature will be kept in balance.

Other activities of people, such as farming, release large quantities of dust into the air. Some studies propose that the excess dust will increase the greenhouse effect and warm the climate. Other studies suggest that excess dust will reflect sunlight and cool the earth.

Scientists do not agree about how our climate may change. They do agree, however, that climate research is vital for our survival.

For Discussion
1. What might happen if the earth gets warmer?
2. What activities of people change the climate?

Alaskan glacier

321

Chapter Summary

- The earth's atmosphere contains about a dozen different gases. Nitrogen and oxygen are the most abundant gases. Small amounts of carbon dioxide, water vapor, and ozone are also present in the atmosphere. (16–1)

- The earth's atmosphere consists of four layers: the troposphere, the stratosphere, the mesosphere, and the thermosphere. (16–1)

- Three-quarters of the atmosphere is within 11 kilometers of the earth's surface. (16–1)

- Heat is the energy of moving molecules. Temperature indicates how fast the molecules of an object are moving. Temperature is measured in degrees, while heat is measured in calories. (16–2)

- Heat energy is transferred by conduction, convection, and radiation. (16–2)

- Sunlight is either reflected by or travels directly through the atmosphere and is absorbed by the earth's surface. Only a little is absorbed by the atmosphere. The earth, in turn, radiates energy. (16–3)

- The greenhouse effect is the process by which certain gases in the air trap radiation from the earth. (16–3)

- The mass of a planet and its distance from the sun are important factors in the formation of its atmosphere. (16–4)

Interesting Reading

Gore, Rick. "What Voyager Saw: Jupiter's Dazzling Realm." *National Geographic*, January 1980, pages 2–29. Includes discussion of Jupiter's atmosphere.

"Man and His Satellite." *Science Digest*, July, 1981, pages 58–60. Describes how the ozone layer is studied by satellite.

Questions/Problems

1. What is the nitrogen cycle?

2. Why could life probably not survive if the percentages of nitrogen and oxygen in the air dropped suddenly?

3. Name and describe the four layers of the atmosphere.

4. What is the difference between heat and temperature?

5. Describe and give examples of the three types of heat transfer.

6. A planet orbiting another star in our galaxy has more mass and is cooler than the earth. Predict whether or not the planet has an atmosphere. Explain your answer.

Extra Research

1. Use the card catalogue to find a book on weather. Look up the greenhouse effect and how it works. Think of and explain two examples of the greenhouse effect that you might find in your everyday life.

2. Draw a diagram of your house, showing the furnace and heat vents. Use arrows to describe how the heat probably travels within each room. Explain what type of heat transfer helps to heat your house.

Chapter Test

A. Vocabulary   Write the numbers 1–10 on a piece of paper.
Match the definition in Column I with the term it defines in Column II.

Column I

1. a gas in the air that blocks harmful rays

2. layer of the atmosphere where "weather" is found

3. radiation given off by the earth

4. carbon dioxide and water vapor trap infrared radiation

5. gas given off by plants in photosynthesis

6. layer of the atmosphere that reflects radio waves

7. heat moves from one molecule to another

8. warm gas rises while cool gas sinks

9. the transfer of energy through air and space

10. indicates the speed of the molecules

Column II

a. conduction

b. convection

c. greenhouse effect

d. infrared

e. ionosphere

f. oxygen

g. ozone

h. radiation

i. temperature

j. troposphere

B. Multiple Choice   Write the numbers 1–10 on your paper.
Choose the letter that best completes the statement or answers the question.

1. The most plentiful gas in earth's atmosphere is   a) nitrogen.   b) oxygen.   c) ozone.   d) carbon dioxide.

2. The layer of the atmosphere where most of the water vapor is found is the   a) ionosphere.   b) troposphere.   c) stratosphere.   d) ozone layer.

3. The energy of molecules moving from warm things to cooler things is called   a) temperature.   b) heat.   c) Celsius.   d) Fahrenheit.

4. Earth gets most of its heat by means of   a) conduction.   b) convection.   c) reduction.   d) radiation.

5. Infrared radiation from the earth   a) passes directly into space.   b) is trapped.   c) destroys the ozone layer.   d) causes suntans.

6. Nitrogen in the air   a) is not directly usable by life.   b) is changed by soil bacteria.   c) comes partly from decayed plants and animals.   d) all are correct.

7. Which of the following does heat move through mainly by convection?   a) metals   b) space   c) air   d) b and c

8. Most of the radiation from the sun is in the form of   a) ultraviolet.   b) gamma rays.   c) radio waves.   d) visible light.

9. Mercury, a planet close to the sun, lacks an atmosphere because of its   a) small mass.   b) great mass.   c) temperature.   d) a and c.

10. Hydrogen and helium remain in the atmosphere of a planet because   a) of its small mass.   b) of its great mass.   c) of its high temperature.   d) all the other gases have escaped.

Chapter 17
Moisture in the Air

Clouds tell us a number of things. Anyone can "read" clouds to get hints about the weather ahead. Dark, heavy clouds can mean rain for the farmer or flooding to people living along rivers. But clouds also tell us what direction the air is moving. After you read this chapter, you will understand what caused the cloud to form above the mountain in the picture.

This chapter opens with a section on how water gets into the air. Then it considers how this moisture can be measured. Finally, the chapter describes some elements of weather that you are familiar with: clouds, rain, and snow.

Chapter Objectives

1. Explain why evaporation, condensation, and the sun's energy are important factors in the water cycle.

2. Describe how humidity is measured.

3. Explain why clouds form and how they are described.

4. Describe five kinds of precipitation.

17–1

Water in the Air and on the Earth

We would have no clouds, rain, or snow without water in the atmosphere. Answer these questions as you learn how water moves back and forth between the atmosphere and the ground:

a. How do evaporation and condensation change the form of water?
b. How does the water cycle work?

How Water Changes Form

Water appears on earth in three forms—solid, liquid, and gas. Most of the earth's water is liquid. Oceans, lakes, rivers, and even groundwater are liquid water. Ice is solid water. Glacial ice several kilometers deep covers most of Greenland and Antarctica. The rest of the world's water is **water vapor,** a gas in the air. Even though you cannot see water vapor, it is present everywhere—even in the driest desert air.

The total amount of water on earth changes very little over time. Water, however, is always moving from place to place and changing form. Some of the water molecules in your ice cubes may once have bubbled from an oasis in Egypt. You may drink molecules of water that were locked in a glacier for thousands of years.

How do such changes happen? One way is **evaporation,** the process in which a liquid changes into a gas. For example, perspiration on your skin dries as the water in it evaporates. The water on your skin changes into water vapor in the air.

It takes energy to change a molecule of liquid water into a molecule of water vapor. When drops of perspiration on your body evaporate, some of the heat energy for evaporation is furnished by your body. As a result, your body loses heat and you feel cooler. Evaporation is a cooling process.

Wind from an electric fan speeds the evaporation of perspiration from your body. Therefore, you lose body heat rapidly and feel cooler when you sit in front of a fan.

Have You Heard?

Almost all substances can exist as a solid, a liquid, or a gas. But water is one of the few substances commonly found in all three forms at normal earth temperatures.

Warm air can hold more water vapor than cool air. When warm, moist air is cooled, some of the vapor becomes liquid. The process in which a gas changes into a liquid is **condensation** (kon′den sā′shən). On a warm summer day, beads of water often appear on the outside of a cold can or bottle. Warm air is chilled when it touches the cold container. Water vapor in the air condenses into liquid water on the cold can or bottle.

The **dew** that covers grass in the morning is moisture from the air. The moisture condenses on the grass and cool surfaces during the night when the temperature drops. **Frost** forms instead of dew if the temperature of the ground is below freezing. Frost is *not* frozen dew, because the water vapor in the air changes *directly* into ice.

Water Circulates in the Water Cycle

Evaporation and condensation work continuously on the waters of the earth. This movement of water between the ground and the air, shown in the diagram, is called the **water cycle.** The sun furnishes the energy for the water cycle. When the sun shines on the oceans and other bodies of water, the sun's energy changes some of the water into water vapor.

Winds carry the water vapor through the air. When the air cools, the water vapor condenses into little drops of water. Clouds form. Eventually, the water in the clouds falls to the ground as rain or snow. In time, the rain or snow flows into a lake or an ocean. The sun comes out and the cycle starts again.

Review It

1. Describe evaporation and condensation and give an example of each.
2. What furnishes the energy for the water cycle?

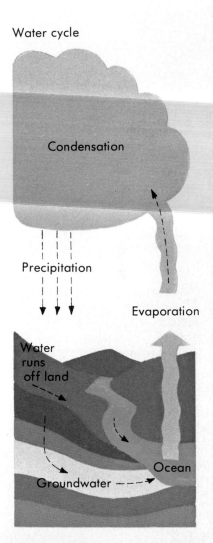

Water cycle

Condensation

Precipitation

Evaporation

Water runs off land

Groundwater

Ocean

327

Activity

Evaporation and Condensation

Purpose
To observe how water gets into and comes out of the air.

Materials
- chalkboard and chalk
- two paper towels
- water
- clock with second hand
- heat source—lamp
- beaker
- plate or saucer
- tongs
- Bunsen burner
- tripod
- wire gauze
- safety glasses
- hot pad

Procedure

Part A
1. With chalk, draw two 15-cm squares on a blackboard. Do not draw them close together or near an air vent in the room.
2. Using wet paper towels, you and your laboratory partner should moisten the two squares at the same time. Make certain each square is thoroughly soaked. Note and record the time.
3. Fan one moistened square with a cardboard or book until it is completely dry. Record how long it took the square to dry. Touch the dried square and the blackboard around it. Record any temperature difference you notice.
4. Record the time it takes for the unfanned square to dry.
5. Repeat steps 1 and 2. This time use a heat source, such as sunlight, a heat lamp, or a desk lamp, to dry one of the moistened squares.
6. Once again, note the drying time for each square.

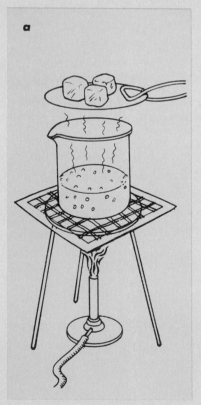

a

Part B
1. Set up a Bunsen burner, wire gauze, and tripod, as shown in *a*. Fill a beaker one-third full with water. Light the burner and bring the water to a boil. *CAUTION: Be very careful when working with fire and boiling water. Wear safety glasses for Part B.*
2. Place 3 or 4 ice cubes on a plate or saucer. Using tongs, hold the saucer above the boiling water for about 2 minutes, as shown.
3. Observe what is happening between the bottom of the saucer and the beaker. Record your observations. Turn off the burner. Use the hot pad to pick up the beaker and pour out the hot water.

Analysis
1. Name the process that you observed in Part A. Explain what happened.
2. Name two factors found on earth that speed up drying time.
3. Name two home appliances that use heat or fanning to speed up drying time.
4. In Part B you made a model of something that happens on earth. What is it?
5. Explain what happened to give you the results found in Part B.

Issues in Earth Science

Acid Rain

How would you like to take a shower in lemon juice? Or water your garden with vinegar? That sounds a bit strange, no doubt, and not very healthful. But in many places around the world, that is just what may be happening.

Rainwater is becoming more acidic. It is becoming more like lemon juice or vinegar. Both are weak acids.

Rainwater is normally slightly acidic. But it is a very *weak* acid. It is no threat to plants, animals, or humans. Now, however, some major changes are taking place. In some locations, the acidity of rainwater is increasing rapidly. In parts of Europe and the United States, rain is from five to thirty times more acidic than normal. Water in some rainstorms may be a thousand times more acidic than normal.

Many human activities are responsible for the change in rainwater. Chemical fertilizers release nitrogen oxides to the air. Industrial plants and automobile exhausts give off sulfur and nitrogen oxides.

Both types of oxides combine with water in the air. The products are sulfuric and nitric acids. When it rains, these acids are carried to the earth. Rainstorms become downpours of weak acids.

The picture shows how acid rains can damage the environment. Over 170 lakes in the Adirondack Mountains no longer have fish. The fish were killed by acid rains. Acid rains can damage plants. They kill bacteria that decay plant and animal remains.

There is no easy answer to the acid rain problem. We need fertilizers to grow our crops. We depend on factories for many of the products we use. However, the time has come to control the compounds that enter the air and reduce acid rain.

For Discussion
1. Why is our rain becoming more acidic?
2. How does acid rain affect the environment?

Fish can die from acid rain

17–2

Water Vapor in the Air

Hot, sticky days are uncomfortable. Often people explain this feeling by saying, "It's not the heat. It's the humidity." This section explains what humidity is and how to measure it. Think about these questions as you read about humidity:

a. What is humidity?
b. What instruments measure humidity?

Humidity Is Moisture in the Air

When water evaporates from oceans, rivers, or lakes, it becomes water vapor in the air. Water vapor in the air is **humidity.** When air feels damp, the humidity is high. The humidity is low if very little moisture is present in the air. Long periods of low humidity can dry your skin and make your lips crack.

The maximum amount of water in the air depends on the temperature of the air. As shown in the margin, warm air can hold more moisture than cold air. The air at 40°C can hold about ten times more water than the air at 5°C.

Air is **saturated** (sach′ə rā′tid) if it contains all the water it can hold at that temperature. The **relative humidity** given in weather reports is the percentage of saturation. A relative humidity of 60%, as shown in the diagram below, means the air is holding 60% of the water it can hold at that temperature.

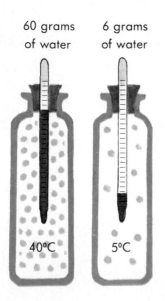

60 grams of water   6 grams of water

40°C   5°C

Equal volumes of air at the same temperature

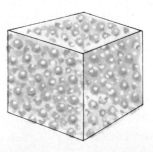

100% relative humidity

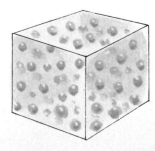

60% relative humidity

What happens when saturated air is cooled? The excess water vapor in the air condenses into drops of water. The **dew point** is the temperature at which these drops begin to appear. The drops of water appeared on the cold glass in the picture when the air next to the glass reached its dew point.

Water vapor condenses at the dew point

Measuring Humidity

One way to measure humidity is to measure changes caused by humidity. Wood, skin, and hair expand as they absorb moisture in the air. If wooden doors or drawers stick in hot, humid weather, you can blame the humidity.

A person's hair looks and behaves differently in rainy and dry weather. A blond hair that is 40 centimeters long can stretch as much as 1 centimeter as the relative humidity moves from 0% to 100%. The **hair hygrometer** (hī grom′ə tər), shown in the margin, is one tool for measuring humidity. One or more human hairs are attached to a pointer. As the hairs change length in response to moisture, the pointer moves.

A **sling psychrometer** (sī krom′ə tər), shown in the picture below, is an excellent tool for measuring relative humidity. The bulb, or rounded end, of one thermometer is covered with a wet cloth. After the thermometers are swung through the air, the wet bulb temperature is lower than the dry bulb. The water evaporating from the cloth lowers the temperature of the wet bulb because evaporation is a cooling process. The relative humidity can then be read from a chart, using the temperature difference between the wet and dry bulbs.

Hair hygrometer

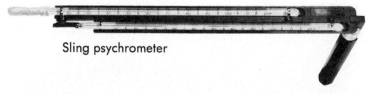

Sling psychrometer

Review It

1. Explain saturated air in terms of relative humidity.
2. Why is hair useful for measuring humidity?

Activity

Dew Point and the Sling Psychrometer

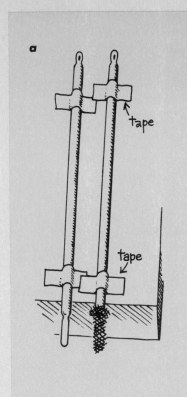

a

tape

tape

Purpose
To find the dew point and the relative humidity of a classroom.

Materials
- empty tin can
- water and ice
- thermometer
- wooden stirring rod
- transparent tape
- 2 identical thermometers
- gauze, about 2-cm square
- thread or rubber band
- piece of cardboard

Procedure

Part A
1. Half fill an empty tin can with water at room temperature. Dry the outside of the can.
2. Gently lower a thermometer into the can.
3. Add two ice cubes, then stir gently with the wooden stirring rod. *CAUTION: Stir carefully so that you do not break the bulb of the thermometer. NOTE: Do not touch the can during the experiment.* Watch the outside of the can for moisture to appear.

4. Add several more ice cubes, stirring as before. Watch the can for changes.
5. When water begins to appear on the outside of the can, note and record the temperature shown on the thermometer in the can. This temperature is the dew point of your classroom.

Part B
1. Make a psychrometer by first wrapping the gauze around one of the bulbs and tying it firmly in place with thread or a rubber band, as shown in *a.*
2. *CAUTION: Be careful because thermometers break easily.* Place the thermometers side by side with the two bulbs just hanging over the edge of a desk or table, as shown in *a.* Tape them to the desk or table at the top and bottom, as in *a.*
3. Thoroughly wet the gauze.
4. Use the cardboard to fan the thermometers.
5. When the temperature of the thermometer with the wet bulb stops going down, record the temperature readings on both thermometers.
6. Subtract the wet bulb temperature from the dry bulb temperature, and record the difference.

7. Look at the relative humidity table, *b*, on this page. The numbers in the left-hand column represent the dry bulb reading (air temperature). The numbers across the top represent the difference between the wet and dry bulb readings. You found this number when you did step 6. The numbers inside the box represent relative humidity.
8. Find the number on the left that is closest to your dry bulb reading. Find the number along the top that matches your temperature difference.

9. Look down the "difference" column and across the dry bulb row until they intersect. Record the number you find at this point. The number you have recorded is the relative humidity of your room.

Analysis
1. What process did you observe happening in Part A when the drops appeared on the can?
2. What causes drops of moisture to appear on the outside of the can?

3. Why is it necessary to stir while adding the ice cubes?
4. Do you think the dew point in your classroom is the same from day to day throughout the year? Explain your answer.
5. Why does the wet bulb thermometer give a lower temperature than the dry bulb thermometer?
6. Why is the difference in the readings of the wet bulb and dry bulb thermometers zero when the relative humidity is 100%?
7. Was the relative humidity in your room high or low? Suggest ways that you can raise or lower the relative humidity in a room to make it more comfortable.

b

Relative humidity table (shown in %)

Dry bulb	Difference between wet and dry bulb readings in Celsius degrees									
C	1	2	3	4	5	6	7	8	9	10
10	88	77	66	55	44	34	24	15	6	
11	89	78	67	56	46	36	27	18	9	
12	89	78	68	58	48	39	29	21	12	
13	89	79	69	59	50	41	32	22	15	7
14	90	79	70	60	51	42	34	26	18	10
15	90	80	71	61	53	44	36	27	20	13
16	90	81	71	63	54	46	38	30	23	15
17	90	81	72	64	55	47	40	32	25	18
18	91	82	73	65	57	49	41	34	27	20
19	91	82	74	65	58	50	43	36	29	22
20	91	83	74	67	59	53	46	39	32	26
21	91	83	75	67	60	53	46	39	32	26
22	92	83	76	68	61	54	47	40	34	28
23	92	84	76	69	62	55	48	42	36	30
24	92	84	77	69	62	56	49	43	37	31
25	92	84	77	70	63	57	50	44	39	33

17–3
Clouds

Clouds are easy to make. When you see your breath on a cold day, you have made a cloud. The water vapor that you exhale condenses when it meets cold air. The answers to the questions below will help you understand more about clouds.

a. How do clouds form?

b. How are clouds described by shape and height?

How Clouds Form

In order for clouds to form, air must be cooled below its dew point. This can happen in several ways. On the left, the picture below shows the sun heating the ground and the air near it. When air is heated, it expands, becomes lighter than surrounding air, and rises. As air expands, it cools. Water vapor condenses when moist air is cooled. The vapor condenses around tiny specks of dust, smoke, or salt from oceans. Each speck becomes a tiny droplet. The droplets are so small that they float in the air. Huge numbers of droplets make up a cloud.

Another way clouds form is shown on the right in the picture. Moist air is forced upward as it passes over a mountain. If the air is chilled enough as it goes up the mountain, clouds form. The clouds pictured on the first page of the chapter developed in this way.

Fog is a low cloud. It forms when moist air near the ground is chilled below its dew point. On a clear night, for example, the ground gets cold when it radiates a great deal of heat. Water vapor condenses into droplets of fog when air near the cold ground is chilled.

Two ways that clouds form

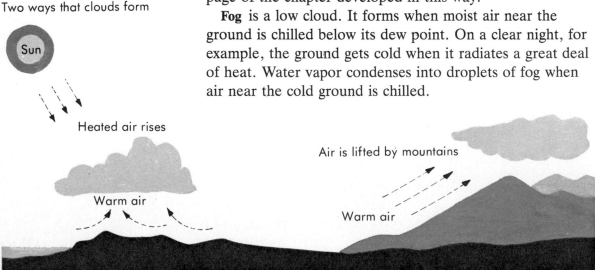

Sun

Heated air rises

Warm air

Air is lifted by mountains

Warm air

Cumulus

Stratus

Cirrus

The Shape and Height of Clouds

Clouds come in many shapes. The pictures above show two common cloud shapes. First, fluffy or lumpy clouds are called **cumulus** (kyü′myə ləs) clouds. Second, spread-out, layered clouds are **stratus** (strā′təs) clouds.

Notice on the diagram that clouds are also grouped as low, middle, or high clouds. On overcast days, low stratus clouds often spread across the sky, blotting out the sunlight. **Cirrus** (sir′əs) clouds, also shown in a photograph above, form at high altitudes above the ground. They are thin feathery-looking clouds made of ice crystals. Big, heaped-up cumulus clouds may extend through all cloud levels, from low to high altitudes.

The term **nimbus** (nim′bəs) added to a cloud's name means rain. A **cumulonimbus** (kyü′myə lō nim′bəs) is a huge, black rain cloud that often produces an electrical storm. **Nimbostratus** (nim′bō strā′təs) are spread-out dark rain clouds that may cover the whole sky. They bring long, steady rains.

Jet trails from high-flying airplanes are artificial cirrus clouds. Some meteorologists think that many jet trails could change our weather, making it rainier or warmer.

Review It

1. What causes clouds to form near mountains?
2. What are two kinds of information used to describe clouds?

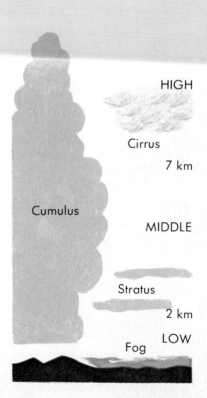

Cumulus

Cirrus

HIGH

7 km

MIDDLE

Stratus

2 km

Fog

LOW

335

17–4
Types of Precipitation

People in Kansas headed for shelter in September 1970, when hailstones as big as grapefruit fell during a storm. The noise of the hailstones hitting buildings and pavement sounded like bombs exploding. Hailstones as large as grapefruit are unusual. But smaller hailstones and other types of precipitation are not unusual. Think about this question as you read:

What are the different kinds of precipitation?

Precipitation

All forms of moisture that fall from the air to the ground are called **precipitation** (prē sip ə tā′shən). Moisture falls as **snow, rain, freezing rain, sleet,** and **hail.**

Rain and Snow Some clouds are made entirely of water droplets because the air temperature within the cloud is above freezing. Clouds of this type are common from the equator to about 30° north and south latitudes. Precipitation from these clouds falls as rain.

On the other hand, clouds that form over much of the earth extend above the freezing level in the sky, where the air is colder than 0°C. As a result, these clouds are made of water droplets and tiny ice crystals.

As air moves within these clouds, the ice crystals and water drops sometimes collide. Water drops then freeze around the ice crystals. When the ice crystals become too heavy to remain in the air, they fall from the cloud. If the air temperature beneath the cloud is above freezing, the precipitation falls as rain. If the air temperature beneath the cloud is below freezing, the precipitation falls as snow.

Each snowflake is one or more crystals of ice. The picture shows that snowflakes have six sides. Snowflakes contain so much air that, on the average, a 10-centimeter snowfall melts into 1 centimeter of water! You can use a meter stick to measure the depth of level, undrifted snow. The **rain gauge** (gāj), shown in the margin, measures the depth of rainfall. You can make a rain gauge with a bucket and a ruler.

Snowflakes

Rain gauge

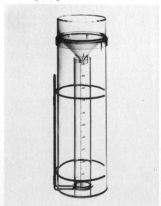

Freezing Rain   Sometimes rain falls through air that is below 0°C, but the rain does not freeze until it hits the ground or any solid object. The result is freezing rain. The photograph shows what an ice storm of freezing rain does to objects on the ground.

Sleet   Sleet is ice pellets that form when rain freezes as it falls through the air. Sleet also forms when snow melts as it falls and then refreezes. Sleet makes a noise and even bounces as it hits hard ground or buildings.

Hail   Hail or hailstones are balls or lumps of ice. These balls of ice form within cumulonimbus, or storm clouds. Hailstones start as ice crystals. Strong winds toss these crystals up and down within a cloud, as shown in the diagram. As they go up and down, drops of water freeze around the ice crystals. This process makes the onionlike layers that you see in the photograph. In severe storms, strong winds can hold the hailstones in the cloud until they grow very heavy. The average hailstone is about the size of a pea, but hailstones may get much larger.

Freezing rain

Hailstone

Review It

1. Why is the temperature within and beneath a cloud important?
2. Describe five types of precipitation.

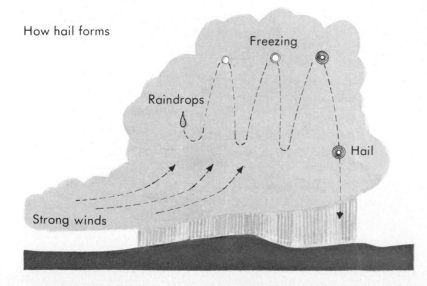
How hail forms
Freezing
Raindrops
Hail
Strong winds

Have You Heard?

Baseball- and softball-sized hail occur frequently in "Hail Alley," which includes portions of northeast Colorado and southeast Wyoming.

Chapter Summary

- Water on earth occurs as liquid water, water vapor, and ice. (17–1)

- Water changes form in the processes of evaporation and condensation. (17–1)

- Water circulates between the air and ground in the water cycle. (17–1)

- Humidity is the water vapor in the air. Relative humidity indicates the amount of water vapor present in the air compared to the greatest amount the air can hold at that temperature. (17–2)

- The hair hygrometer and the sling psychrometer are instruments that measure relative humidity. (17–2)

- Clouds are condensed water vapor or ice crystals in the air. They form when air is cooled as it rises or is lifted. (17–3)

- A cloud is described by its shape and altitude above the ground. (17–3)

- Precipitation is moisture in the air that falls to the ground as rain, snow, hail, or sleet. (17–4)

Interesting Reading

Graves, C. K. "Rain of Troubles." *Science 80,* July/August 1980, pages 75–79. Describes acid rain and the problems it brings.

Milgrom, Harry. *Understanding Weather.* Crowell-Collier, 1970. Includes a good explanation of the water cycle and of cloud classification.

Questions/Problems

1. Explain why a piece of bread gets very hard when it is left out on a table overnight.

2. Why do the windows inside a car "fog up" when several people are riding in a car on a cold day?

3. Give three examples of changes around your home that are probably due to high or low humidity.

4. How can you raise a volume of air from 75% to 100% relative humidity?

5. How do particles of salt and dust in the air affect the formation of clouds?

6. Predict the difference in wet and dry bulb temperatures when a sling psychrometer is used in saturated air.

7. Think of a way to prove that there is water vapor even in dry desert air.

Extra Research

1. Pack a tall tin can with alternate layers of ice and salt, using twice as much ice as salt. Describe any changes that you observe. Explain what happened.

2. Many clouds have a name that is in two parts. The first part usually tells the altitude of the cloud. The second part describes the shape. Look up "cloud" in an encyclopedia. Make your own cloud chart that shows name, cloud level, a description, a drawing, and the type of weather associated with each cloud.

3. Twice each day for thirty days, observe and record the weather and the types of clouds that you see. Predict the weather that goes with each cloud type. Hand in your record and conclusions.

Chapter Test

A. Vocabulary   Write the numbers 1–10 on a piece of paper.
Match the definition in Column I with the term it defines in Column II.

Column I

1. the process in which a liquid changes into a gas

2. the process in which a gas changes into a liquid

3. temperature at which the air is saturated

4. a measure expressed in percent of the amount of moisture in the air

5. instrument for measuring humidity, consisting of two thermometers

6. flat, layered cloud

7. heaped-up cloud that may extend from low to high altitudes above the earth

8. thin, featherlike cloud made of ice crystals

9. ice pellets that form when rain freezes on its way to the ground

10. balls of ice that form during thunderstorms

Column II

a. cirrus

b. condensation

c. cumulus

d. dew point

e. evaporation

f. hail

g. relative humidity

h. sleet

i. sling psychrometer

j. stratus

B. Multiple Choice   Write the numbers 1–10 on your paper.
Choose the letter that best completes the statement or answers the question.

1. Clouds may form when   a) warm, moist air rises.   b) cool, moist air sinks.   c) moist, cool air glides down a mountain.   d) b and c.

2. Hailstones   a) are associated with thunderstorms.   b) freeze when they hit the ground. c) are layered inside.   d) a and c.

3. The main key to the water cycle is energy from the   a) sun.   b) clouds.   c) wind. d) rain.

4. Laundry hanging out in the sun soon dries because of   a) precipitation.   b) evaporation. c) condensation.   d) saturation.

5. Most of the earth's water is in the form of a) water vapor.   b) glaciers.   c) liquid.   d) a solid.

6. A cloud that forms next to the ground is called   a) cirrus.   b) cumulus.   c) fog. d) nimbus.

7. Low, spread-out clouds that produce prolonged rain or snow are   a) nimbostratus. b) stratocumulus.   c) cirrocumulus. d) cumulonimbus.

8. A rain gauge may be made of   a) a bundle of hairs.   b) two thermometers.   c) a bucket and a ruler.   d) a, b, and c.

9. When air contains all the water vapor it can hold at that temperature   a) the relative humidity is 100%.   b) the air is saturated. c) the air has reached its dew point.   d) a, b, and c.

10. One cubic meter of air contains 8 grams of water vapor. This air is saturated when it contains 24 grams of water vapor. The relative humidity of the volume of air is   a) 33%. b) 67%.   c) 42%.   d) 300%.

Chapter 18
Air Pressure and Winds

Hang gliding is exciting, but dangerous. The person in the picture has just soared off the cliff above. The flyer is hoping to catch a "thermal," which is a column of warm rising air. The thermal will lift the hang glider and prolong the ride. Good hang glider pilots know a great deal about air and how it moves.

This chapter begins with an explanation of air pressure and the instruments used to measure it. Next it describes winds of different kinds. This chapter will give you a basic understanding of how air circulates around the globe.

Chapter Objectives

1. Describe air pressure and the units used to indicate air pressure.
2. Describe two instruments that measure air pressure.
3. Briefly explain three forces that determine what direction the winds blow.
4. Name the instruments that measure wind direction and speed.
5. Identify the global winds and jet streams and tell where they are found.
6. Give two examples of local winds.

18–1
Air Pressure

What part of the weather report interests you the most? If you are like many people, you are interested in how hot or cold it will be tomorrow and whether it will rain or snow. Few people wonder about air pressure. Yet air pressure is a very important part of our weather. As you read, try to answer these questions about air pressure:

a. What is air pressure?
b. What instruments and units are used to measure air pressure?

Understanding Air Pressure

You can use a bicycle pump to fill a basketball with air. The basketball inflates because the air you pump into it pushes against the insides of the basketball, as shown in the diagram. This push of air is called **air pressure.**

Air in the atmosphere exerts pressure too. At sea level, air pushes down on the earth's surface with a pressure of about one kilogram per square centimeter. Notice in the diagram that the air in the cells of your body pushes out with the same pressure that the air around you pushes in. The inside and outside pressures are equal. Therefore, you do not feel the pressure of the air.

The average weight of air at sea level is the standard for air pressure everywhere on earth. We need a standard because air pressure rarely remains the same. It can vary daily, even at one location.

Challenge!

Explain why a bicycle or automobile tire collapses when it is punctured by a nail or a piece of glass.

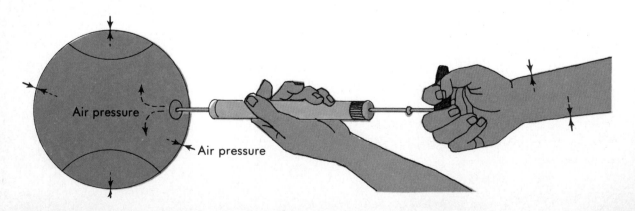

Air pressure

← Air pressure

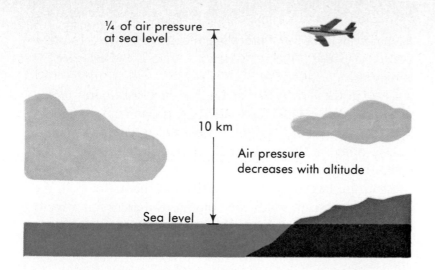

¼ of air pressure at sea level

10 km

Air pressure decreases with altitude

Sea level

Altitude affects air pressure. As you rise higher in the atmosphere, air pressure is less because there is less air above you pushing down. Therefore, the weight of the air and air pressure are greatest near the earth. The pull of gravity keeps three-fourths of the air molecules within 10 kilometers of the earth. Many commercial jets fly 10 kilometers above sea level, as shown in the diagram. Air pressure at this height is one-fourth of the pressure at sea level. Airplane cabins have air added to "pressurize" them. Passengers need this higher air pressure for comfort and safety.

The average air pressure at any place on the earth's surface depends on the altitude. Albuquerque, New Mexico, is 1,620 meters (5,314 feet) above sea level. Omaha, Nebraska, is only 299 meters (982 feet) above sea level. The layer of air is thicker over Omaha than it is over Albuquerque. Therefore, the average air pressure in Omaha is higher than it is in Albuquerque.

You may not be aware of how air pressure changes with altitude. But your body responds to even small changes. For instance, the air pressure decreases as an elevator rises. When you ride in a rapidly rising elevator, your ears pop. They pop because they are adjusting to the drop in air pressure.

Have You Heard?

When you suck on a straw, you pull some air out of it. The air pressure pushing down on the liquid inside the glass is then greater than the air pressure inside the straw. As a result, the liquid rises up the straw.

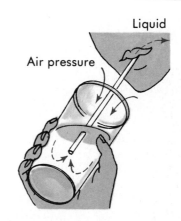

Liquid

Air pressure

Barometers and Units Used to Measure Air Pressure

A **barometer** (bə rom′ə tər) is an instrument used to measure air pressure. One very accurate type is the **mercury barometer.**

Look at the illustration of the mercury barometer to see how it works. A long glass tube that is open at one end is filled with mercury. The tube is placed, open end down, in a dish. Some of the mercury flows out of the tube into the dish, leaving a space with no air at the top of the tube. Air pressure pushes down on the surface of the mercury in the dish. This pressure holds the column of mercury at a certain height inside the tube. If air pressure decreases, the column of mercury falls. If air pressure increases, the column rises.

The standard height of a mercury column at sea level is 76.0 centimeters (29.92 inches). Changes in the height of the mercury column mean changes in air pressure. These changes are useful for predicting weather. A falling barometer often means that rain and stormy conditions are ahead. A rising barometer often means that fair weather is coming.

Weather forecasters on radio and television often report air pressure in units called **millibars** (mil′ə barz). Millibars indicate how much the air actually presses on the surface of the earth. Standard sea level air pressure is 1013.25 millibars (mb). The table lists the units ordinarily used for air pressure.

Mercury barometer

No air

76 cm of mercury

Air pressure   Air pressure

Air pressure at sea level

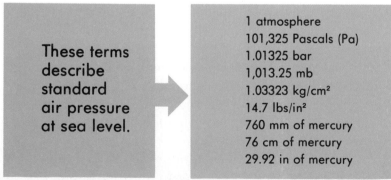

These terms describe standard air pressure at sea level.

1 atmosphere
101,325 Pascals (Pa)
1.01325 bar
1,013.25 mb
1.03323 kg/cm²
14.7 lbs/in²
760 mm of mercury
76 cm of mercury
29.92 in of mercury

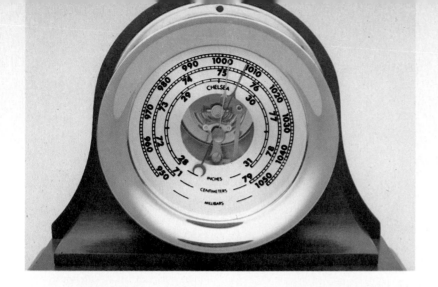

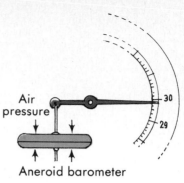

Air pressure

Aneroid barometer

You may have seen another kind of barometer, called an **aneroid** (an′ə roid′) **barometer,** in your home or at school. The aneroid barometer is a metal can with most of the air removed. An aneroid barometer acts like an accordion. It expands when air pressure goes down, and it contracts when air pressure goes up. As air pressure changes, the can changes shape. The diagram shows how a pointer attached to the can indicates the pressure reading on a scale.

Most aneroid barometers have numbers on the dial that range from 28 to 31. These numbers represent what the height of a mercury column would be in inches.

Some aneroid barometers give the air pressure reading in three different units. Examine the dial of the barometer in the picture. The long arrow indicates that air pressure is 1007.5 millibars, 75.5 centimeters, or about 29.7 inches.

The short arrow on the barometer does not move automatically. It is set to an earlier pressure reading. The short arrow in the picture is to the left of the long arrow, so air pressure is rising. When the short arrow is to the right of the long arrow, the air pressure is falling.

Barometers are valuable tools. They tell us what the air pressure is and what kind of weather might be coming.

Challenge
An altimeter (al tim′ə tər) is a special kind of aneroid barometer used in airplanes. Find out what it does and how it works.

Review It

1. How does altitude affect air pressure?
2. How are mercury and aneroid barometers different?

345

Activity

Air Pressure

Purpose
To demonstrate that air exerts pressure.

Materials
- drinking glass
- water
- bowl
- 3 pieces of clay, each about 1 cm in diameter
- 2 plungers or other suction cups
- drinking straw

Procedure

Part A
1. *NOTE: Do Part A over the sink or a large basin.* Fill the glass with water. Press the pieces of clay on the rim of the drinking glass.
2. Place the bowl over the glass as in *a*. The clay should separate the bowl from the glass by a few millimeters.
3. Quickly invert the glass and bowl together, as shown in the middle and bottom drawings. Draw a picture that shows the result.

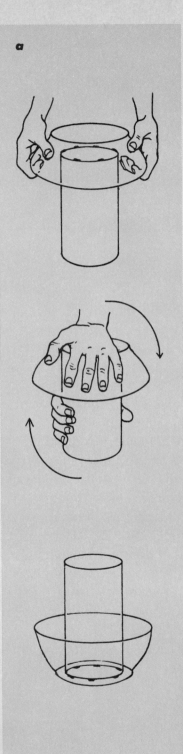

a

Part B
1. Put the straw part way into a glass of water.
2. Put your finger over the top of the straw and take the straw out of the water.
3. While holding the straw over the water, remove your finger. Record what happens.

Part C
1. Wet the rims of two plungers. Place the plungers rim to rim and push them together. When you stop pushing, they should stick together.
2. Try to pull them apart. Record what happens.

Analysis
1. What determines how high the water remains in the inverted glass in Part A?
2. Compare what you made in Part A with a type of air pressure instrument.
3. Explain why the water does not run out of the straw while your finger is on one end.
4. Explain what happened to air pressure inside the plungers when you pushed them together.
5. What holds the plungers together?

346

Did You Know?

Return of the Sailing Ships

Sailing ships are back! It has been nearly two centuries since giant clipper ships roamed the oceans. The invention of the steam engine marked the end for huge sailing vessels. The world's energy crisis, however, has made sails and wind power practical once more.

Some advantages of sail-power are obvious. The winds are free and nonpolluting. On certain ocean routes, winds are dependable most of the time. With these benefits in mind, a number of experimental ships have been built. Tugboats, fishing ships, cargo vessels, and oil tankers have all been fitted with sails. The results are promising.

One of the most ambitious projects has been the movement of oil rigs. In the summer of 1980, a combination sail- and motor-driven tug towed an offshore drilling platform from Texas to Canada. Fuel costs and travel time were less than with a conventional steam-powered ship.

The 900-ton Japanese oil tanker *Shin Aitoku Maru,* shown in the photograph, is the largest sail- and motor-

driven ship used commercially. Compare the sails of the ship in the picture to sails from earlier sailing vessels. A computer on board decides when the ship's sails should be used and how they should be set. The computer automatically directs the sails. The computer also tells the engine when to slow down or speed up. On its first trips, the tanker received up to 53% of its power from the wind and saved nearly half its fuel costs.

Ship designers are working to make computerized sailing ships a success.

For Discussion
1. Why are sailing ships becoming popular again?
2. How do modern sailing ships differ from sailing ships made in the 1800s?

18–2
Why Winds Blow

On a hot summer day in Chicago, people swelter as the thermometer reaches 35°C. Suddenly a wind begins blowing from Lake Michigan, the temperature drops, and people feel more comfortable. As you read about winds, keep these questions in mind:

a. How is air pressure related to wind direction?
b. How is wind measured?

Pressure Differences Cause Winds

Differences in air pressure cause winds. These pressure differences develop when the earth's surface is heated unevenly. When air is warmed, it expands, becomes less dense, and pushes down with less pressure than before. Locally, the area with the most dense air also has the highest pressure. A force, known as the **pressure gradient** (grā′dē ənt) **force,** moves air away from a high-pressure center toward a lower pressure. Thus, wind, which is moving air, blows from high to lower pressure, as shown below.

Because the earth rotates, the wind moving away from the high-pressure centers is turned toward the right in the Northern Hemisphere. In the Southern Hemisphere, winds are turned toward the left. This turning of the wind's path is caused by a second force, called the **Coriolis force.**

You can demonstrate the turning effect with a piece of chalk and a globe. Notice the drawing to the right above.

Have You Heard?

The paths of rockets and long-range bullets also appear to move toward the right in the Northern Hemisphere and toward the left in the Southern Hemisphere because of the Coriolis force.

Pressure gradient force

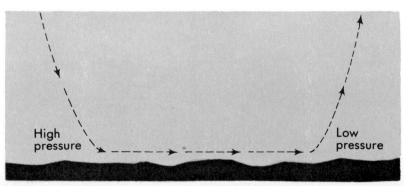

High pressure

Low pressure

While one person draws a line from the North Pole to the equator, another person looking down rotates the globe counterclockwise. The chalk line will curve because the globe is rotating out from under the north-south chalk line.

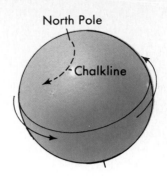

The Coriolis force is strongest at the poles and weakest at the equator. The faster the wind, the stronger the Coriolis force. The rotation of the earth causes a similar turning of east-west winds.

Within the first kilometer above the earth's surface, a third force—**friction**—works on the winds. Friction affects winds just as it affects a heavy box sliding across the floor. The box stops because of friction between the box and the floor. Winds slow down because of friction between the ground and air molecules.

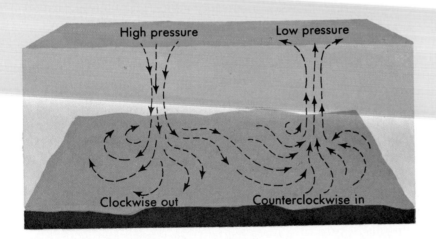

The diagram shows how the combined forces of pressure gradient, Coriolis, and friction affect the direction of surface winds. In the Northern Hemisphere, winds move counterclockwise into the center of a low-pressure system. Winds move clockwise out of the center of a high-pressure system. In addition, wind moves from high pressure to lower pressure.

Another name for a low-pressure system is a **cyclone** (sī′klōn), which means "revolving" in Greek. Another name for a high-pressure system is **anticyclone** (an′ti sī′klōn).

Challenge!

Explain why this statement is true: When the wind is blowing against your back (in the Northern Hemisphere), the higher pressure is located to your right, and the lower pressure is to your left.

Wind vane

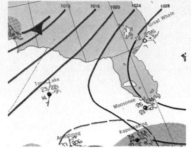
Weather map

Anemometer

Wind Measurement

When you step outside the door on a cold, windy day, chances are the wind is coming from the north. The wind that comes from this direction is called a north wind. Winds are named for the direction from which they come.

The picture shows a **wind vane,** which is sometimes called a weather vane. It is an instrument used to indicate wind direction. Wind hits the large "feathers" of the vane and pushes the feathered end away from the wind direction. The pointer, therefore, indicates the direction from which the wind is coming.

You can tell wind direction by reading a weather map. Meteorologists mark air pressure readings from many locations on the map. Then they connect the points of equal air pressure to form curving lines, such as those in the picture. A line connecting points of equal air pressure is an **isobar.** The closer the isobars are on the map, the faster the wind speed.

The **anemometer** (an ə mom′ə tər) in the photograph is an instrument that measures wind speed. The wind pushes the cups attached to the arm's ends. The harder the wind blows, the faster the arms turn. The wind speed is recorded on a dial connected to the anemometer. The table tells you how to estimate wind speed without an instrument.

How you can estimate
wind speed

Speed of wind in mph	
0	Calm; smoke rises straight up
4-7	Wind vane moves; leaves rustle; wind felt on face
13-18	Lifts dust and loose paper; small branches move
25-31	Large branches move; hard to use an umbrella
39-46	Twigs break from trees; walking difficult
55-63	Great damage to buildings
Above 64	Buildings destroyed

Review It

1. Why does a wind *not* blow directly into a low?
2. What instruments measure wind speed and direction?

Activity

Wind Vane

Purpose
To construct a model wind vane.

Materials
- block of wood
- 2 straws
- construction paper
- plastic lid
- transparent tape
- push pin
- clay
- pencil with eraser
- stapler
- 2 small washers
- scissors
- cm ruler
- compass

Procedure
1. Look at the completed model in *a* as you work through the procedure. Use the block of wood for a base. Put the clay in the middle of the wood.
2. Stand the pencil up by sticking its sharpened end into the clay.
3. Trim the plastic lid until it is a circle about 4 or 5 cm in diameter.
4. Punch or cut a small hole in the center of the lid. The hole should be about as large as the hole in the washers.

5. First thread a washer, then the plastic lid, and finally, the other washer onto the push pin, as in *b*.
6. Cut the head and tail of the arrow from construction paper, using the design shown in *a* as a guide. Staple the head and tail of the arrow between the straws as shown.
7. Tape the straws to the lid, as in *a*. Make certain that the push pin is securely in the eraser but that the lid can spin freely.

8. Take the wind vane and compass outside into the wind or use a fan indoors. Note how the wind vane moves in the breeze. If outdoors, find and record the compass direction from which the wind is coming.

Analysis
1. Name the wind (by direction) that was blowing when you tried your model.
2. In what direction does the head of the arrow point?

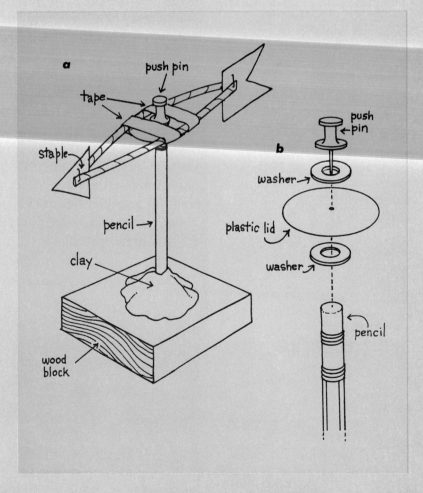

18-3
Global and Local Winds

Global and local winds are as important to today's airplane pilots as they were to sailors on sailing ships many years ago. Answer the questions below as you read about winds:

a. What are semi-permanent pressure features and global winds?
b. What causes local winds?
c. What are the jet streams?

Semi-Permanent Pressure Features and Global Winds

If daily weather maps were averaged for many years, several high- and low-pressure features would appear. You can see some of these features on the diagram. These features are semi-permanent, which means they are present a good deal of the time. For example, low pressure is common around the equator because warm, equatorial air expands and rises.

Oceans around 30° north and south latitudes are usually colder than the continents at those latitudes. The air over the oceans is also colder and denser. Thus, the ocean air at this latitude has higher pressure than the air over the land. This temperature difference between land and water exists through most of the year. As a result, semi-permanent highs are found over the oceans at about 30° north and south. These highs are the **subtropical highs.**

The winds that move toward the equator from the subtropical highs are called the **trade winds.**

Have You Heard?

The doldrums near the equator and the horse latitudes at about 30° north and south latitudes are between wind belts. They are regions of very little wind where sailing ships were often stalled for many days.

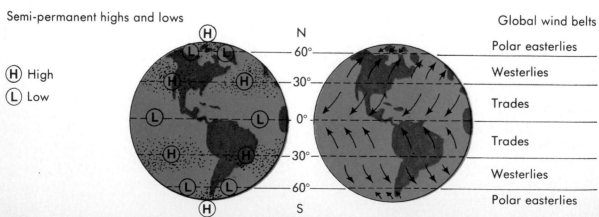

Semi-permanent highs and lows

Ⓗ High
Ⓛ Low

Global wind belts

Polar easterlies
Westerlies
Trades
Trades
Westerlies
Polar easterlies

N
60°
30°
0°
30°
60°
S

The winds that move from the subtropical highs toward the poles are the **westerlies.** As you see in the diagram, trades and westerlies cover large areas of the world. They are global winds.

Oceans at 60° north and south latitudes are generally warmer than the surrounding continents. Low pressure is common over the oceans at these latitudes. These lows are called **subpolar lows.**

High pressure is usually found over the poles because cold polar air is very dense. Air flows from the poles toward the equator—from high to lower pressure. This air flow is the global wind known as the **polar easterlies.**

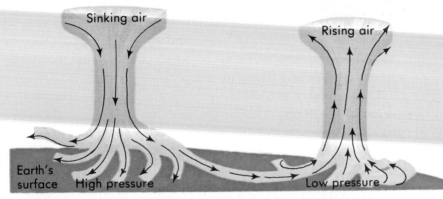

Sinking air

Rising air

Earth's surface   High pressure   Low pressure

Near the surface of the earth, air moves from high to low pressure. Therefore, air tends to accumulate near the center of lows. This air rises from the center of the low much as air rises in a chimney, as the drawing above shows. The rising air cools until condensation takes place, forming clouds and perhaps precipitation. As a result, areas of the earth with lows are often more cloudy than surrounding areas.

On the other hand, air moves away from a high near the earth's surface. It is replaced by air from above that sinks into the center of the high. Sinking air tends to block cloud growth, so highs are typically cloud-free. Polar areas, for instance, are regions of low precipitation. The poles seem to be snowy regions because most of the snow that falls does not melt. Instead, it accumulates.

Challenge!

Locate the major deserts of the world on a globe or map. At what latitudes are most of the deserts found? Can you think of an explanation for your answer?

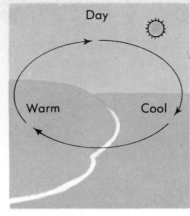

Sea breeze

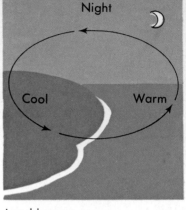

Land breeze

Have You Heard?

Chinook is an Indian name for the hot, dry wind that sometimes blows down the eastern slopes of the Rocky Mountains. This wind is warm and dry enough to melt two feet of snow in one day. The Indians also called this wind the "snow eater."

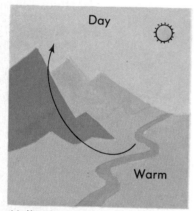

Valley breeze

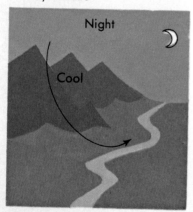

Mountain breeze

Local Winds

At some places in the world, the wind direction is almost constant throughout the year. This is not the case, however, from about 30° to 60° north and south latitudes. One day, the wind may be from the south. By the next morning, it may be blowing from the north.

In addition, some places have local winds that change regularly each day. During the day, the wind blows from one direction. During the night, it blows from another.

Land-Sea or Land-Lake Breezes Land and sea breezes are types of local winds. The diagram above shows how the winds over the land and water change between the night and day. When the sun is out, land heats more quickly than water. The air above the land becomes warmer and rises as the cooler air moves in from the water. This movement of cool air is called a **sea breeze.** At night, land cools more quickly than water. The warmer air over the water rises as the air from the land moves off shore. This flow of cool air is a **land breeze.**

Another local wind develops in the mountains. The diagram to the left shows that during the day the side of a mountain heats more quickly than the valley below. Cool air over the valley pushes down with enough pressure to force air up the side of the mountain. This moving air is a **valley breeze.** At night, the situation reverses. The mountain cools more quickly than the valley. Air flows down the mountain, creating a **mountain breeze.**

354

Jet Streams—Rivers of Air

During World War II, pilots learned a great deal about the upper part of the troposphere. Sometimes pilots in the upper troposphere had problems making progress above the ground, even though they were flying through the air at high speeds. They were the first people to fly against the jet stream.

The **jet stream** is a fast river of air in the upper troposphere. It twists and loops through moving air at heights of 6,000 to 12,000 meters. The speed of these winds may be as fast as 370 kilometers per hour. Like fast currents in a river, they rush through the sky in streams that are up to several hundred kilometers wide.

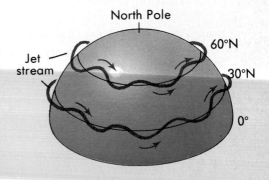

The picture shows the usual position of the polar jet stream over the United States and Canada. This jet stream flows west to east. A second jet stream is usually found at about 20° to 30° north latitude. It sometimes crosses the southern United States. In the summer, these jet streams weaken and move toward the poles. In the Southern Hemisphere, another jet stream flows from southeast Asia toward North Africa during the summer. It disappears in the winter.

The jet stream affects airplanes that fly in the upper troposphere. For example, the flight from Hawaii to Chicago moves in the same direction as the jet stream. This flight takes about seven and one-half hours. But the flight from Chicago to Hawaii, which is against the jet stream, can take as long as 9 to 10 hours.

Meteorologists do not yet understand how the jet stream influences, and is influenced by, the air around it. But they do know that the movements of the jet stream affect our weather.

Review It

1. Name the global wind belts and their locations.
2. What causes land and sea breezes?
3. How is a jet stream like a river?

Chapter Summary

- Air pressure is the weight of air above the earth's surface. (18–1)

- Mercury barometers and aneroid barometers measure air pressure. (18–1)

- Air pressure is indicated by a number of different units, such as pascals, millibars and inches or centimeters of mercury. (18–1)

- Unequal heating of the earth's surface causes winds. (18–2)

- The pressure gradient force, Coriolis force, and friction determine the direction the wind blows. (18–2)

- Semi-permanent high and low pressures exist around the earth. They are present because of differences in temperatures on various parts of the globe. These same temperature differences create global winds. (18–3)

- The trades, westerlies, and polar easterlies are global winds. (18–3)

- Land and sea breezes and mountain and valley breezes are types of local winds. (18–3)

- Jet streams are fast west winds in the upper troposphere. (18–3)

Interesting Reading

Smith, Norman. *Gliding, Soaring, and Skysailing*. Julian Messner, 1980. Explains why gliders fly and how pilots use wind and air currents to their advantage.

"Written on the Wind," *Time*, July 21, 1980, page 59. Discusses the pros and cons of wind power.

Questions/Problems

1. Explain why peoples' ears pop when they ride in aircraft.

2. Would the average height of a mercury column be higher on Mount Everest or at Atlantic City, New Jersey?

3. What is a weather forecaster talking about when he uses the term *millibar?*

4. Why is the force of friction that acts on winds greatest in the first kilometer above the earth's surface?

5. Explain how the distance between the isobars on a weather map may indicate how fast the wind is blowing.

6. Why does air tend to pile up at the center of a low?

7. What proof do we have that the upper air winds are different from those at the earth's surface?

Extra Research

1. Describe what would happen if a window or door of a jet airplane suddenly opened while the plane was flying high in the troposphere. Explain your answer.

2. Look up "wind chill factor" in an encyclopedia. Describe it and give some examples.

3. Find a book in the library that explains how airplanes are able to fly. Report your findings to the class. Use a paper or model airplane to demonstrate.

Chapter Test

A. Vocabulary Write the numbers 1–10 on a piece of paper.
Match the definition in Column I with the term it defines in Column II.

Column I

1. sea-level air pressure

2. any low-pressure system

3. common pressure systems over oceans at 60° north and south latitudes

4. instrument that tells wind direction

5. wind belt from about 30° to 60° north and south latitudes

6. instrument used to measure air pressure

7. causes winds to move from high to lower pressure

8. instrument that measures wind speed

9. common air-pressure system over oceans at 30° north and south latitudes

10. line connecting points that have the same air pressure

Column II

a. aneroid barometer

b. anemometer

c. cyclone

d. isobar

e. 1 kg/cm^2

f. pressure gradient force

g. subpolar lows

h. subtropical highs

i. westerlies

j. wind vane

B. Multiple Choice Write the numbers 1–10 on your paper.
Choose the letter that best completes the statement or answers the question.

1. All barometers a) contain mercury.
b) are easily moved. c) are metal containers
that change shape. d) measure air pressure.

2. Mountain breezes blow a) during the day.
b) during the night. c) from a valley up a
slope. d) when the mountainside is very
warm.

3. The bending of wind to the right in the
Northern Hemisphere is caused by the
a) Coriolis force. b) pressure gradient force.
c) force of friction. d) force of gravity.

4. Jet streams a) occur only in the Northern
Hemisphere. b) do not vary in location.
c) do not vary in wind speed. d) affect
earth's weather.

5. Standard sea-level air pressure is a) 1020
mb. b) 28.2 inches of mercury. c) 78 cm of
mercury. d) 760 mm of mercury.

6. The weather associated with a very rapidly
falling barometer is probably a) fair.
b) slightly rainy. c) cold. d) stormy and
rainy.

7. The way air circulates around the earth is
determined mainly by a) unequal heating and
the earth's rotation. b) the force of friction.
c) rising air. d) sinking air.

8. The force that moves air from high pressure
to lower pressure is called the a) Coriolis
force. b) pressure gradient force. c) friction.
d) a, b, and c.

9. In the Northern Hemisphere, air moves
counterclockwise into a a) high. b) low.
c) cyclone. d) b and c.

10. The polar easterlies and trades are
a) local winds. b) global winds. c) found in
both hemispheres. d) b and c.

Chapter 19
Understanding the Weather

The word *hurricane* may come from an Indian name for evil spirit. The people of Mississippi and Alabama probably think the name is appropriate. Hurricane Frederic swept through this region in 1979. You can see in the photograph how the high winds and rain of the storm lashed the coastline.

In this chapter you will learn a little about what causes our day-to-day weather. You will read about storms that develop between blocks of moving air. You will find out how weather forecasters gather the information that they use to predict weather. Finally, you will read about evidence of storms on other planets in our solar system.

Chapter Objectives

1. Describe four air masses that move across North America.
2. Compare the passage of a warm front with that of a cold front.
3. Explain how highs and lows affect our daily weather.
4. Compare tornadoes, hurricanes, and thunderstorms.
5. Explain how meteorologists gather data and make weather forecasts.
6. Compare storms on Earth with those on other planets.

19–1
Air Masses Affect Our Weather

Television weather forecasters often show maps of weather conditions throughout much of North America. This section explains how weather conditions 1,000 kilometers away from your home can affect you. Answer these questions as you read about weather:

a. What is an air mass?
b. What types of air masses affect the weather in North America?

What Is an Air Mass?

An **air mass** is a giant body of air that has similar temperature and moisture throughout. The mass forms when air moves very slowly over one place on the earth's surface. The air takes on the temperature and humidity of that region. For example, an air mass that forms over snow-covered land is cold and dry. An air mass that forms over a tropical ocean is warm and moist. When the air mass moves away, it carries its temperature and humidity to other regions.

As an air mass moves, it changes. Little by little, it takes on the temperature and humidity of the surface over which it moves. In time, the air mass loses its distinct temperature and moisture features.

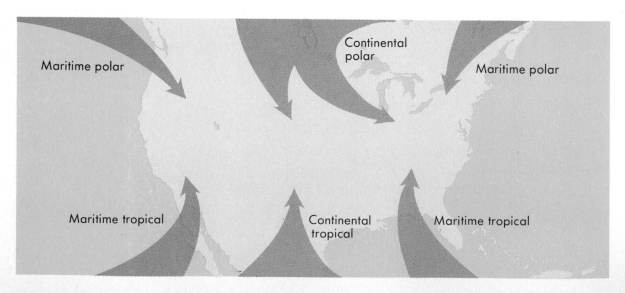

Four Types of Air Masses

Four main types of air masses influence our weather. The map shows where these air masses form. The direction they travel is shown by the arrows. **Continental polar** (cP) air masses form over northern Canada and Alaska. These cold, dry air masses move south and east. They cause winter cold waves in the central and eastern United States.

Continental polar air picks up moisture as it moves south and east across the Great Lakes. The moisture falls as snow. The snow showers on the eastern shores of the Great Lakes come from the continental polar air mass. When the air mass moves farther east, the Appalachian Mountains also get snow.

Maritime polar (mP) air masses develop over the northern Pacific Ocean all year. These air masses bring winter rains to the West Coast. As a maritime polar air mass moves east, it rises over the Rockies and loses its moisture. This moisture becomes the heavy snows that often make good skiing on the slopes of the Rockies.

Maritime polar (mP) air masses also form over the north Atlantic. These air masses generally move eastward toward Europe. Sometimes, however, they move into the New England states, causing *northeasters*. These storms bring strong northeast winds, snow, and cold weather.

Maritime tropical (mT) air masses form in the south. They come from the tropical waters of the Pacific, Atlantic, and the Gulf of Mexico. These warm moist air masses move north. They bring hot, humid days in summer and warm spells in winter.

Continental tropical (cT) air masses are born in the southwestern United States and Mexico. These hot, dry air masses form during the summer. If they remain over an area for too long, drought may result. They sometimes move into Oklahoma and Kansas, bringing warm, dry weather.

Review It

1. Why does an air mass become cold and moist?
2. What four types of air masses affect our weather?

19–2
Fronts and Lows

During World War I, enemy armies faced each other at battle fronts. At the same time, a group of Norwegian scientists used the word *front* in another way. They compared the region separating two air masses to the land separating two armies. As you read, try to answer the following:

a. What is a front?
b. What causes the traveling storms in the middle latitudes?

How Fronts Form

Air masses are always moving and bumping into each other over North America. Cold air and warm air do not mix easily because they have different densities. Instead, a boundary forms between these air masses. The boundary separating two air masses is called a **front.** Like air masses, fronts usually move from west to east.

Fronts form when one kind of air mass enters an area occupied by another kind of air mass. A **cold front** and its weather map symbol are shown in the picture. A cold front is the boundary along the leading edge of a cold air mass that is pushing out a warm air mass. As a cold front nears your region, the barometer falls. The cold air behind the front wedges under the warm air and lifts it sharply off the ground. Large cumulonimbus clouds appear. These clouds often bring thunderstorms and rain showers during the summer.

Have You Heard?

When the air feels cooler and drier after a thunderstorm on a hot, summer day, a cold front has passed through. The air temperature can drop 15 or 20 degrees in a few minutes, because cool air sharply lifts warm air at a cold front.

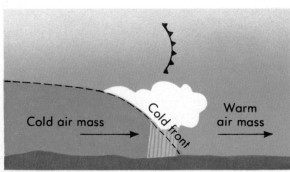

Cold air mass
Cold front
Warm air mass

Cold front

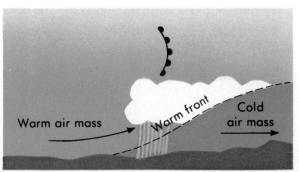

Warm air mass
Warm front
Cold air mass

Warm front

As the cold front passes, the wind changes direction. The weather becomes clear and colder, and the barometer rises again. When the front moves away, the storms end.

A **warm front,** shown in the diagram, is the boundary along a warm air mass that is pushing out a cold air mass. The warm air behind the front glides up and over the cold air. As a warm front approaches, high cirrus clouds appear. These are followed by stratus and nimbostratus clouds. The barometer falls and a long, steady rain or snow begins. Gradually, the front passes and the sky clears. Temperatures rise as warm air replaces cold air, and the barometer stops falling.

Sometimes two air masses will remain over a region for several days. The front that forms between them does not move. This is called a **stationary** or a **static front.** Both terms—stationary and static—mean "not moving." The weather along a stationary front is similar to weather along a warm front—a long, steady rain or snow.

An **occluded** (o klüd′əd) **front** forms when a cold front overtakes a slower-moving warm front. The occluded front is more complicated than the others because *two fronts* interact. Notice that diagram *a* contains both a cold front and a warm front. Colder air is wedging under warm air at the cold front. Warm air is gliding up and over another cold air mass at the warm front. The result of what is happening in diagram *a* is pictured in diagram *b*. The warm air is squeezed out and lifted above the ground. Steady rain or snow falls at an occluded front.

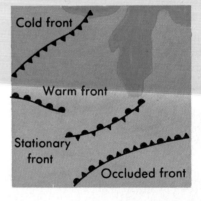

Front symbols

Cold front

Warm front

Stationary front

Occluded front

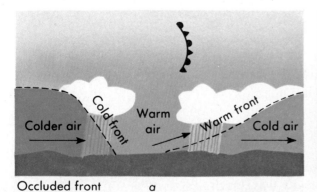

Occluded front   *a*

Colder air

Cold front

Warm air

Warm front

Cold air

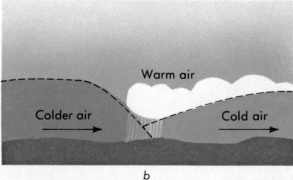

b

Warm air

Colder air

Cold air

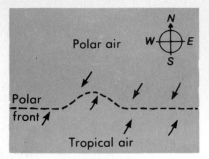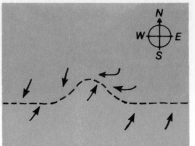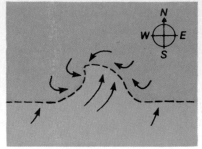

The development of a wave cyclone

Have you heard?

Did you know that you are living under a battle zone? Cold, polar air clashes with hot, tropical air over much of the United States. The moving front that separates the clashing air is called the polar front.

Day-to-Day Weather in the United States

Large high- and low-pressure systems move from west to east across the United States. They cause the changeable weather that is common in many parts of this country.

Cool, dry air masses that form over continents are often moving centers of high pressure—highs. Some highs, however, do form over oceans. You can expect high barometer readings and fair weather when a high is present.

Many large low-pressure systems develop at the **polar front.** The polar front is the moving boundary between the cold polar air and warmer air from the equator. These lows, called **wave cyclones,** start when a tongue of cold, polar air pushes into the warmer air to the south. When this happens, a kink, or wave, develops in the polar front. The diagram shows stages in the development of a wave cyclone. The arrows indicate wind direction.

The wave cyclone moves across North America from west to east along the polar front. The low that surrounds a wave can cover thousands of square kilometers. Cloudy and rainy weather accompany a wave cyclone. This cyclone usually lasts three or more days before it disappears.

Highs and lows sweep across the continental United States regularly. They are very important weather makers in the middle latitudes.

Review It

1. How are cold fronts and warm fronts different?
2. Where do many wave cyclones start?

Activity

Fronts Move

Purpose
To measure the speed at which a front or a high moves.

Materials
• cm ruler

Procedure
1. Locate the front along the West Coast on the map of Day 1.

2. Calculate and record the distance in km that the front moved in one day. Use the ruler and the scale on the map to measure the distance.
3. Divide the distance you found in step 2 by the number of hours in one day. This gives the average speed of the front in km/hr. Record your answer.
4. Find the high in Canada on the map of Day 1. Repeat steps 2 and 3 to find out how fast the high is moving.

Analysis
1. Describe the general direction or path of the highs, lows, and fronts on the maps.
2. Describe the wind direction near lows and highs on the maps. Use these terms: in, out, clockwise, counter-clockwise.
3. What has happened to the north end of the cold front in the West by Day 2?
4. What are the weather conditions in Wyoming and Montana on Day 2?
5. Predict the weather where you live for the day after Day 2.

Day 1

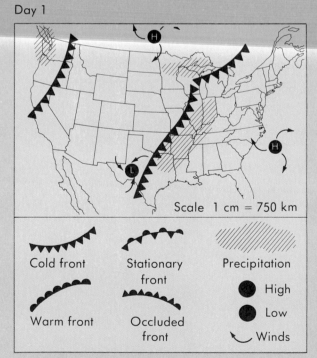

Scale 1 cm = 750 km

Day 2

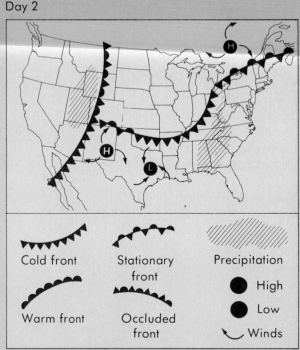

19–3
Storms

People on low-lying islands are often at the mercy of a hurricane's wind and high water. Their houses may collapse in high winds. Some people have even lashed themselves to trees to avoid being washed or blown away. As you read, try to answer the following:

a. What is a hurricane?
b. What are tornadoes and thunderstorms?
c. In what weather conditions do tornadoes develop?

Hurricane—A Powerhouse of Energy

A **hurricane** is a spiral-shaped low, or cyclone, that forms over tropical oceans. The diagram below indicates possible paths of a hurricane. It has no fronts. Instead, it is a mass of swirling clouds, rain, and winds that may reach 240 kilometers per hour.

The picture shows the spiraling clouds in a hurricane that stretches for hundreds of kilometers. In the center of a hurricane is a calm region called the **eye.** The sky is clear or only partly cloudy in the eye of the storm. There is no rain and almost no wind.

As a hurricane passes over the ocean, ships at sea can be in distress for several days. If it hits a coastal area, a hurricane brings heavy rains, high waves, and severe floods.

A hurricane

Have You Heard?

Hurricanes are known as typhoons in the western Pacific, as willy willys in Australia, and as cyclones in the Indian Ocean.

Hurricane regions of the world

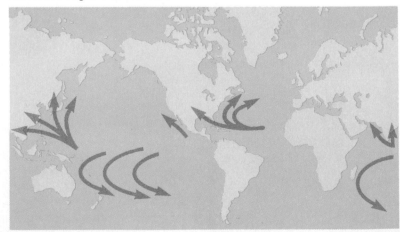

Most hurricanes that affect the weather in North America form in late summer or early fall. Often they move inland over the Gulf or Atlantic Coasts. When hurricanes move inland, they soon weaken and die. They weaken because their source of energy—the heat and moisture of tropical seas—is removed. Friction with the land also slows the storm.

Thunderstorms

Thunderstorms are also common along fronts where air is rising rapidly. The picture shows the lightning and cumulonimbus clouds that are typical of a thunderstorm. Thunderstorms also bring gusty winds and sometimes hail.

Lightning is a flash of light in the sky. It occurs when electricity travels between two clouds, from one part of a cloud to another part, or from a cloud to the earth's surface. The release of electricity heats the air. Air expands rapidly when it is heated and produces the loud noise that we call thunder.

Challenge!
Would you expect tornadoes to be accompanied by thunderstorms? Why?

367

Have You Heard?

Many strange events occur during a tornado. One story says that a chicken swept into a funnel cloud lost its feathers but was not killed. People have even reported "showers of frogs" when frogs lifted from a pond by a funnel cloud were dropped somewhere else!

Tornadoes

A **tornado** is a small but violent cyclone. Tornadoes occur most often from April to June in North America. Hundreds of tornadoes are reported in all parts of the United States every year. They are most common, however, in the South and Midwest.

One or more tornadoes may form and move along a cold front. When warm air along the cold front is pushed rapidly upward, it may begin to twist. A funnel-shaped cloud, like the one in the picture, forms. Funnel clouds are attached to cumulonimbus clouds.

A tornado skips rapidly and unpredictably along the cold front. Winds *within* tornado clouds may reach 500 kilometers per hour. If the funnel cloud touches the ground for a few minutes, it can destroy whole neighborhoods. Then it may rise above the earth and leave the next neighborhood untouched. The extremely low pressure within the funnel causes strange accidents. Tornado reports tell about buildings that explode and straws that are driven into telephone poles.

Review It

1. What happens to a hurricane when it moves inland?
2. What causes thunder?
3. Why is a tornado so destructive?

Issues in Earth Science

Weather Modification: How Far Have We Advanced?

Mark Twain once said, "Everybody talks about the weather, but nobody does anything about it." Now, however, scientists can do something about the weather.

The first real scientific breakthrough in weather control was made in 1946, when scientists discovered cloud-seeding. To seed clouds, dry ice (solid carbon dioxide) or silver iodide crystals are dropped into clouds. Ice crystals or drops of water form around the chemicals.

The goal of most cloud-seeding has been to increase the amount of rain or snow that falls. Scientists do not agree as to how successfully this goal has been met. It is difficult to tell how much rain would have fallen if the cloud had not been seeded. Some scientists think that seeding some clouds might even reduce rainfall!

Some people fear that weather modification may harm the environment. Studies show that silver iodide, which falls with the precipitation, can build up in the soil after repeated cloud-seedings. Silver iodide damages tiny organisms and bacteria in the soil.

Cloud-seeding can also slow the wind speeds within hurricanes. In August, 1969, hurricane Debbie was seeded for two days in a row. After each seeding, wind speeds dropped. But there is some concern that hurricane control, even if it can be achieved, might backfire. People in many places depend on the rainfall from hurricanes for their water supply. They could be harmed more by drought than by a hurricane's floods.

Seeding is most successful in clearing *certain types* of fog from over airports. The pictures show how visibility improved over Elmendorf Air Force Base, Alaska, one hour after cloud-seeding.

For Discussion
1. State one reason for and one reason against cloud-seeding.
2. What are two chemicals used for cloud-seeding?

19–4
Forecasting the Weather

In 1854, a storm smashed a fleet of English and French ships just outside a European seaport. This disaster could have been avoided if news of the coming storm had been known. A few years later, France and England set up the first network to send weather information from city to city. Today we have better networks. We use the information collected by these networks to make up-to-the-minute weather forecasts. As you read, think about the following:

a. How are weather data observed and collected?
b. How are weather forecast maps prepared?

Collecting Weather Data

Meteorologists in over 8,000 weather stations around the world make observations of weather conditions at least four times a day. They record temperature, air pressure, winds, clouds, humidity, precipitation, and visibility.

Reports are made not only by land stations but also by airplane pilots, ships at sea, and radar stations. The weather balloon in the picture carries instruments that record weather conditions in the upper atmosphere. The information is then returned by radio to the station below.

Satellites also give us weather information. They can observe the earth's oceans as well as other areas where there are few or no weather stations.

Have You Heard?

During the 18th century, scientists began going aloft in balloons to measure weather conditions. In 1785, Dr. John Jeffries made the first measurements of temperature, humidity, and air pressure at heights of almost 3,000 meters above Europe.

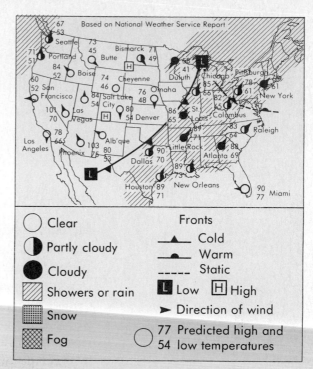

Based on National Weather Service Report

Clear
Partly cloudy
Cloudy
Showers or rain
Snow
Fog

Fronts
Cold
Warm
Static
L Low **H** High
Direction of wind
77 Predicted high and
54 low temperatures

Some satellites remain above the same place on the earth. They send back pictures that show how weather changes from hour to hour. Now we can follow the flow of large weather patterns. This information has greatly improved the accuracy of our weather predictions.

Weather data from satellites and all weather stations is gathered by the **National Weather Service** (NWS). This government agency has computer centers in Washington, D.C., and Kansas City, Missouri. The NWS uses computers to make daily weather maps and forecasts. Television, radio, airlines, and newspapers use the NWS data.

Nearly all newspapers have a daily weather forecast and a simple weather map. Newspaper maps usually show fronts, highs, lows, precipitation, and temperatures. Compare the newspaper weather map above to the satellite picture taken earlier the same day. The map predicts where the fronts will be at 7:00 p.m. Eastern Standard Time. Many newspapers and television stations now carry daily satellite pictures of weather patterns.

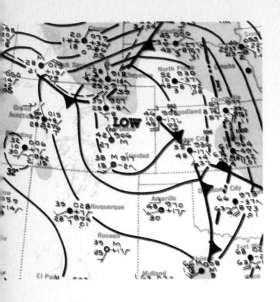

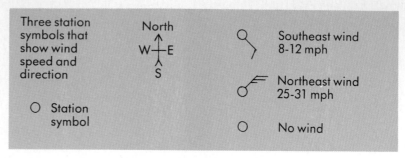

Three station symbols that show wind speed and direction	North W—E S	Southeast wind 8-12 mph
Station symbol		Northeast wind 25-31 mph
		No wind

Some common weather symbols	
Precipitation	**Some types of high clouds**
☰ Fog	⊐ Scattered cirrus
✳ Snow	⊐) Dense cirrus in patches
● Rain	Veil of cirrus—covering sky
Thunder storm	Cirrus—not covering sky
Wind speed and direction	**Some types of middle clouds**
1 to 3 mph	Thin stratus layer
4 to 7 mph	Thick stratus layer
8 to 12 mph	Thin stratus in patches
13 to 18 mph	Thin stratus in bands
19 to 24 mph	
25 to 31 mph	
Sky coverage	**Some types of low clouds**
◯ No cover	Cumulus of fair weather
◗ 2/10 to 3/10	- - - Cumulus of bad weather
◑ 1/2	Stratus of fair weather
◕ 7/10	
● Complete overcast	

National Weather Service Maps

Meteorologists at weather stations use symbols such as those in the tables to represent weather data on maps. Weather stations in every country use the same symbols.

Weather maps, such as the one you see, contain a great deal of information. Closed isobars on the map indicate where highs and lows are found. Front symbols are shown. Each small group of numbers represents data from one weather station. The numbers tell wind direction and speed, dew point, precipitation, air pressure, change in air pressure, temperature, visibility, and cloud cover. Some weather maps contain **isotherms** (ī′sə thėrmz′). These lines connect points on the map that have the same temperature at the same time. Isotherms help meteorologists find the boundaries of cold air masses and fronts.

Weather forecasts are based on many factors. These factors include the speed and direction that highs, lows, or fronts are moving when the forecast is made. Forecasts made by the National Weather Service for the next day's weather are 75 to 85 percent accurate.

If the air conditions change unexpectedly, the forecast will be wrong. The possibility of such change is very likely in forecasts for four or more days. Therefore, long-range NWS forecasts are much less accurate than daily forecasts.

Review It

1. Name three ways weather data is collected.
2. What type of information is on National Weather Service weather maps?

Activity

Reading and Plotting Weather Data

Purpose
To practice reading and using the standard symbols that are found on weather maps.

Materials
• paper and pencil

Procedure
1. Examine the Weather Symbol Table on page 372.
2. Draw a complete weather station map entry for Abilene, Texas. Start by drawing a small circle. Use the Weather Station Model, *b*, as your guide. Convert the information in *a* to weather map symbols.The numbers or symbols on your drawing should be in the same position as they are on *b*. For example, the symbol for type of low clouds should always appear just below the circle. Wind speed and direction is the only symbol that is found in different locations around the circle.
3. Repeat step 2 for the stations at Fort Myers, Florida, and Eureka, California.

Analysis
1. Explain what the weather is like at each of the stations in *a*.
2. Why is the change in air pressure important?
3. What type of change in air pressure would you find at a station where a cold front has recently passed?
4. Find Eureka, California, on a map. Why is it often foggy or rainy if there is a west wind in Eureka?

a

Location of station	Abilene, Texas	Fort Myers, Florida	Eureka, California
Temperature in (°F)	66	60	37
Precipitation	None	Rain	Fog
Wind speed in miles per hour	15	20	4
Wind direction	North	Southwest	West
Dew point temperature	61	64	38
Cloud type:			
High	Scattered cirrus	Veil of cirrus	Dense cirrus
Medium	Thin stratus layer	Thick stratus layer	Thin stratus in bands
Low	Cumulus—fair weather	Cumulus—bad weather	Stratus of fair weather
Sky coverage	2/10	Complete overcast	7/10
Air pressure (in mb)	1012.3	1002.5	1018.0
Change in air pressure (in mb)	Up 1.4	Down 2.8	Down 1.6

b

Weather station model

(Location of station)
City, State

245
30
+ 34
28
Type of low clouds
Dew point temperature
Wind direction
Wind speed
Type of precipitation
Temperature (°F)
Type of middle clouds
Type of high clouds
Amount of sky covered by clouds

Change in air pressure in last 3 hours (mb)
Change in air pressure = up 3.4 mb
Omit decimal point

Air pressure is 1024.5 mb
Use last three numbers and omit the decimal point

19–5
Clouds and Storms in the Solar System

Studying the clouds and storms on other planets will help meteorologists verify weather models used here on Earth. As you read, try to answer these questions:

a. What factors affect the movement of air on a planet?
b. How do storms on other planets compare with Earth's?

The Movement of Air Around Jupiter

The Great Red Spot and the white ovals, which you can see on the picture of Jupiter, are storms. These weather features and clouds are larger and longer-lasting than those on Earth. The Great Red Spot, which is about 10,000 kilometers across, has lasted for more than 300 years. Jupiter's "storms" are actually huge anticyclones. Air spirals out from the center of these features. Small anticyclones and cyclones are also common in Jupiter's atmosphere. The bands of light and dark clouds may be Jupiter's jet streams.

The Great Red Spot

Scientists do not fully understand what causes the air to circulate as it does on Jupiter. The speed at which the planet rotates is important. Jupiter rotates faster than the Earth. A day lasts about 10 hours on Jupiter.

The temperature and density of a planet's upper layers are also important. Jupiter is covered with a thick layer of clouds and has no solid surface.

In addition, the energy that powers a planet's atmosphere affects air circulation. Heat from inside Jupiter heats the atmosphere from below much more than the sun's energy heats Jupiter's atmosphere. This heat may be one reason why the Great Red Spot has lasted so long.

Many Planets Have Storms

Violent storms each spring in Mars' southern hemisphere carry dust around the planet. The storms cover and uncover dark areas with reddish dust, making seasonal changes that we can see even from Earth. Some storms on Mars have a spiral form, like many storms on Earth.

Heavy clouds shield the surface of Venus from our view. The clouds circle Venus rapidly every four Earth days. Spacecraft that went down through the clouds of Venus saw signs of lightning.

Jupiter has many smaller storms in addition to its Great Red Spot. All these storms rotate. The *Voyager* spacecraft that flew by Jupiter also detected gigantic lightning bolts.

The *Voyagers* discovered rotating storms on Saturn as well. By following the storms, scientists could see for the first time how fast different bands in Saturn's atmosphere rotate. When the information is analyzed, it will help meteorologists understand and predict our weather on Earth.

Review It

1. Compare the Great Red Spot with a storm on Earth.
2. Which planets have rotating storms?

Chapter Summary

- An air mass is a large body of air that takes on the humidity and temperature of the region over which it forms.   (19–1)

- A front is the boundary between two air masses.   (19–2)

- Many cyclones that affect our weather develop at the polar front.   (19–2)

- A hurricane is a huge rotating storm that begins over tropical oceans.   (19–3)

- A tornado is a funnel-shaped cloud that develops from a cumulonimbus cloud.   (19–3)

- A thunderstorm is a cumulonimbus cloud accompanied by lightning and thunder. (19–3)

- Meteorologists collect and record weather data at stations around the world. They use the data to make weather maps and forecasts.   (19–4)

- Daily weather maps contain a great deal of information. They list weather conditions, such as wind direction and speed, dew point, precipitation, and air pressure. They also show highs, lows, and fronts across the country.

- Space research has proved that storms similar to Earth's storms occur on other planets in the solar system.   (19–5)

Interesting Reading

Cohen, Daniel. *What's Happening to Our Weather?* M. Evans, 1979. Discusses trends in weather.

Sattler, Helen R. *Nature's Weather Forecasters.* Thomas Nelson, 1978. Describes weather signs found in nature.

Schechter, Bruce. "Hurricane!" *Discover,* October, 1980, pages 15–20, 24. Describes Hurricane Allen and hurricane-seeding.

Questions/Problems

1. Describe the air mass that may have caused the following weather: a northeaster in Maine; hot, humid weather in Indiana; a dust storm in west Texas.

2. How are cyclones, such as hurricanes, tornadoes, and lows, alike?

3. A weather report says a storm is coming. You are advised to board up the windows of your home. Are you expecting a tornado or a hurricane? Explain your answer.

4. Until the 1960s, weather forecasts for Seattle, Washington, were less reliable than those for Columbus, Ohio. Explain why this was true.

Extra Research

1. Keep a daily record of the weather for one month. At the same time each day, record how overcast or clear the sky is, the kinds of clouds in the sky, the current temperature and air pressure, the wind speed and direction, and the humidity. Also, include observations about special occurrences, such as lightning, thunder, or air pollution.

2. Cut out and read the daily weather maps in your newspaper for seven days. Briefly describe the movements of highs, lows, and fronts from the first day to the last day.

3. Write to the American Meteorological Society for information about weather data collection. You can get the address from your teacher.

Chapter Test

A. Vocabulary   Write the numbers 1–10 on a piece of paper.
Match the definition in Column I with the term it defines in Column II.

Column I

1. line on weather map connecting places with the same temperature

2. any low pressure system

3. cold, dry air mass

4. severe tropical storm with winds that may be over 240 kilometers per hour

5. small destructive cyclone that may occur at a cold front

6. boundary between air masses that are not moving

7. boundary that forms where a cold air mass is wedging under a warm air mass

8. makes weather maps and forecasts

9. what is present where a cold front overtakes a warm front

10. warm, moist air mass

Column II

a. cold front

b. cP

c. cyclone

d. hurricane

e. isotherm

f. mT

g. National Weather Service

h. occluded front

i. stationary front

j. tornado

B. Multiple Choice   Write the numbers 1–10 on your paper.
Choose the letter that best completes the statement or answers the question.

1. Maritime tropical air masses form in
a) Canada and Alaska.   b) the North Pacific.
c) the Gulf of Mexico.   d) a, b, and c.

2. Maritime polar air from the North Atlantic
affects weather mainly in   a) the Southern
Great Plains.   b) the Central United States.
c) Europe. d) a, b, and c.

3. When two unlike air masses meet   a) they
always mix together easily.   b) a front forms.
c) the cold air rises.   d) a high forms.

4. Which of the following is found along a
warm front?   a) steady rain   b) cold air
wedged under warm air   c) hurricanes
d) tornadoes

5. A low that develops along the polar front
a) has clockwise winds in the Northern Hemisphere.   b) moves from west to east.   c) lacks
fronts.   d) a, b, and c.

6. Hurricanes are usually associated with
a) two air masses.   b) fronts.   c) flooding.
d) a, b, and c.

7. Weather satellites   a) provide information
about areas with few or no weather stations.
b) radio weather data back to earth.   c) help
locate hurricanes.   d) a, b, and c.

8. Thunder follows lightning because
a) heated air expands.   b) heated air contracts.   c) cooled air expands.   d) lightning
splits molecules of air.

9. What kind of data do weather maps contain?   a) temperature   b) cloud types
c) wind speed and direction   d) a, b, and c

10. The Great Red Spot is   a) a red region on
Mars.   b) the ozone layer of the Earth's atmosphere.   c) a giant storm on Jupiter.
d) caused by the greenhouse effect.

Chapter 20
Climate

Homes like the one in the picture are common on islands in the South Pacific. The unfinished house is elevated to keep people dry during the rainy season and when there are very high tides. The roof and walls of the house will be thatched to let cool ocean breezes circulate through the house. Although thatched houses look flimsy, they are very flexible. They can often withstand high winds better than more rigidly constructed buildings. For thousands of years, islanders have built their homes to take advantage of their climate.

This chapter begins by explaining why there are so many different climates on the earth. Later, you will learn what causes seasons. Finally you will read about the movement of glaciers during the most recent Ice Age.

Chapter Objectives

1. Describe the factors that make and change climates.

2. Explain what causes seasons on the earth.

3. Describe the most recent Ice Age.

20–1

Factors That Influence Climate

Weather is just one thread in a big piece of cloth called climate. Just as many threads woven together make cloth, weather and seasonal changes over twenty years or more make up climate. Answer these questions as you read:

a. How does the angle of the sun's rays affect climate?
b. How does a large body of water change a climate?
c. What effects can surface features have on climate?

The Angle of the Sun's Rays Creates Climate Zones

Because the earth is shaped like a sphere, the sun's rays strike the earth's surface at different angles. The drawing shows two beams of sunlight that hit the earth's surface. If you were standing in shaded area A, the sun would be directly overhead. In shaded area B, the sun's rays would be at a lower angle.

The sunlight gives the same amount of energy to A and B. The sunlight at A, however, is concentrated into a smaller area than the sunlight at B. The surface at A, therefore, is warmer than it is at B.

Places, such as the equator, where the sun is nearly overhead all or most of the time, have warm climates. Latitudes near the poles, such as B, always get the sun's rays at low angles. These regions have cold climates. In the middle latitudes, where the United States is, the angle of the rays varies from rather low in the winter to higher in the summer. The sun's rays are directly overhead in the United States only in Hawaii.

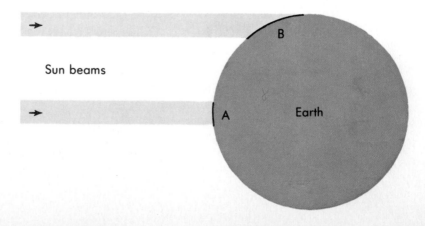

Sun beams

How Large Bodies of Water Affect Climates

The equator is warm and the poles are cold because of the angle at which the sun's rays hit the ground. The change of average temperatures from the equator to the poles is not steady, however. Large bodies of water, such as oceans or very large lakes, have a great effect on climate.

Land near a large body of water often has a humid climate. Water from the ocean or lake evaporates into the air. The hot, equatorial regions around the world are mostly oceans, and these regions tend to be humid. This heat and humidity breed the hurricanes and tropical storms that move across the world's oceans.

Oceans warm slowly and cool slowly. Ocean temperatures in one region usually do not vary much throughout the year. The climate of land that is surrounded by water is influenced by the temperature of the water. For example, the temperature of the ocean water surrounding the Hawaiian Islands changes little from month to month. The Hawaiian Islands, therefore, also experience very little temperature change.

Land, on the other hand, heats and cools quickly. Kansas City is located in the middle of a large continent. This city has great temperature changes between winter and summer. Kansas City has very hot summers and very cold winters.

Climates in the interior of large continents at middle latitudes, such as North America, are not influenced by oceans. Instead, air that comes from the north clashes with air that comes from the south. The continents of the middle latitudes are regions of traveling storms.

Large bodies of water also have warm and cold currents that can alter climates. The Gulf Stream, for instance, is a warm current that flows north through the Atlantic Ocean. Air masses form over the part of the Atlantic Ocean that is warmed by the Gulf Stream. These warm air masses move north to England. As a result, England's climate is warmed. Even though England is as far north as Hudson Bay in Canada, its climate is similar to the climate of the New England states.

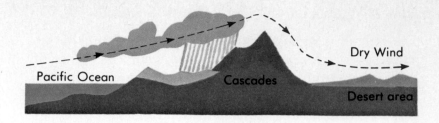

Pacific Ocean   Cascades   Dry Wind   Desert area

How Surface Differences Affect Climate

In addition to oceans, surface differences like mountains affect climate in many ways. For example, the Cascade Mountains run through western Oregon and Washington. Moist winds blow inland from the ocean, as shown in the diagram. When the moist air rises up the western slopes of the Cascades, rain falls. By the time the winds move east, beyond the mountains, the air is dry. Parts of eastern Oregon and Washington, therefore, have dry climates.

Different climates can exist side by side because of differences in elevation. San Bernardino, California, which is at a low elevation, has a hot, desert climate. At Big Bear Lake on a mountain nearby, the summers are cool and the winters are snowy and cold.

Surface differences and oceans can create seasonal winds, such as the **monsoons** (mon sünz′). In the summer, the monsoon is a moist wind that blows from the ocean toward the warm land. The moist air rises when it is heated by the land. The moisture in the air condenses and falls as rain. In the winter, the monsoon is a dry wind that blows from the cool land toward the warmer oceans.

Monsoons bring wet and dry seasons to southeast Asia, India, and parts of north Africa. A weak monsoon system also blows in the southeastern part of the United States.

Review It

1. Why is the equator warmer than the poles?
2. What ocean current warms the climate of England?
3. Why does Kansas City have cold winters and hot summers?

Activity

Climate

Purpose

To explore two factors that affect climate—the angle of the sun's rays and the distribution of land and water.

Materials

- flashlight
- construction paper
- graph paper
- black tape
- 2 containers
- sand or soil
- water
- heat lamp
- meter stick
- 2 thermometers

Procedure

Part A

1. Roll the construction paper into a tube slightly smaller than the glass of the flashlight.
2. Attach the paper tube to the glass of the flashlight with the tape, as shown in *a.*
3. Hold the flashlight and tube pointing straight down at the graph paper, as in *a.* Assume the light is a sun ray and the graph paper is the ground.

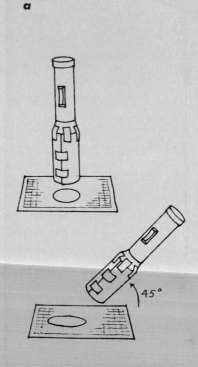

a

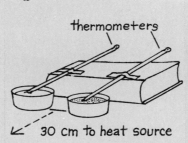

b

thermometers

30 cm to heat source

4. Draw a line around the lighted area on the paper. Count and record the number of lighted squares.
5. Repeat step 4, but hold the flashlight at a 45° angle with the paper, as in *a.*

Part B

1. Fill one container with water at room temperature (about 20°C) and the other with sand.
2. Place a thermometer in each cup, using tape to hold them in place as shown in *b.* The bulbs of the thermometers should be placed so that they are covered by no more than .5 cm of soil or water. Record the temperature of the sand and water.
3. Place a heat lamp 30 cm away from each cup. Record the temperature in each cup 1, 3, and 5 minutes after the lamp is turned on.
4. Disconnect the lamp. Record the temperature of the sand and water after 4 minutes.

Analysis

1. In Part A, compare the light intensity and number of lighted squares in the two trials.
2. Explain why the sun's rays from overhead make the ground warmer than low angle rays.
3. Compare the way that sand and water absorb and lose heat.

383

20–2
Seasons

The climate where you live does not change quickly. The weather, however, may change from day to day, month to month, and season to season. Winter, spring, summer, and fall bring regular weather changes that happen every year. Consider these questions as you read:

a. What is meant by the tilt of the earth's axis?
b. How does the tilt of the axis cause seasons?

The Earth's Axis

The tilt of the earth's axis is responsible for the seasons. The axis is an imaginary line that cuts through the earth from the North to the South Pole. The earth spins on its axis. Imagine that the earth's path around the sun is on a huge flat surface—or plane—like the one in the picture below. The solid vertical line in the diagram to the right below makes a 90° angle with the plane. As you can see, the dashed line that represents the axis meets the plane at a different angle. The axis and the plane meet at an angle that is 23.5° less than a 90° angle.

The Tilt of the Axis Causes Seasons

The diagram to the right above illustrates why there are seasons. From June 20 or 21 to September 22 or 23, it is summer in the Northern Hemisphere. This hemisphere tilts toward the sun. Each square meter of the ground receives more solar energy because the sun is more nearly overhead. The tilt makes the days warmer and longer.

Path of the earth around the sun

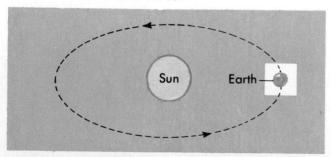

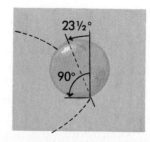

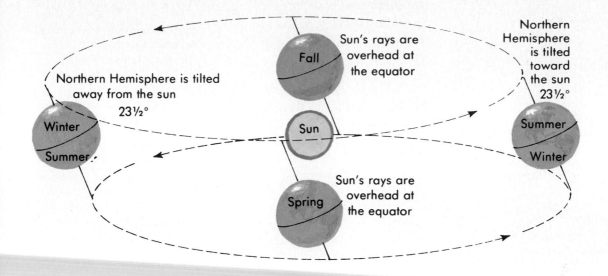

Fall

Sun's rays are overhead at the equator

Northern Hemisphere is tilted toward the sun 23½°

Summer

Winter

Northern Hemisphere is tilted away from the sun 23½°

Winter

Summer

Sun

Sun's rays are overhead at the equator

Spring

When it is summer in the Northern Hemisphere, it is winter in the Southern Hemisphere. The Southern Hemisphere is tilted away from the sun.

From December 20 or 21 to March 20 or 21, the Northern Hemisphere has winter. The hemisphere is tilted away from the sun. The sunlight hits the ground at a low angle and is very spread out. Therefore, each square meter of the ground receives less energy from the sun. When it is winter in the Northern Hemisphere, the Southern Hemisphere has summer. In Australia, January and February are the hottest months.

The drawing also shows both hemispheres in the spring and fall. March 20 or 21 is the first day of spring in the Northern Hemisphere. September 22 or 23 is the first day of fall. The sun is directly above the equator on the first day of spring and the first day of fall.

Review It

1. How many degrees is the axis tilted?
2. Describe the position of the axis when we have winter in the United States.

Have You Heard?

The earth is closest to the sun in January, when it is winter in the Northern Hemisphere. The earth is farthest from the sun in early July, when it is summer in the Northern Hemisphere. The distance between the earth and sun is not responsible for seasonal changes.

385

Activity

Seasons Model

Purpose
To observe how seasons change as the earth moves in its orbit.

Materials
• polystyrene ball
• flashlight
• cm ruler
• straight wire
• protractor
• straight pins
• transparent tape
• paper
• scissors

Procedure
1. Copy table *a* on your paper.
2. You will use the ball to make a model of the earth. Run the wire, which is the axis, through the center of the ball. Measure and record the diameter and circumference of the ball in cm.

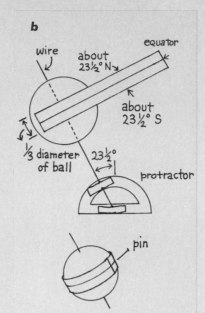

3. Cut a strip of paper to pin around the ball, as shown in *b*. The length of the strip equals the circumference of the ball. The width of the strip equals the diameter of the ball divided by 3. Pin the strip to the ball.
4. Tape the axis to the protractor, as shown in *b*.
5. Put four pieces of tape on your desk or table and label them, as in *c*.
6. Set a flashlight on books in the middle of your desk, as in *c*.
7. Hold your model at position #1 with the bottom of the protractor at right angles to the table edge.
8. Fill in the blanks in *a* for #1, using some of these terms: fall, spring, summer, winter, sun overhead, low angle rays, high angle rays. You will not use all the terms at each position.
9. Repeat steps 7 and 8 at positions #2, #3, and #4. The position of the protractor changes, as shown in *c*. Complete the table as you work. When you are finished, the table should have some blanks.

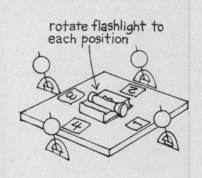

rotate flashlight to each position

Analysis
1. Where and at what season was part of the earth dark for more than 24 hours?
2. Are there seasons at the equator? Explain.
3. Explain what would happen to seasons and climates on earth if the axis made a 90° angle with the plane of the orbit.

a

Season

	1	2	3	4
Northern Hemisphere				
Southern Hemisphere				

Angle of sun's rays

	1	2	3	4
Equator				
23½° N				
23½° S				

Breakthrough

Ideas for the Future

Attention, water-poor countries of the world! Icebergs for sale.Enough frozen water for 10,000 people.
Guaranteed to solve your water problems!

This ad is no joke. Some people think icebergs can be used as a source of fresh water. The icebergs can be collected in the Antarctic region.

A huge amount of ice flows out into the ocean from the ice-covered continent of Antarctica. Ice that formed on land is pure and free of salt. Icebergs from the ocean around Antarctica could be towed to any country that needed water. One plan calls for seven tugboats to tow an iceberg that weighs 100 million tons from the Antarctic to countries that need fresh water. Nuclear submarines could be used to pull even larger icebergs.

Of course, there are problems with this plan. It could take as long as four months to get an iceberg to its destination. An iceberg will melt as it is towed into warmer waters. One solution is to cover the ice with a sheet of plastic. That would keep some heat out and reduce the amount of melting.

Many countries are interested in the iceberg plan. Saudi Arabia, for instance, is very short of fresh water. Some of Saudi Arabia's water now comes from the ocean. But removing the salt from seawater is very expensive. In time, it may be cheaper to tow icebergs to Saudi Arabia than to remove the salt from seawater.

The United States also needs more fresh water. As our fresh water supply gets low, we will be looking for new sources of fresh water.

Using icebergs from the Antarctic presents many problems. But if these problems are solved, the world has a huge, untapped source of fresh water.

For Discussion
1. Why do people want to use Antarctic icebergs?
2. How can icebergs be protected from heat as they are towed into warmer waters?

20–3
Ice Ages

Over the years, the climate in various parts of the world has changed. If you live anywhere in Canada or the northern United States, large masses of ice may once have covered your home town. This ice formed most of Minnesota's and Wisconsin's 15,000 lakes. As you read about glaciers, look for answers to the following:

Where and when did glaciers cover the land in the most recent Ice Age?

Ice Sheets Cover Much of the Earth During an Ice Age

In the past, sheets of ice have covered large parts of the continent. A period during which ice sheets extend over many parts of the world is called an **ice age.** Scientists have studied ancient climates. They believe that the climate has alternated from one ice age to a warm age to another ice age, and so on.

The most recent ice age began about 1.75 million years ago and ended about 10,000 years ago. Often when people speak of "the Ice Age," they mean the most recent one. The map shows how much of the earth was covered with ice. All recorded history has taken place since this Ice Age ended 10,000 years ago.

Have You Heard?

Scientists believe there were also great periods of glaciation 230, 400, and 500 million years ago.

Places covered by glaciers during the Ice Age

Some scientists believe that the most recent Ice Age has not ended. They think we are now in a short warm period between glaciations.

During this Ice Age, there have been at least seven periods of glacier formation in Europe. In North America, there have been four major periods of glaciation. Glaciers also formed in Asia, South America, Africa, Australia, and New Zealand.

At the beginning of this Ice Age, ice thousands of meters thick formed near Hudson Bay in Canada. The map shows that, at one time, glaciers advanced into the United States as far south as the Ohio River. The Greenland icecap is the largest glacier that remains from the Ice Age.

Heavy rains that fell during the Ice Age created many large lakes in the West. **Lake Bonneville** covered about one third of Utah. Eventually, it drained into the Pacific Ocean. All that remains is the Great Salt Lake.

Melting glaciers filled the **Great Lakes, Lake Agassiz** (ag′ə sē), and other large lakes in the Midwest and Canada. Lake Agassiz, which has disappeared, once covered more land than all five Great Lakes put together. Ancient shorelines and beaches are left to remind people that a great body of water was once present.

Many theories have been suggested for the causes of ice ages. One theory is that the weather cools when many erupting volcanoes produce a heavy cloud cover. Another theory states that when the sun puts out less energy, the earth cools. At the present, many scientists believe that changes in the angle of the axis or changes in the shape of the earth's orbit—or path—around the sun may be partly responsible.

Scientists simply do not know exactly what causes ice ages. Nor can they be sure how pollution particles or excess carbon dioxide in the air will affect climate in the years ahead.

Have You Heard?

Scientists have been watching to see if the dust from Mount St. Helens caused any cooling of the climate in the Northwest. A cooler climate could mean a shorter growing season in this rich farmland. So far, the eruptions have not altered the weather.

Review It

1. When did the glaciers last cover North America?
2. What were two sources of water for glacial lakes?

Chapter Summary

- The average temperatures tend to drop from the equator to the poles. Average temperatures depend on the angle that the sun's rays strike the ground. (20–1)

- Surface differences and the distribution of land and water affect climate. (20–1)

- The seasons occur because the earth's axis is tipped 23.5° with respect to its orbit around the sun. (20–2)

- The earth has had a series of ice ages followed by warm periods. Ice sheets last covered large parts of North America about 10,000 years ago. (20–3)

- Many huge lakes developed during the Ice Age. Most of the largest have since disappeared. (20–3)

- Scientists do not know what caused the glaciers to advance and retreat during the ice ages. (20–3)

Interesting Reading

Gilfond, Henry. *The New Ice Age.* Watts, 1978. Raises the question of whether or not a new ice age is coming soon.

Hays, James D. *Our Changing Climate.* Atheneum, 1977. Describes the forces that shape and change climate.

LaBastille, Anne. "On the Trail of Wisconsin's Ice Age." *National Geographic,* August 1977, pages 182–205. Discusses the effect of the glaciers on the Ice Age Trail in Wisconsin.

Questions/Problems

1. How would our seasons be different if the earth's axis were parallel to the plane of its orbit?

2. Explain why all places at the same latitude do not have the same climate.

3. Explain why the hours of daylight in Fairbanks, Alaska, range from 4 per day in the winter to 21 per day in the summer.

4. The height of the sun's path across the sky each day varies with the season. Explain.

5. Which of the large lakes that formed in the United States during the Ice Age remain?

6. How might great volcanic activity cause glaciers to form?

Extra Research

1. List features in your house or apartment that were built or added because of your climate.

2. Write to the electric company in your area to find out how climate affects the amount of energy needed.

3. Write a short science fiction story or play about the return of the glaciers in the year 2050. Describe how humans and animals survive the cold.

4. Write meteorologists at a university, television station, or airport. Find out what weather changes they think might signal the return of the ice ages.

Chapter Test

A. Vocabulary Write the numbers 1–10 on a piece of paper.
Match the definition in Column I with the term it defines in Column II.

Column I

1. seasonal wind

2. continents of the middle latitudes

3. region where the sun's rays are directly overhead

4. region where the sun's rays are at a low angle

5. features that remained when the glaciers melted

6. time when more ice grew than melted

7. caused by the tilt of the earth's axis

8. ice age lake that disappeared

9. weather changes over twenty years or more

10. warm current in the Atlantic Ocean

Column II

a. climate

b. equator

c. Great Lakes

d. Gulf Stream

e. ice age

f. Lake Bonneville

g. monsoon

h. polar region

i. region of traveling storms

j. seasons

B. Multiple Choice Write the numbers 1–10 on your paper.
Choose the letter that best completes the statement or answers the question.

1. Which of the following has definite wet and dry seasons? a) high mountains b) large continents in the middle latitudes c) India d) England

2. Inland areas often have a) hot summers. b) monsoons. c) a climate similar to coastal areas. d) very little seasonal change.

3. Glaciers moved as far south in the United States as a) Alabama. b) Oklahoma. c) Utah. d) Ohio.

4. The tilt of the earth's axis a) is 45°. b) is 90°. c) remains the same throughout the earth's orbit. d) none of the above.

5. The largest glacier that remains from the last Ice Age is a) in Hudson Bay. b) the Greenland icecap. c) in northern Alaska. d) none of the above.

6. The climate in England is warmed by a) its high altitude. b) ocean currents. c) low humidity. d) its low latitude.

7. The amount of the sun's energy received by a solar collector on the earth depends on a) the angle the rays make with the ground. b) the spherical shape of the earth. c) the earth's distance to the sun. d) a, b, and c.

8. After June 20 or 21 in the Southern Hemisphere, the hours of daylight a) increase. b) decrease. c) stay the same. d) none of the above.

9. The climate of Hawaii is probably determined largely by a) latitude. b) how fast water heats and cools. c) land. d) a and b.

10. During the Ice Age, how many major periods of glaciation occurred in North America? a) two b) three c) four d) seven

Chapter 21
Exploring the Ocean

The weather on the earth's surface often changes rapidly. But beneath the ocean, conditions remain the same year after year. The diver in the picture is examining living things around a coral reef 20 meters beneath the ocean's surface. The corals live in shallow oceans that are always warm. Scientists use diving equipment, research ships, and satellites to investigate the oceans. They find out about the conditions under the oceans, living things in the oceans, and resources of the oceans.

In this chapter you will learn about the oceans—their water, floors, life, and mineral resources. You will also read about inventions that help scientists study the oceans.

Chapter Objectives

1. Locate the four major oceans on a map of the world.
2. Define salinity and thermocline.
3. Describe the sediments and features of the ocean bottom.
4. Describe where living things can be found in the ocean.
5. Explain how we get minerals and fresh water from the ocean.
6. Explain how people explore the ocean today.

21–1
Oceans of the Earth

Of all the planets in our solar system, only earth is covered by vast oceans of liquid water. This water is like a thin soup. It teems with living things and is seasoned with salt and other minerals. As you read about the ocean, keep the following questions in mind:

a. How much of the world is covered by oceans?
b. What are the major oceans of the earth?

Oceans Cover Most of the Earth

Oceans cover more than 70 percent of the earth's surface. Astronauts looking at the Pacific Ocean from space see only cloud-covered water dotted with small islands and ringed with continents. The other side of the globe contains almost all the earth's land.

The oceans contain 97 percent of all the water on earth. Rivers, lakes, streams, and ponds hold less than 1 percent of the earth's water. The remaining 2 percent is frozen into ice in glaciers and around the North and South Poles. Water circulates among the oceans, the land, and the air by means of precipitation and evaporation in the water cycle.

Satellite views of the Pacific Ocean (left) and the Atlantic Ocean (right)

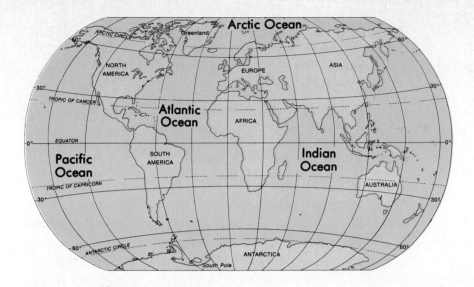

Major Oceans of the World

The water of all the oceans circulates in one vast ocean. Geographers divide this great ocean into four separate bodies of water, as shown on the map. The Pacific is the largest and deepest ocean. It covers more than a third of the earth's surface. Next in size is the Atlantic. The third largest is the Indian Ocean. The Arctic is the smallest ocean. Much of the surface water in the Arctic is frozen most of the year.

Scientists who study the movements of the earth's crust find that the Pacific Ocean is getting smaller. Most of the crust beneath the Pacific is one huge plate. At its boundaries, the Pacific plate sinks under the surrounding continental plates. In the center of the Atlantic Ocean's floor, however, two plates are moving apart. The Atlantic is slowly getting larger because new crust forms at the spreading boundary. The plates of the ocean floor move at about the same speed your fingernails grow.

Review It

1. How much of the earth's surface do oceans cover?
2. Name the four major oceans, from largest to smallest.

Have You Heard?

The Pacific Ocean is so large that all the continents put together could fit into it. It covers 165,200,000 square kilometers.

21–2
Waters of the Ocean

A mouthful of seawater tastes saltier than a mouthful of potato chips. To understand why, you must know about the minerals in ocean water. Keep these questions in mind:

a. What is salinity?
b. How do the temperature and pressure of seawater vary?

Dissolved Salts Make Seawater Salty

Dissolved salts and minerals make ocean water salty. Notice in the table that sodium chloride—common table salt—is the most abundant salt in the ocean. Almost all elements found on earth are also found in seawater.

The ocean's crust is the main source of the minerals in seawater. Water seeps down through pores and tiny cracks in the ocean floor. Minerals in the crust dissolve in this water. The kinds of minerals and their ratio to each other are the same in seawater everywhere. An amount of water equal to the entire ocean filters into and out of the crust every eight million years.

Salinity (sə lin′ə tē) is a measure of how salty seawater is. If you boil away all the water from 1,000 grams of seawater, about 35 grams of salt will remain, as shown below. Only 965 grams is water. The average salinity of the oceans is 35 parts of salt in 1,000 parts of seawater.

In warm, dry climates, such as near the Mediterranean Sea, ocean water evaporates rapidly. The salts that remain make the water saltier than average. Salinity is low where rivers, melting ice, or heavy rains pour fresh water into the ocean.

The most abundant minerals in seawater

	Parts per thousand
Sodium chloride	27.2
Magnesium chloride	3.8
Magnesium sulfate	1.7
Calcium sulfate	1.3
Potassium sulfate	0.9
Calcium carbonate	0.1
Magnesium bromide	0.1

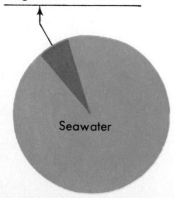

Seawater

Average salinity of seawater

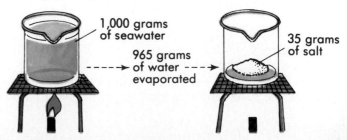

1,000 grams of seawater

965 grams of water evaporated

35 grams of salt

Temperature and Pressure of Ocean Water

Temperature   The sun warms the water on the ocean's surface. Wind and waves mix the heated surface water with cold water beneath it. Notice in the diagram that water temperature is almost the same throughout the top layer of water. The temperature of this layer—the **mixed layer**—is different in different parts of the ocean. At the poles, it is usually colder than 0°C. Near the equator, surface water can be as warm as 30°C. In the middle latitudes, the surface temperature changes with the seasons. The mixed layer is 100 to 300 meters deep.

Beneath the mixed layer is the **thermocline** (thėr′mō klīn)—a layer of water that rapidly gets colder with increasing depth. Seawater at the bottom of the thermocline is very cold. Even near the equator, the bottom of the thermocline is colder than 5°C. The thermocline can be as deep as 1,000 meters.

Below the thermocline, temperatures drop slowly. The freezing point of seawater of average salinity is −2°C. The temperature of deep ocean water is always near freezing.

Pressure   Air above the earth presses on the earth's surface. The air pressure that results can be measured in "atmospheres." Average air pressure at sea level is one atmosphere. In the same way that air presses on the earth's surface, water presses on the ocean's bottom. Pressure becomes greater with depth. Water pressure on the sea floor increases by an amount equal to one atmosphere of pressure for every increase of 10 meters beneath the ocean's surface. Forty atmospheres of water press on objects 400 meters below the surface. Deeper in the ocean, pressures are even greater.

Temperature of layers
of the ocean

Depth		Temperature
0 m		25°C
100 m	Mixed layer	24°C
200 m		23.5°C
300 m		21°C
400 m		15°C
600 m	Thermocline	10°C
700 m		7°C
800 m		6.5°C
1,000 m		5°C
1,200 m		4.5°C
1,400 m	Deep ocean	4°C
1,600 m		3.5°C
3,000 m		2°C

Review It

1. What is the average salinity of seawater?
2. What is the thermocline?
3. How many atmospheres of pressure would the ocean put on an object 6,000 meters beneath the surface?

21–3
Exploring the Ocean Floor

Most people know more about the surface of the near side of the moon than they know about the bottom of the ocean. Answer these questions as you read about the ocean floor:

a. How do oceanographers measure the depth of the ocean?
b. How is sediment brought up from the ocean bottom?
c. What are the features of the sea floor?

Measuring the Water's Depth

Soundings are measurements of the depth of water. In the past, sailors took soundings by lowering ropes with weights. When the weight touched bottom, the length of wet rope showed the depth of the water. In deep water, a sounding was inaccurate because of the water's movement.

Today, scientists find the depth of water by using an **echo sounder.** This device measures depth by bouncing sound waves off the ocean floor. Notice in the diagram to the lower left that sound waves hit the ocean bottom and bounce back to the ship as an echo. The echo sounder measures how long a sound wave takes to reach the ocean bottom and return to the ship. Since the speed of sound in seawater is known, the sounder can calculate the ocean's depth at that spot. As the ship moves, the echo sounder makes a map like the one at the lower right.

Have You Heard?

Since twain means two, "By the mark twain," indicates a water depth of two fathoms or twelve feet. Samuel Clemens, a Mississippi river boat pilot, took the name Mark Twain as his pen name.

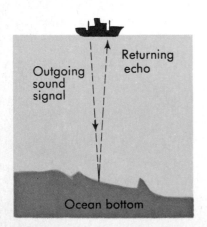

Outgoing sound signal

Returning echo

Ocean bottom

Profile of the ocean floor

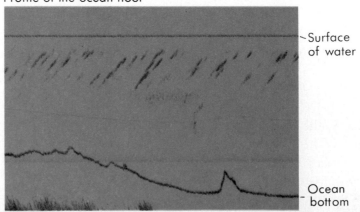

Surface of water

Ocean bottom

A core

Corer tubes

Sediments on the Ocean Bottom

The layers of rock that make up the sea floor are covered with sediments. Near the continents, most of these sediments were washed off the land as sand, clay, dust, or volcanic ash. Far from land, however, many sediments are the remains of organisms—or living things. As sea organisms die, their bodies fall to the ocean floor. Some parts of the ocean are so deep that bodies of organisms dissolve before they reach the bottom.

The deepest sea floors are covered by tiny particles of clay carried from the continents by rivers. The particles slowly drift through the ocean until they sink to the bottom. It can take 1,000 years for two millimeters of sediment to accumulate on the bottom of the sea floor.

Scientists use several devices to gather samples from the ocean bottom. A grab sampler has jaws that close when they reach bottom. It takes bites out of the sediment beneath shallow water. A dredge is like a bag made of steel links. A ship drags the dredge along the ocean bottom. Dredges pick up large objects, such as loose rocks.

A corer works like a huge hollow drill. It brings long cylinders of sediment—**cores**—up to the surface in metal tubes like those shown above. Special research ships, such as the *Glomar Challenger,* bring up cores from beneath the water along the edges of continents. Scientists learn about the history of the sea floor by studying the layers of sediments in cores like the one above.

Challenge!

In seawater, sound travels 1,524 meters per second. If an echo is sent out and returns to a ship in 10 seconds, how deep is the water?

In warm ocean water, a coral reef may grow around a volcanic island. If the volcano sinks beneath the ocean's surface, only the reef remains. It becomes a ring-shaped atoll (at′ol) surrounding a shallow lagoon.

The Features of the Sea Floor

The drawing below shows a side view of the ocean's floor. At the far left is the **continental shelf**—a broad, gently sloping plain near the shoreline. Its width ranges from less than 3 kilometers off the west coast of Peru and Chile to more than 1,000 kilometers off the northeastern coast of Siberia. In most places, the shelf extends about 75 kilometers from the shoreline. The ocean averages 135 meters deep on the shelf. Scientists believe that fast-flowing currents containing mud or sand erode deep valleys—or submarine canyons—into the continental shelf. The Hudson River Canyon, for example, is a deep cut in the continental shelf off New York City.

The slightly steeper **continental slope** begins beyond the continental shelf. It drops to a depth of about 4,000 meters. Sand or mud washed down from the slope may form a gentle **continental rise** at the base of the slope.

The **ocean basin** extends hundreds of kilometers beyond the continental slope. Its depth averages more than 4,000 meters. Low hills, called abyssal (ə bis′əl) hills, cover parts of the ocean basin. If a hill is more than 900 meters high, it is called a **seamount.** The ocean floor is flat where sediment collects and covers the hills. These large flat regions are abyssal plains.

Volcanoes rise from the ocean basin in many areas. Some reach above the ocean's surface to form volcanic islands, such as the Hawaiian Islands. A volcano with a flat top is called a **guyot** (gē′ō). Oceanographers believe guyots are volcanoes that rose above the ocean's surface until waves eroded and leveled their tops.

Side view of the ocean floor

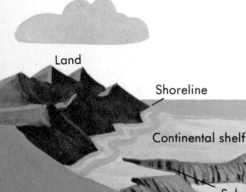

Land

Shoreline

Continental shelf

Seamount

Guyot

Abyssal plain

Submarine canyon

Continental slope

Continental rise

Abyssal hills

Rift

Trench

Trenches are deep cracks in the ocean floor where two plates are colliding. Crust material sinks back into the mantle at the trenches. Trenches are the deepest places in the ocean. Most trenches cut 2 to 4 kilometers down into the ocean floor. They may be thousands of kilometers long, but only about 100 kilometers wide. Deep ocean trenches run around the edges of the Pacific Ocean.

Mid-ocean ridges are mountain ranges that zigzag along the ocean floor. Ridges form where plates are spreading apart. Magma pushes up into rifts—or valleys—that cut through the center of the ridges. This magma forms new sea floor. The Mid-Atlantic Ridge runs along the center of the Atlantic Ocean. Spreading boundaries with lower, less rugged mountains are called rises.

Underwater earthquakes and volcanoes often occur at mid-ocean ridges and trenches. Studies of these ocean bottom features led to the theory of sea-floor spreading. From this theory, scientists developed the theory of plate tectonics.

Have You Heard?

The deepest spot in all the oceans is Challenger Deep. It is in the Marianas Trench in the western Pacific Ocean. It is more than 11,000 meters deep! Challenger Deep is 1,600 meters deeper than Mount Everest, the highest mountain on land, is tall.

Review It

1. How do oceanographers use sound waves to measure the depth of the ocean?
2. What is a source of sediment found in the deepest part of the ocean?
3. Name three types of features on the ocean floor.

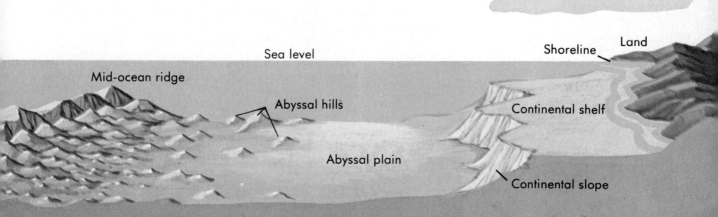

Mid-ocean ridge

Sea level

Abyssal hills

Abyssal plain

Shoreline   Land

Continental shelf

Continental slope

21–4
Ocean Life

When you think of organisms that live in the ocean, you probably think of whales or sharks. But most organisms in the ocean are so small they can only be seen through a microscope. As you read about ocean life, ask yourself:

a. What organisms in the ocean need sunlight?
b. What organisms exist in the dark?
c. How is the ocean important as a source of food?

Sunlight and Ocean Life

Sunlight reaches only about 100 meters into the water. Because plants need energy from the sun, ocean plants live only as far down as the sunlight reaches. Most sea animals live in or just below this layer of sunlit water. Fish, squid, porpoises, and whales are some organisms that swim in the surface waters of the ocean.

Plankton (plangk′tən) are organisms that drift with ocean currents. Most plankton, such as the ones below, are less than 1 millimeter long. They are an important food for many sea animals. Many kinds of plankton make their own food. Some kinds of plankton feed on others.

Plankton

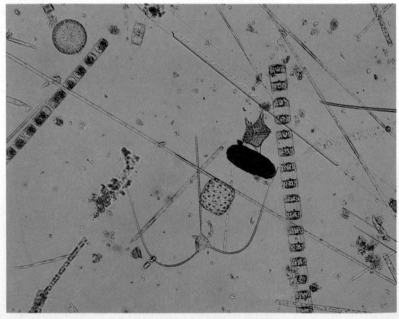

Some fish eat seaweed and plankton. Many kinds of fish eat other fish. These, in turn, are eaten by still larger fish. The relationship among organisms that feed on each other is a food web.

Life in the Depths

The deep parts of the ocean are dark and cold. No plants can grow there and the pressure is enormous. Yet some life exists even in the deepest parts of the ocean.

Almost all complex organisms need oxygen to release energy from food. Surface water contains oxygen from the air and from plants that live in the water. Water sinking from the surface carries oxygen down to deeper levels. Organisms in deep water need this oxygen to survive.

Some fish and other organisms live at great depths and adapt to the pressure. Most of them could not survive near the surface where the pressure is lower. Some animals that live in the depths eat the bodies of plankton and other organisms that die and sink to the bottom. Other animals digest the decayed remains of organisms in sediment on the ocean floor. Still others prey on the living organisms that swim in the cold, dark water.

Have You Heard?

Fireflies flicker like sparks in the dark night sky. In the same way, some animals that live in the continuous darkness of the deep ocean glow in the dark water. Bioluminescence (bī′ō lü′mə nes′ns) is the ability of an organism to give off light. Scientists think the light helps the animals attract food or mates.

Life in dark waters

Food from the Ocean

Plants of the ocean are important as food for fish. But people also eat sea plants, such as seaweed. Chemicals taken from some kinds of seaweed are used to make ice cream and salad dressing. Kelp, an ocean plant, can grow more than 80 meters in height. It is harvested for food, iodine, and potassium.

Sea animals such as fish are an important food for many people. Fish make up 90 percent of the sea life caught each year. The picture at the left shows a day's catch of fish. Whales and crabs, shrimp, oysters, and their relatives are also caught. More than half the fish caught in the oceans are used to feed poultry and livestock.

One way to increase the production of food from the sea is sea farming. The number of fish that live in an area will increase if more food is provided for them. Minerals that plankton need for life could be brought up from the deep waters. Other sea life that eat the plankton could then grow in greater numbers.

Problems arise as people depend more and more on sea life for food. One problem is **overfishing**—or the removal of so many fish from an area that the fish population cannot reproduce itself. Overfishing for just one year means there will not be enough fish for years to come.

Pollution of the ocean is another problem for people who depend on fish for food. Most of the fish we eat live in waters above the continental shelves. Insecticides and toxic wastes wash off the land into the water. Some fish in these polluted waters die, and some produce eggs that cannot hatch. Poisons stored in the bodies of other fish make them unsafe for people to eat. Oil spills from ships at sea or from oil drilling on the continental shelves can also pollute fishing areas.

The day's catch

Review It

1. What are plankton?
2. How do fish living deep in the ocean get their food?
3. How does pollution of ocean water affect sea life?

Activity

How Depth Affects Water Pressure

Purpose
To observe the effects of water pressure.

Materials
- plastic foam cup
- sheet of rubber to cover mouth of cup
- rubber band
- cm ruler
- tank of water
- large cardboard or plastic milk container
- nail
- masking tape
- empty basin or sink

Procedure

Part A
1. Stretch the rubber sheet over the mouth of the cup. Hold it on with the rubber band, as in a.
2. Place the ruler over the top of the cup. Draw or describe the rubber sheet's shape.

3. Lower the cup into the tank of water until the cup's top is 10 cm below the water's surface. Use the ruler to measure any change in the rubber sheet. Describe or draw what you see.

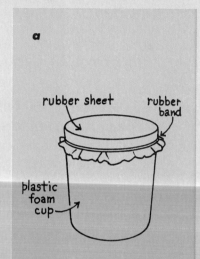

4. Roll up your sleeves. Repeat step 3 with the cup near the bottom of the tank.
5. While the cup is at the bottom of the tank, make a hole in the side of the cup with the nail. Let the cup fill with water. Record what happens to the rubber sheet.

Part B
1. With the nail, make three small holes in the milk container, as in b.
2. Cover the holes with masking tape.
3. Place the carton in the empty basin or sink. Fill the carton with water to a higher level than the top hole.
4. While the carton is in the sink, remove the masking tape from all the holes. Record what happens. Clean and return all equipment.

Analysis
1. Explain the results of Part A, step 3.
2. Explain your results in Part A, step 5.
3. In Part B, why did the water squirt farther out of one hole than the others?
4. How much pressure would an underwater research vessel have to withstand at the bottom of Challenger Deep, 11,000 meters beneath the ocean's surface? (Hint: See page 397.)

21–5
Ocean Resources

Each year, enough sand and gravel is dredged from the bottom of the sea to build a four-lane highway 2,000 kilometers long. The sea is also the source of other products. As you read, think about the following:

a. How can seawater be changed into fresh water?
b. What minerals do we get from the sea?
c. What devices do oceanographers use in their research?

Fresh Water from the Ocean

People use water for drinking, washing, farming, and manufacturing. Seawater is too salty for drinking, and it kills most crops and rusts most machines. The process of removing salts and minerals from seawater is **desalting.**

One way to desalt water is to boil it until it turns into water vapor and evaporates. In the process of **distillation** (dis′tl ā′shən), water evaporates, leaving the salts and minerals behind. The water vapor cools and condenses into distilled water, which is fresh water.

Fresh water can also be produced by melting frozen seawater. When seawater freezes, only about a third of the salts are frozen into the ice. The rest remain behind in the unfrozen water. The salt crystals can be removed from the ice, leaving fresh water.

Desalting uses a lot of energy. In some countries, solar energy is used to desalt ocean water. The drawing below shows a simple way to use solar energy to distill seawater. This method, however, does not produce enough water for use on a large scale.

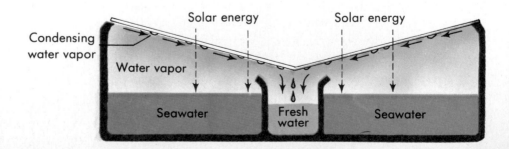

Harvesting salt

Minerals from the Ocean

Many useful minerals are removed from seawater. The photograph above shows one way to harvest salt from seawater. The seawater is gathered into shallow pools. When most of the water evaporates, crystals of common table salt remain behind. Seawater also supplies salts containing magnesium, sulfur, potassium, and bromine.

Minerals are also taken from the ocean bottom. More than ten percent of the world's tin comes from sand dredged from the sea floor. About ten percent of the world's sand and gravel comes from the bottom of the ocean. Many rich oil and natural gas deposits are in sedimentary rock layers in the ocean.

Manganese nodules

Nodules (noj′ülz) are lumps of minerals commonly found near plate boundaries on the ocean floor. They contain mostly manganese, with some iron, copper, cobalt, and nickel. Layers of the minerals can form around bones, sharks' teeth, and bits of rock. Nodules like the ones to the right may someday be a rich source of manganese and other metals. Today, however, bringing nodules up from the ocean bottom is more expensive than mining even poor ores from the land.

407

Ocean Research Today

New devices let oceanographers work deep beneath the ocean's surface. Submersibles are research vessels that operate under water. Some can dive as deep as 6,000 meters. Their strong, thick walls withstand enormous pressures. Scientists inside the vessels can observe the sea floor. Some submersibles do not carry people. Scientists in ships on the surface guide the submersible and operate its instruments. Television cameras send up pictures of the ocean floor.

Some scientists explore the ocean floor wearing diving suits. Rigid suits protect divers from the water's pressure and allow divers to go down more than 300 meters. Other divers, such as the one in the picture, wear flexible suits that allow easier movement. But they can go down only about 100 meters. In shallow water, divers can carry their air supply in tanks on their backs. They cannot dive as deep or stay down as long as divers in diving suits.

Habitats, like the one shown below, are pressurized underwater dwellings. More than 50 undersea habitats have been built since 1969. The habitat *Tektite* is 15 meters under the sea off the Virgin Islands. Some scientists lived in it for 58 days. Others spent 45 days in *Sealab II* off California. Using a habitat as a base, scientists can spend their days exploring the ocean. They study marine life, sea-floor geology, and human reactions to living underwater.

Have You Heard?

Divers in *Sealab II* found that one diver living underwater could do as much work in a 6-hour period as 35 divers going back and forth between the surface and the bottom. One day, research sites or even whole cities may be built beneath the sea.

A habitat on the ocean bottom

Large research ships travel over the ocean like floating laboratories. They carry instruments that gather and record information about water temperature, salinity, and depth. Some instruments are towed through the water. Television cameras towed along the ocean bottom send back pictures so clear that viewers could have read the headlines of newspapers, if any were lying on the ocean floor.

The *Glomar Challenger,* shown above, was specially designed to drill cores from the ocean floor. In the 1970s, scientists studying these cores found evidence to support the theory of sea-floor spreading. The cores showed that the crust beneath the ocean is younger than the continental crust.

Oceanographers also get information about the ocean from satellites that orbit the earth. Some satellites map the temperature and movement of ocean water. Computers interpret the information sent back to earth.

Review It

1. Explain two ways to get pure water from seawater.
2. List five minerals we get from the sea.
3. What is a habitat?

Activity

Desalting Water by Distillation

Purpose
To observe how minerals are removed from seawater.

Materials
- flask
- stopper or cork with hole
- 25-cm glass tube with a bend
- glass jar
- bowl
- Bunsen burner
- ringstand with clamp
- pinch of table salt
- pinch of copper sulfate crystals
- water
- ice cubes
- safety glasses

Procedure
1. Arrange the flask, stopper, tubing, jar, ringstand, and burner as shown.
2. Add a generous pinch of salt and a pinch of copper sulfate crystals to the flask.
3. Fill the flask with water. Shake it until the salt and copper sulphate crystals dissolve. Record the color of the liquid.
4. CAUTION: Wear safety glasses and observe safety rules when you use the burner. Light the burner and bring the water to a boil.
5. Record any color changes you see as the water boils. CAUTION: Turn the burner off before all the liquid boils away.
6. Record the color of the liquid that drips into the jar. Record the color of the liquid left in the flask.

Analysis
1. Without tasting the liquid, how do you know the liquid in the jar is distilled water?
2. What is the function of the copper sulfate crystals?
3. Explain this method of desalting. Use the words evaporation and condensation.
4. Is desalting water in this way practical for home use? Explain your answer.

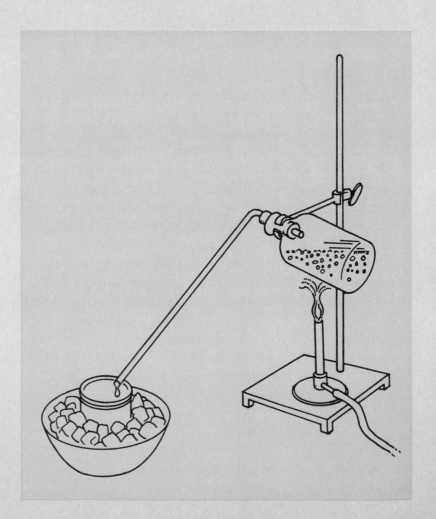

Breakthrough

Strange Features on the Ocean Floor

Since 1977, divers in the *Alvin* and other submersibles have made remarkable discoveries at plate boundaries on the sea floor. They found giant cracks in the earth's crust, huge mountain ranges, active volcanoes, and unusual lava formations. But the strangest discoveries were the hot springs near the spreading boundaries in the eastern Pacific Ocean, shown below.

These hot springs, also called "black smokers" and "white smokers," spurt hot water from vents in the ocean floor. The water from a black smoker like the one in the picture is at least 350°C. It is hot enough to melt the plastic rods that hold the oceanographers' thermometers. The water in the white smokers is not quite as hot.

The hot springs are about 2,500 meters beneath the ocean's surface. Because of the great pressure at these depths, the hot springs' water does not boil.

Geologists believe the hot springs develop when cold ocean water that seeps into the crust is heated by magma rising from the mantle. The heated water dissolves minerals in the magma. The hot springs erupt into the ocean and are cooled by the ocean water. As the water cools, the minerals in it are deposited around the vents in chimney-like structures. These structures are mounds of valuable mineral deposits that are sometimes 10 meters high.

Many strange organisms, such as giant tubeworms, thrive at the hot springs. These unique animals feed on bacteria that do not depend on energy from the sun.

Scientists will continue to study the unusual formations and organisms found near hot springs.

For Discussion
1. Where are the hot springs?
2. What is a black smoker?

A black smoker

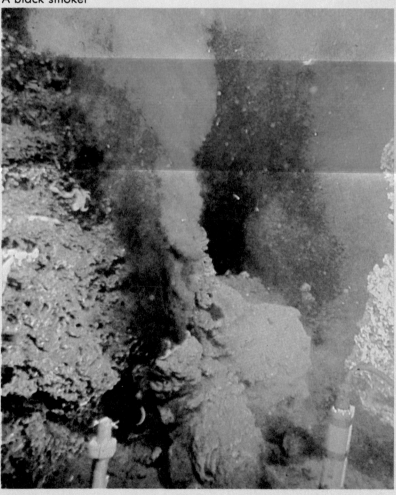

Chapter Summary

- Oceans cover more than 70 percent of the earth's surface.   (21–1)

- Out of 1,000 grams of seawater, about 965 grams is water.   (21–2)

- Deep ocean water is near freezing. Water pressure increases with depth.   (21–2)

- Features on the sea floor include the continental shelf and slope, mid-ocean ridges, rifts, trenches, abyssal hills and plains, seamounts, and guyots.   (21–3)

- Most ocean organisms live in or just below the layer of water reached by sunlight. (21–4)

- Salts and minerals must be removed from seawater before it is useable.   (21–5)

- Minerals and other resources can be obtained from seawater and from the ocean bottom. (21–5)

- Oceanographers study the oceans using submersibles, diving suits, research ships, and undersea habitats.   (21–5)

Interesting Reading

Earle, Sylvia A. "A Walk in the Deep." *National Geographic,* May, 1980, pages 624–631. The diver wears a rigid diving suit to explore the ocean floor at a depth greater than 400 meters.

Colby, C. B. *Undersea Frontiers.* Coward, McCann & Geoghegan, Inc., 1977. Describes devices oceanographers use for exploration and research.

Davis, Eryl. *Ocean Frontiers.* Viking Press, 1979. Explains the difficulties of undersea exploration.

Questions/Problems

1. A ridge runs through the Indian Ocean. What is probably happening to the size of that ocean? Explain your answer.

2. Much of the Arctic Ocean is frozen. What do you know about the salinity of the unfrozen water nearby? Explain your answer.

3. Describe the process of echo sounding, and explain why it is useful.

4. At this time, removing the salt from ocean water is not a solution to the world's freshwater shortage. Explain.

5. What might happen to a deep ocean fish that suddenly rose to the surface?

Extra Research

1. Write a one-page report describing the explorations of the *H.M.S. Challenger,* an English research ship that circled the globe from 1872 to 1876.

2. Partly freeze a bowl of salty water. Remove the ice from the bowl and let it melt. Taste a drop of melted ice water. Also taste a drop of the unfrozen water left in the bowl. Do not swallow the water, just taste it. Compare the tastes and explain your results.

3. Imagine you are going to spend a week in an underwater habitat. You will live inside a cylinder 4 meters in diameter. Draw a floor plan including what you would need for a week beneath the ocean.

4. Draw and describe kelp and other sea plants. Tell at about what depth they live. Explain their usefulness to humans or other organisms. Describe any unusual features about them that you find interesting.

Chapter Test

A. Vocabulary Write the numbers 1–10 on a piece of paper.
Match the definition in Column I with the term it defines in Column II.

Column I

1. number of grams of minerals in 1,000 grams of seawater

2. layer of the ocean in which temperature drops rapidly

3. a method of finding the depth of the ocean

4. mineral deposits found on the ocean floor

5. long cylinder of sediment from the ocean bottom

6. taking so many fish out of an area that the fish population cannot reproduce itself

7. flat parts of the ocean basin
8. the deepest places in the ocean

9. ocean organisms that drift with the currents

10. removing salts and other minerals from seawater

Column II

a. abyssal plain

b. core

c. desalting

d. echo sounding

e. nodule

f. overfishing

g. plankton

h. salinity

i. thermocline

j. trenches

B. Multiple Choice Write the numbers 1–10 on your paper.
Choose the letter that best completes the statement or answers the question.

1. Most of the earth's water is in the form of
a) glaciers. b) rivers. c) oceans. d) lakes.

2. The continental shelf is a) a gently sloping plain near the shoreline. b) a flat-topped sea-mount. c) made of sand or mud washed off the continental slope. d) about 1,000 meters deep.

3. The most abundant mineral in seawater is
a) tin. b) magnesium. c) manganese.
d) sodium chloride.

4. Mid-ocean ridges are a) at spreading plate boundaries. b) near trenches. c) located on the continental rise. d) low hills on the ocean basin.

5. The average salinity of seawater is a) 700 parts per thousand. b) 35 parts per thousand.
c) 40 parts per million. d) 20 parts per hundred.

6. Pressure in ocean water a) decreases with depth. b) increases with depth. c) decreases with temperature. d) is the same throughout the ocean.

7. Plants live in the layer of the ocean that
a) receives sunlight. b) is about −2°C. c) is saltier than average. d) is always dark.

8. The temperature of the mixed layer a) is −2°C. b) always changes with the seasons.
c) is the same as the temperature at the bottom. d) is different in different places.

9. The main source of the minerals in seawater is a) gases from the air. b) the ocean crust.
c) organisms that die and sink to the bottom.
d) nodules.

10. Some submersibles a) drill cores from the ocean floor. b) can dive as deep as 100,000 meters. c) carry scientists deep beneath the ocean. d) are lived in for weeks at a time.

Chapter 22
Motions of the Sea

The waters of the ocean are always moving. Winds whip up storm waves much more powerful than those in the picture of Oregon's coastline. The sharp rocks in the picture are the result of the relentless pounding of waves. The foaming breakers eventually pulverize rocks into sandy beaches. Beneath the foam and breaking waves, silent currents snake through the dark, cold depths. A ship's captain must be familiar with the motions of waves, currents, and tides in order to bring the ship safely into port.

In this chapter you will learn about the motions of ocean water. You will read about currents that travel like rivers through the oceans. You will find out about huge waves that can move unnoticed across thousands of kilometers of open ocean. When the giant waves surge onto a coastline, they cause great destruction. Finally, you will learn what causes the tides that raise and lower the ocean's surface.

Chapter Objectives

1. Explain the causes of surface and density currents.
2. Describe water waves and their effects.
3. Explain the causes and effects of tides.

Centuries ago, sailors learned to use currents on the ocean's surface. American ships in the 1700s rode a strong, fast current eastward across the Atlantic. When they sailed west, they avoided the current. Benjamin Franklin charted the course of this great river in the sea. As you read about ocean currents, think about these questions:

a. What makes most surface currents move?
b. Why are some currents called density currents?
c. How do scientists measure currents?

Wind-Driven Currents

Steady winds blowing across the surface of the ocean move masses of water. The winds create **surface currents** that flow like streams through the surface water of the ocean. Most surface currents reflect the patterns of the winds.

The presence of land and the earth's rotation also affect how surface currents move. Land masses block a current's motion. When a current nears a land mass, it turns and flows along the coast. The Coriolis force, which is the result of the earth's rotation, affects the way winds blow. It also determines which way currents turn. The earth's rotation shifts the currents slightly away from the direction of the winds, as shown in the diagram below. In the Northern Hemisphere, surface currents are shifted to the right of their path of flow. In the Southern Hemisphere, they are shifted toward their left. The Coriolis force is strongest at the poles. As a current in the Northern Hemisphere moves north, it shifts more and more to its right.

Prevailing winds and surface currents

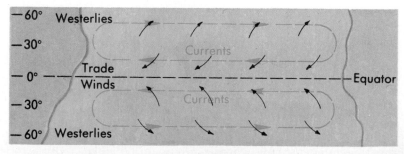

Circulation patterns of surface currents

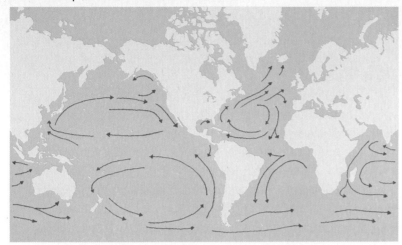

Northern
Hemisphere

0° equator

Southern
Hemisphere

Notice on the map above that most currents flow in great loops. Currents flow basically clockwise in the Northern Hemisphere and counterclockwise in the Southern Hemisphere. Warm currents flow westward along the equator. They are pushed by trade winds that blow from east to west. When they reach land, the currents turn toward the poles. About halfway to the poles, other winds—the westerlies—cause the currents to change direction. The westerlies blow from west to east. The currents turn eastward about halfway between the equator and the poles. When the currents meet land again, they turn toward the equator, completing their loops.

The **Gulf Stream** is part of the swift current that loops through the Atlantic Ocean north of the equator. The Gulf Stream travels up to 10 kilometers per hour. It carries warm water from the Gulf of Mexico up the east coast of the United States. Near Newfoundland, the Gulf Stream turns east and moves more slowly toward Europe. The Japan Current is a warm current in the North Pacific. It travels up the eastern coast of Asia.

Inside the loop of the ocean currents is a quiet area. Winds are light and water moves slowly. In the North Atlantic, this region is the Sargasso (sär gas′ō) Sea.

Have You Heard?

The Sargasso Sea in the North Atlantic gets its name from sargassum, a kind of seaweed. Tangled masses of this brown seaweed float on the surface of the water. They are held within the still area surrounded by a loop of surface currents. Hundreds of years ago, sailors feared the seaweed would trap their ships.

Density Currents

Currents also flow deep beneath the ocean's surface. These deep currents—**density currents**—are denser than the water around them. Gravity makes dense water sink beneath less dense water.

Cold Density Currents   Cold water is denser than warm water, and salty water is denser than less salty water. Water near the poles is both cold and salty. When seawater freezes, most of its salt is left behind. So the unfrozen water is more salty. As the cold, very salty water moves away from the poles, it meets warmer water. The dense, cold, salty water sinks deep beneath the surface. Then it travels slowly away from the poles. The slow movement of these cold, deep polar currents is called **polar creep.** Water from the ocean's surface is rich in oxygen. Polar creep brings surface water into deep parts of the ocean. Animals at the bottom of the ocean use the oxygen carried to them by polar creep.

Upwelling is the process by which deep currents rise to the surface. Observe in the top diagram that winds blowing away from land may push surface water out to sea. Cold water from deep currents rises to replace the warmer surface water. A deep current may also rise to the surface when it collides with a land mass in its path.

When sea organisms die, their bodies sink to the ocean bottom. They decompose and dissolve. Water carried to the surface by upwelling is rich in dissolved minerals from the organisms. Areas of upwelling teem with plankton that live on the minerals. So many fish feed on the plankton and each other that these areas are good for fishing.

Salty Density Currents   Some density currents consist of very salty, warm water. In the Mediterranean Sea, for example, the dry, warm climate causes surface water to evaporate. The remaining water is saltier than water nearby in the Atlantic Ocean. The lower diagram shows how less salty ocean water enters the Mediterranean Sea and replaces water lost by evaporation. Dense, salty water from the Mediterranean moves out into the Atlantic. The saltier water flows under the current coming in from the ocean.

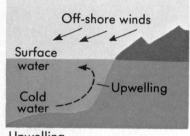

Upwelling

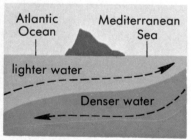

Salty density current

An infrared photograph of the Gulf Stream along the East Coast

Turbidity Currents Currents made up of water, mud, and sand are **turbidity** (tėr′bid/ə tē) **currents.** This water is denser than clear water. Rivers that empty into the ocean carry mud or sand. They may flow deep in the sea as turbidity currents. Underwater landslides also create turbidity currents. The landslide sweeps water ahead of it. Mud and sand mix with the water. Quickly moving turbidity currents can carve canyons on the ocean floor.

Measuring Ocean Currents

Each ocean current has its own special temperature and mineral content. Scientists trace currents by measuring the temperature and mineral content of water samples. They use instruments, called current meters, to measure and record the speed and direction of currents. Some satellites carry instruments that sense temperature differences among surface currents. They send back maps, such as the one above, that show warm and cold currents. The warmest currents in the picture are red.

Review It

1. List three factors that affect how surface currents move.
2. Name and explain three kinds of density currents.
3. How do satellites track currents?

Challenge!

Produce a density current in a shallow bowl. Gently squeeze a few drops of food coloring out of a medicine dropper down the inside of a shallow bowl of water. The food coloring is denser and should slide down the side of the bowl under the water. What happens when you use cold food coloring and warm water? Try squeezing the coloring into the bottom of the bowl.

22–2
Waves

Strong storm waves beating against the shore can change the shape of the shoreline. Gentle waves lapping at the beach may deposit or carry away sand. As you read about waves, try to answer the following questions:

a. What characteristics describe waves?
b. What causes most waves to move?
c. How do waves affect the shoreline?
d. What causes tsunamis?

Describing a Wave

Regardless of the size or height of waves that come in and break on any beach, all water waves share certain characteristics. Notice in the diagram at the lower left that each wave has a **crest,** which is its highest point. The **trough** is the wave's lowest point. The **wave height** is the distance from its crest to its trough. The **wavelength** is the distance from the crest of one wave to the crest of the following wave.

Waves in the water move the same way waves move along a rope. If you tie one end of a rope to a tree and shake the free end, a wave moves along the rope. The picture at the lower right shows how the rope moves up and down as the wave passes. The wave moves forward, but the rope does not. In the same way, water rises and falls as waves move forward on the ocean's surface. But the water does not move forward.

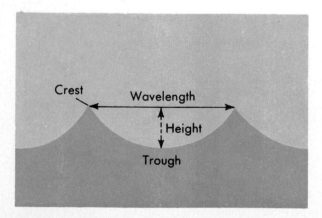

Water moves onto the beach

Movement of Ocean Waves

If you watch a twig bobbing on waves, you will see that as each wave passes, the twig rises on the crest and drops into the trough. In the same way, water particles move up and down as a wave passes. A particle moves a little forward on the wave's crest. As the wave passes, the particle moves a little backward into the trough. Notice in the diagram that each water particle moves in a circular loop. It ends up just about where it started.

The movement of your arm was the force that produced the wave on the rope. Wind energy produces most waves in the ocean. When wind blows across the water's surface, it pushes up tiny waves. As the wind continues to blow, it pushes the tiny waves up into larger waves.

The heights and wavelengths of waves in the open ocean depend on the speed of the wind, how long the wind blows, and the amount of open sea over which the wind blows. Strong winds that blow for many hours over a large area produce the biggest, fastest waves. Most ocean waves are about 3 meters high. Storm waves can be 30 meters high.

When a wave reaches shallow water, its wavelength gets shorter. The ocean bottom pulls at the wave and slows it down. The crest gets ahead of the rest of the wave and begins to tilt forward. The front of the crest is unsupported. Finally, it tumbles over into the trough. The collapsing wave is a **breaker.**

After a wave breaks, the foaming water rushes up the beach. Now water particles no longer move in circles as they did in the wave. The water actually moves forward onto the beach, as shown in the photograph above.

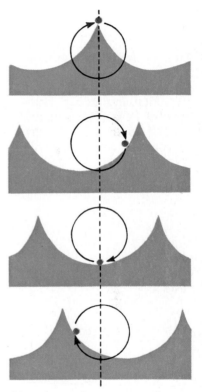
Movement of water particles as a wave passes

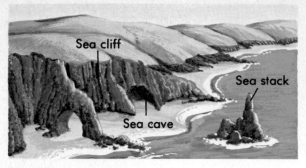

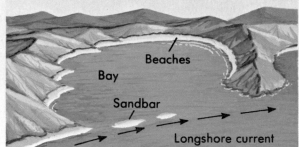

Have You Heard?

Storm waves have enormous energy. At Tillamook Rock, Oregon, waves hurled a huge rock high into the air. The mass of the rock was more than 61 kilograms. It crashed through the roof of a building 30 meters above the water.

Waves and the Shoreline

Waves pounding on the shore wear down the land in some places and build it up in others. Storm waves can do severe damage to land along a seacoast. Breaking waves hurl tons of water against a coast. They can move huge rocks, destroy buildings, and dash uprooted trees onto the beach.

When strong waves hit the shoreline, water rushes into cracks in the rocks. Eventually, the cracks widen and the rocks break apart. Bits of rock and sand in the waves act like sandpaper and grind up rocks. Seawater slowly dissolves some kinds of rock. Waves often drag beach sand with them when the water runs back into the ocean. Waves can erode many meters of land in a single season.

The diagram to the upper left shows some rock formations produced by waves. Sea cliffs form when waves wear away rock at the base of a rocky shoreline. Overhanging rocks fall into the water, leaving a steep sea cliff. Sea caves form where waves hollow out soft rock in a sea cliff. Sea stacks are columns that remain when the rest of the rock has eroded.

Longshore currents form along the shore when waves strike the shoreline at an angle. These currents move parallel to the shore, carrying sand and bits of rock. Waves pick up some of the sand from the currents. They deposit it in bays, where it forms beaches. Sand dropped by the current parallel to a beach forms a sand bar. The diagram to the upper right shows some shoreline features that form as waves deposit sand. Waves and currents constantly change the shape of a beach.

Tsunamis

A **tsunami** (sü nä′mē) is a series of waves caused by sudden movements of the ocean floor. Tsunamis are often called tidal waves, but they have nothing to do with tides. Most tsunamis are caused by underwater occurrences, such as landslides, earthquakes, or eruptions of volcanoes.

An underwater earthquake releases large amounts of energy. A series of waves may fan out from the earthquake's center. The waves race across the ocean's surface at more than 700 kilometers per hour. Their wavelengths may be greater than 200 kilometers. In deep water, tsunamis are less than a meter high. Sailors on the open ocean may not even notice that waves are passing. When a tsunami reaches shallow water, however, it slows down. The rushing water piles up and the waves get taller. Tsunami waves reach shore as walls of water up to 50 meters high. Tons of water crashing onto a coastal town can cause great destruction, as the photograph to the right shows.

Oceanographers have set up a tsunami warning system in the Pacific Ocean. They observe seismic waves and sudden changes in water level to help predict when a tsunami will hit. Tsunamis fanned outward from an earthquake in Alaska in March, 1964. Waves damaged towns on Alaska's coast only minutes after the earthquake. Four hours later, waves did millions of dollars of property damage to Crescent City, California. The city had a half hour of warning. Waves reached Hilo, Hawaii, 5.5 hours after the earthquake and 2 hours after warning sirens sounded. The tsunamis reached Sydney, Australia, after 17 hours. They arrived at Antarctica after traveling 22 hours.

A person in the path of a tsunami wave

Review It

1. Name and define four characteristics of a wave.
2. List three factors that determine the height and wavelength of waves in the open ocean.
3. How do longshore currents affect beaches?
4. How high are tsunamis on the open ocean?

Have You Heard?

What would you do if you were at an ocean beach and the water suddenly pulled back, exposing the ocean bottom? You *should not* go out to look at stranded fish or beached boats. Instead, you should head for high ground. When waves retreat suddenly, it probably means the trough of a tsunami has arrived and the tsunami is about 10 minutes away.

Activity

Waves

Purpose
To observe how waves are formed.

Materials
• paint tray
• water
• small block of wood
• black cloth or paper
• waterproof tape
• electric hair dryer

Procedure
1. Cover the bottom of the paint tray with black paper or cloth. Tape the cloth or paper in place with waterproof tape.
2. Add water to the paint tray until it reaches within 2 or 3 cm of the shallow end, as shown in the picture.
3. Blow gently on the surface of the water near the deep end. Record and draw what you see.
4. Blow harder on the surface of the water. Record and draw what you see.
5. Direct the stream of air from a hair dryer at the deep end of the water. *CAUTION: Do not let the hair dryer get wet or touch it with wet hands. Do not touch the hair dryer and the water at the same time.* Record what you see after the hair dryer has blown for a short period of time. Now observe as the hair dryer blows over the water for several minutes. Record any difference you see in the size of the waves.

Analysis
1. What happens to the surface of the water when you blow on it?
2. What change can you see when you blow harder on the water's surface?
3. What happens to the wave size when the hair dryer blows for several minutes?
4. What two factors seem to affect the size of the waves?

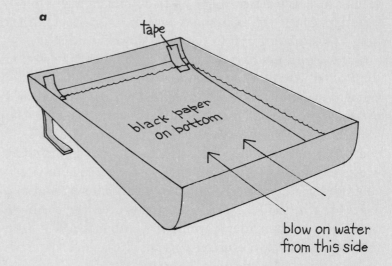

a

tape

black paper on bottom

blow on water from this side

Breakthrough
El Niño

The warm ocean current called El Niño—the little one —has sometimes brought disaster to Peruvian fishermen. The anchovies they catch for a living depend on the up-welling of cold water along the coast of South America. But about once every ten years, the warm waters of El Niño move southward along the coast. Anchovies cannot live in these warm waters. The fishing boats come back empty, and many Peruvians go hungry.

Anchovies are also used as fish meal, which is an important part of chicken feed. As the price of fish meal rises, the price you pay for fried chicken also goes up.

No one can tell when El Niño will show up and ruin the fishing business.

Oceanographers believe that the ocean and winds work together to create El Niño. In some years, the trade winds, which blow from east to west, are stronger than usual. They push surface water in the Pacific Ocean westward. It piles up along the coasts of China, Indonesia, and Australia.

Eventually, the trade winds quiet down. Water that was pushed westward begins to flow back. The current of returning water moves eastward along the equator. When it reaches the coast of South America, it turns south as El Niño.

By watching winds and weather conditions in the Pacific, scientists think they may be able to predict when El Niño is coming. In 1974, they warned Peruvian fishermen four months in advance that the warm current was coming. In time, meteorologists will learn more about how air and ocean interact. Then, they may be able to forecast weather all over the world for months ahead.

For Discussion
1. How does El Niño affect people other than fishermen?
2. What is the value of predicting the paths of ocean currents?

Processing anchovies

22–3
Tides

The water level on most seacoasts rises and falls twice each day. Waves creep higher up the beach. Then they retreat. As you read about tides, think about the following questions:

a. What is the main cause of the tides?
b. How does the sun affect the tides?
c. Are tides the same at all coasts?

The Effect of the Moon

The pull of the moon on the earth is the main cause of tides. The moon's gravity pulls on the earth and on the water of the oceans. The waters pile up in a bulge. The moon pulls on solid parts of the earth too. But they are not as free to move as water is. Tides of the solid earth are much smaller than the tides of the ocean.

The moon's gravity has a greater effect on parts of the earth closer to the moon. Notice in the diagram below that ocean water piles up on the side of the earth below the moon. This bulge of water is a **high tide**. A bulge also forms on the opposite side of the earth. The solid earth is pulled more strongly toward the moon than is the water on the side of the earth farthest away from the moon. So water heaps up in a high tide bulge on the side away from the moon. **Low tides** are between the bulges.

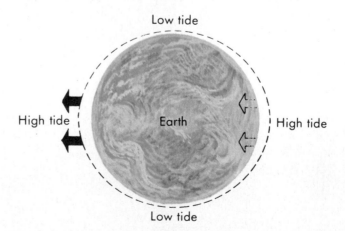

The earth rotates on its axis once every 24 hours. Meanwhile, the moon moves in its orbit around the earth. The earth must rotate 24 hours and 50 minutes before the moon returns to the same position overhead. High tides occur wherever the moon is either overhead or halfway around the earth. High tides are separated by about 12 hours and 25 minutes. High and low tides alternate about every 6 hours.

The Sun Affects the Tides

The pull of the sun's gravity also affects the tides. The sun has much more mass than the moon, but it is much farther away from the earth. The effect of the sun on the tides is about half that of the moon. Twice each month, the sun and moon are lined up with the earth, as shown in the diagram to the lower left. Their pulls combine to produce the **spring tides,** which are higher-than-average high tides. At spring tides, the low tides are lower than average.

Twice each month the sun and moon are at right angles to each other, as shown in the diagram to the lower right. Their gravity forces then pull in different directions. They work against each other to produce **neap** (nēp) **tides,** which are lower than average high tides. At neap tides, the low tides are higher than average. The difference between high and low tide is less than usual during neap tides.

Have You Heard?

The term *spring tide* has nothing to do with the season of spring. It comes from an old word *springen,* which means "to leap up."

Spring tide

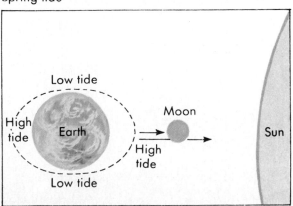

Neap tide

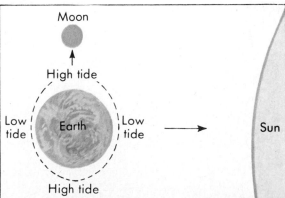

427

High tide

Low tide

Patterns of Tides May Vary

Many places have two equal high tides and two equal low tides each day. But the shape of the ocean floor and the location of currents can affect the tides' heights and the times the tides appear. For example, in shallow water, the movement of the tide may be slowed down.

Where the land forms a narrow inlet, incoming tide waters pile up as they flow into the narrow place. The difference between high and low tides may be great. In the photographs above, notice the water's height during high and low tides in New Brunswick, Canada. The water level can be more than 13 meters higher at high tide than at low tide. In the open ocean and in places where incoming water can spread out, the tide usually changes the water level only about a half meter. Some places have no tides at all because the action of the sun and moon is balanced by the effects of the ocean and land.

Review It

1. Define neap tide and spring tide.
2. What parts of the earth are affected by the moon's gravity?
3. Why does the height of the tide vary at different places?

Activity

Tide Model

Purpose
To demonstrate how parts of the earth pass beneath the moon as the earth rotates and how the sun affects the tides.

Materials
- pencil
- construction paper
- compass
- scissors
- 3 thumbtacks
- corrugated cardboard

Procedure
1. Using the compass, draw three circles on the sheet of construction paper, as shown in *a*. Label the moon, sun, and earth. Draw an X on one edge of the circle labeled "earth."
2. Cut out the circles.
3. At the center of the cardboard, draw a circle the same size as the earth circle. Draw tidal bulges on opposite sides of the circle, as in *b*.
4. Use a thumbtack to fasten the moon to the cardboard opposite one of the tidal bulges, as in *c*.
5. Use another thumbtack to fasten the earth over the circle you drew on the cardboard. Turn the earth so the X is beside one of the tidal bulges, as in *c*.
6. Rotate the earth slowly clockwise one quarter turn. In your notebook, record what the tide would be like at X. Continue turning the circle clockwise. Record the tides at X for each quarter turn.
7. Place the sun on the model where it would be at spring tide. Draw your model on a piece of paper.
8. Move the sun to its position at neap tide. Draw your model.

Analysis
1. How many high tides and low tides occur at point X during one full rotation of the earth?
2. How does the sun affect the height of the spring and neap tides?

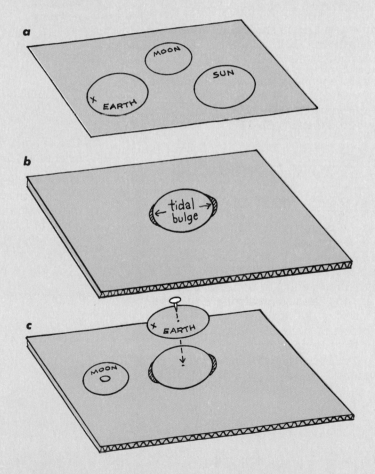

429

Chapter Summary

- Surface currents of the ocean reflect the patterns of global winds. (22–1)

- Deep ocean currents consist of water denser than the water around them. (22–1)

- Scientists study the temperature and mineral content of currents and measure their speed and direction. (22–1)

- A wave's highest part is its crest, and the lowest is its trough. (22–2)

- Wind is the force that produces most waves in the ocean. (22–2)

- Waves wear down the shoreline in some places and build it up in others. (22–2)

- Tsunamis result from sudden movements of the ocean floor. They reach great heights as they near the shore. (22–2)

- The pull of the moon and sun on the earth causes the tides. Local currents and the shape of the ocean floor affect the height and timing of the tides. (22–3)

Interesting Reading

Ashkenazy, Irvin. "Benthic Currents." *Oceans,* November 1979, pages 34–36. Describes the characteristics and movements of deep ocean currents.

Cromie, William J. "When Comes El Niño?" *Science 80,* March-April 1980, pages 36–43. Changes in upwelling in the Peru Current may provide clues to predicting weather in other parts of the world.

Zim, Herbert S. *Waves.* Morrow, 1967. Describes the principles governing water in motion and contains an excellent explanation of tsunamis.

Questions/Problems

1. If you were exploring the ocean floor in a submersible, what kinds of currents would affect your motion?

2. If a sealed bottle is dropped into the ocean off the coast of California, where do you think it might wash ashore?

3. If you planned to build a cabin on the ocean front, what would you need to check?

4. In May, 1960, an earthquake occurred in Chile, and a tsunami damaged Hilo, Hawaii. How might the two events be related? Which do you think took place first?

5. Some planets have several moons. What would the tides be like if Earth had two moons?

Extra Research

1. Use drops of colored dye and a stream table or shallow bowl to investigate currents in water.

2. Use an encyclopedia to find out what seiches are and what causes them.

3. Draw a map showing what might happen to the surface currents in the ocean if the earth began to rotate from east to west instead of from west to east. Remember that this change would affect the direction of the winds.

Chapter Test

A. Vocabulary   Write the numbers 1–10 on a piece of paper.
Match the definition in Column I with the term it defines in Column II.

Column I

1. process by which deep currents rise to the surface

2. density current that contains mud and sand

3. collapsing wave

4. highest high tide

5. distance from a wave's crest to its trough

6. distance from the crest of one wave to the crest of the following wave

7. instrument used to trace currents

8. current that flows parallel to the shore and carries sand and bits of rock

9. waves caused by an underwater earthquake

10. movement of cold polar currents under the ocean

Column II

a. breaker

b. current meter

c. longshore current

d. polar creep

e. spring tide

f. tsunami

g. turbidity current

h. upwelling

i. wave height

j. wavelength

B. Multiple Choice   Write the numbers 1–10 on your paper.
Choose the letter that best completes the statement or answers the question.

1. Surface currents   a) travel mostly in loops. b) all carry warm water.   c) are unaffected by the earth's rotation.   d) all flow counterclockwise.

2. Ocean waves   a) carry water along with them as they move across the ocean.   b) build up all shores.   c) break when they near shore. d) are not affected by the wind.

3. Tides are caused   a) by the sun alone. b) by the moon alone.   c) equally by the sun and moon.   d) mostly by the moon.

4. Tsunamis can be detected   a) by ships at sea.   b) only when they reach shore.   c) by observing seismic waves and sudden changes in the water level.   d) only in the Atlantic Ocean.

5. From one high tide to the next high tide is about   a) 6 hours.   b) 12 hours and 25 minutes.   c) 24 hours.   c) 24 hours and 50 minutes.

6. Water in deep polar currents is   a) cold and salty.   b) warm and salty.   c) filled with mud and sand.   d) less dense than the surrounding water.

7. When a wave breaks,   a) water rushes up the beach.   b) water particles move in circles. c) it can erode the land.   d) a and c.

8. When a surface current nears a land mass, it a) piles up, forming a wall of water. b) reverses its direction.   c) turns and flows along the coast.   d) sinks to the bottom.

9. High tides tend to be extremely high   a) in the open ocean.   b) in narrow inlets.   c) at the neap tides.   d) in the spring.

10. The Mediterranean Sea is saltier than the Atlantic because   a) deep currents churn the water.   b) evaporation replaces the salt lost in currents.   c) its water is colder.   d) the climate causes surface water to evaporate.

Careers

Weather observer

Who gives a news program its weather information? Observers from all around the country do when they report the weather in their area. Weather observers often work for the National Weather Service or other government agencies.

Weather observers watch the sky for changes in the clouds. They use instruments that constantly record the temperature, wind direction, humidity, and precipitation. In addition, weather balloons return news about conditions at high altitudes to the observer. Observers combine this information onto teletype machines that send the data around the world.

Weather observers learn how to use technical weather equipment and computers during one or two years at a trade school or junior college.
Career Information:
American Meteorological Society, 45 Beacon St., Boston, MA 02108

Airport meteorologist

Long before an airplane lands, the pilot can tell passengers about weather conditions on the ground. Airport meteorologists radio the weather picture to pilots.

These meteorologists forecast weather conditions along airplane flight routes, so airplanes can avoid hazardous weather conditions. Satellites and ground stations provide the data to make the forecasts. An airport meteorologist uses the data to draw weather maps and charts.

Meteorology students take four years of science and drawing in college. Airport experience is also important to the job.
Career Information:
American Meteorological Society, 45 Beacon St., Boston, MA 02108

Climatologist

Some people believe that glaciers will cover the U.S. at some time in the future. Other people think that the North Pole will get warmer and existing glaciers will melt. A climatologist tries to figure out world weather trends.

Climatologists are meteorologists who do not forecast the everyday weather. Instead, they predict weather conditions for much longer periods of time. Past weather records are often fed into computers to help a climatologist forecast weather patterns for the next season, the next year, or even the next ten years.

Climatologists study meteorology in college. They learn to draw weather maps and to make weather predictions. They must also learn what climates were like in the past.
Career Information:
American Meteorological Society, 45 Beacon St., Boston, MA 02108

Fisher

Most people who fish for a living concentrate on ocean fishing. But lakes and rivers support a smaller fishing industry as well.

Men and women who fish for a living go out winter and summer. They may work alone or in groups to bring in their catch. They use hooks and lines, traps, or nets, depending on the type of fish they want. Each catch then gets weighed, stored, and delivered.

Fishers must learn about the currents, tides, and waves in the water where they work. Whether they seek whitefish in lakes or tuna in the oceans, they must also know a great deal about weather and how it changes. These workers learn their skills from on-the-job training.

Career Information:
American Fisheries Society, 5410 Grosvenor Lane, Bethesda, MD 20014

U.S. Coast Guard member

In 1912, the *Titanic* hit an iceberg and sank. Since then, U.S. Coast Guard ships have patrolled seas for hazards to ships. The Coast Guard works to make the seas safe. It performs many services, such as tracking icebergs, stopping smugglers, and rescuing ships in distress.

People enlist in the Coast Guard, a military service, to serve on ships. Some guard boats only go out on safety patrol cruises, but others travel around the world. Crew members serve from one to four years. During this time, they may run weather stations, check shipping lanes, or study oceanography.

People who enlist in the Coast Guard spend nine weeks at training camp. Officers must pass written exams after taking training classes.

Career Information:
Commandant, U.S. Coast Guard, 2100 2nd St., SW, Washington, DC 20593

Oceanographer

Oceanographers may scuba dive to find out about the growth of coral reefs. Or they may take a submarine ride to great depths. Oceanographers do many exciting things. But they also perform more routine tasks. They learn about water, its movements, and the shape of the ocean bottom.

An oceanographer may work on land as well as on the sea. However, an oceanographer often may make long voyages to collect ocean data. He or she then studies the data in a laboratory that is on the ship itself. Research findings are usually published in reports, articles, or books.

Ocean experts need a master's or doctor's degree. They generally do research or teach.

Career Information:
N.O.A.A., National Sea Grant College Program, 6010 Executive Blvd., Rockville, MD 20852

433

UNIT FIVE
ENERGY AND ENVIRONMENT

Where besides a science fiction movie could you see a scene like this? Is this a "special effect" for a movie? Does the picture show equipment used in the space program? Might the photograph have been taken on one of the lunar landings?

Fort Scott, Kansas—not the moon—is the setting of the picture. The photograph is a time exposure taken during the night shift at a coal mining operation. The yellow splash of light near the bottom of the picture is the cab of a huge piece of equipment used to mine coal. A miner in the cab rotates a long, thin arm, called a boom. Three sets of lights on the boom created the bands of light in the picture. A tremendous bucket, suspended from the boom, scoops up soil until a layer of coal is exposed. Coal is one important energy source described in this unit. Environmental problems, which are often caused by our use of energy, are also discussed.

Chapter 23 Energy
We rely on fossil fuels and nuclear energy. Solar and geothermal energy may become more useful in the future. Conservation is a key part of our energy program.

Chapter 24 The Environment
Protecting our water, air, and land will improve the quality of our lives.

Chapter 23
Energy

Each of the strange-looking structures in the photograph is a windmill on a windfarm. People have used windmills for centuries, but windfarms are something new. The blades in these windmills are thinner than windmill blades once were, but they do as much work. They capture the energy of the wind and use it to make electricity. Although wind will probably never be a major source of energy, wind energy can become important in some places around the world.

This chapter describes many sources of energy we use today. It also tells about some energy sources that are still in the experimental stage. The chapter will also suggest ways that you and your family can save energy.

Chapter Objectives
1. Explain the advantages and disadvantages of using fossil fuels.
2. Describe how fission and fusion can produce energy.
3. Describe four renewable energy sources.
4. List six ways of conserving energy.

23–1
Energy Use and Fossil Fuels

You may have heard your parents groan when they fill the car's gas tank or when they pay large heating bills. Their unhappiness with the high cost of fuel reflects the energy problems that face all of us. Keep the following questions in mind as you read about common energy sources:

a. How do we use energy?
b. What are the types of coal?
c. How can we expand our oil supply?

Energy

Energy is the ability to do work or move objects. We use energy every day in many ways. We use it to keep warm and to run our machines.

We get energy from many sources including oil, gas, coal, and the nuclei of atoms. The bar graph below shows how the United States used energy resources during a recent year. As you can see, the United States used oil to meet almost half its energy needs. Most of this oil is refined into gasoline for transporting people and goods from place to place. Both oil and natural gas are used to heat homes and run industries. Coal is also an important energy source for industry.

How the United States uses its energy

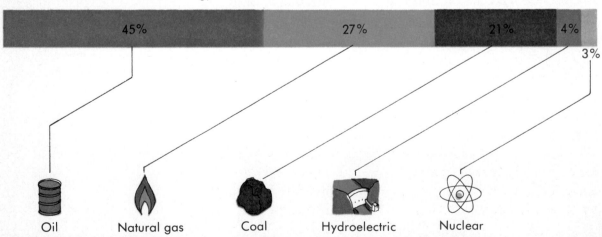

45%	27%	21%	4%
3%

Oil   Natural gas   Coal   Hydroelectric   Nuclear

Generators

Sometimes we use energy directly, such as when we burn natural gas to cook our food. Often, however, we use one energy source, such as coal, to make another form of energy—**electricity.** Electric energy is convenient because it is easily transported through wires, and is available at the flip of a switch.

Electricity is produced in a machine called a **generator.** The picture shows one type of generator. This machine uses the energy from oil, gas, coal, atoms, falling water, wind, or other sources to turn large loops of wire. When the wire moves near a magnet, electricity flows in the wire. This electricity moves over power lines to homes, schools, factories, or wherever it is needed.

Our most important sources of energy—oil, gas, and coal—are called fossil fuels. They formed hundreds of millions of years ago from the remains of buried organisms. When we use up our fossil fuels, no more will be available for millions of years. They are, therefore, **nonrenewable resources.** Energy from other sources, such as the sun or wind, will not run out. They are **renewable resources.**

Coal has been used as a fuel for over 3,000 years. But it has been used in great amounts only since the industrial revolution in the 1800s. Burning coal for homes and industry caused the killer smogs that plagued European cities in the 1800s. Now people are concerned that burning coal will add so much carbon dioxide to the air that the earth's climate will change.

Coal Is an Energy Source

Hundreds of millions of years ago, plants died in swamps and decayed into peat, shown on the left below. As time passed, sediments buried the peat. Pressure and heat turned the peat into different kinds of coal. Increasing pressure and heat turned the peat first into lignite, then bituminous and finally, anthracite. In the picture below, lignite is to the right of peat. Bituminous is next. Anthracite is on the right.

Lignite and bituminous are soft coals. Bituminous is very abundant and gives off a great amount of heat when it burns. It is, therefore, often used to generate electricity. Two-thirds of the coal we mine is used to make electric energy. Anthracite is a hard, clean-burning coal. But only one percent of the United States coal is anthracite.

Some coal contains many particles and elements such as sulfur. When high-sulfur coal burns, it pollutes the air. Much of the low-sulfur coal in the United States is located in the West, far from most industrial centers. Therefore, it must be shipped long distances to the cities.

The stages of coal formation

A strip mine in Pennsylvania

Later, the land was restored

Because of the way coal forms, we find it in layers—or beds. Some coal beds are so far underground that deep mines must be built to reach the coal. If the coal is close to the surface, it can be strip-mined. In strip mining, soil and rock at the earth's surface are stripped away to reach the coal. This stage of strip mining is economical, but it presents problems. The wastes from strip mines often wash into streams, clogging or polluting them. The waste also kills vegetation. Strip mining destroys valuable farmland that could be used to produce food. Now laws have been passed that require mining companies to restore the land after the coal is strip-mined. The pictures show strip-mined land before and after it was restored.

Coal is usually shipped in railroad cars from the mines to cities and generating plants. But sometimes coal is changed into gas or liquid fuels that can be sent through pipelines. Coal in these forms burns more cleanly than raw coal, but the processing is expensive.

441

Where Can We Get More Oil?

Geologists believe that oil and natural gas formed hundreds of millions of years ago. As tiny organisms died and settled to the bottom of shallow oceans, they were covered with sediments that later became sedimentary rocks. Heat and pressure changed the organisms into natural gas and oil, which is also called **crude oil** or petroleum.

Gas sometimes collects with oil in the pores and cracks of sedimentary rocks. Gas, which is lighter, can float on top of the oil, or it can be dissolved in the oil deposits. Oil and gas that collect in sedimentary rocks can be pumped from the rocks.

Most of the large oil deposits on land in the United States have already been used. The search for new oil reserves in this country has led geologists and oil companies out onto the continental shelf. Offshore drilling in the Gulf of Mexico has already been successful. The picture shows a barge towing part of an oil rig down the Mississippi River on its way to the Gulf waters.

The United States has other sources of oil. The Green River shale of Colorado, Utah, and Wyoming is a thick bed of **oil shale.** Oil shale is sedimentary rock containing organic matter called kerogen. The kerogen, which contains oil, cannot be pumped out of oil shale. Instead, the shale is heated and the oil is removed in an expensive process.

Towing an oil rig

This squeezing process requires a lot of water, which is scarce in many states. Also, oil-shale mining creates huge piles of used shale that litter the countryside. The oil shale in the picture is so rich in oil that it burns at the touch of a match.

Alberta province in western Canada has rich deposits of **tar sands.** These deposits are clay and sand mixed with water and heavy oil—a black, sticky tar. After the deposits are strip-mined, the heavy oil can be separated from the sand and made into crude oil. Separating the sand and oil is difficult and expensive because the sand quickly wears out the machines that process it. The process also requires large amounts of water, steam, and electricity. Removing crude oil from tar sands requires a lot of energy.

Oil and gas are good sources of energy. They burn easily and produce a lot of heat and power. They are also easy to transport. However, like coal, burning oil causes air pollution when the sulfur in it combines with oxygen. Also, oil and gas are nonrenewable. Once our current deposits are used up, it will be millions of years before large new deposits are available.

Fossil fuels have other uses besides providing energy. Industrial chemicals, plastics, some fabrics, and many other products are made from oil and gas. Some people believe that oil and gas should be set aside for use in these important products and not burned as fuels.

Two-thirds of the known reserves of oil and gas are found in the Middle East. Therefore, many industrialized nations have become dependent on that part of the world. As the price of oil rises and our reserves are used, many nations are looking for new sources. Offshore drilling, oil shales, and tar sands are becoming more important.

Have You Heard?

Geologists search for oil by creating small earthquakes with explosives. Underground rock structures reflect the seismic waves from these explosions back to the surface. The seismic record of the shock waves tells geologists about the type and depth of rocks. It also tells them whether or not the rock structures are a good place to find oil.

Oil shale burns

Review It

1. What is the function of a generator?
2. How is bituminous different from anthracite?
3. How might Canada and the United States boost their oil production?

23–2
Nuclear Energy

Many people believe that nuclear energy will solve our energy problems. Other people feel that the hazards of nuclear energy make it too risky. As you learn more about nuclear energy, keep in mind:

a. How does fission produce energy?
b. How does fusion differ from fission?

Nuclear Energy from Fission

Albert Einstein suggested in 1906 that mass can be changed into energy. Later, scientists realized that some of the mass in the nucleus of an atom can be changed into energy by splitting the nucleus into parts. The process is **nuclear fission.** Some uranium nuclei and the nuclei of a few other elements split easily. As the diagram shows, the mass of the pieces is less than the mass of the original nucleus. The small difference in mass is changed into a lot of energy.

During fission, the first nucleus that splits gives off other lighter elements, energy, and about two neutrons. These neutrons split other uranium atoms. Once it starts, the splitting process continues. Thus, it is a **chain reaction.** An atom bomb is an uncontrolled chain reaction.

Engineers have found ways to control chain reactions. They have designed nuclear reactors to produce energy for homes or industry from these controlled nuclear reactions. Nuclear reactors cannot explode because their fuel is not packed closely enough together.

Reactors make electricity indirectly. Their energy boils water to make steam. The steam turns the blades of a machine called a **turbine** (tur′bən). The turbine operates a generator.

A reactor, shown in the photograph to the right, has many safety systems that become active if something goes wrong. For example, metal rods fall into the reactor to slow or nearly stop the chain reaction. Some people fear that all the safety systems might fail at the same time. A lot of radioactivity would escape if that happened, and many people, plants, and animals might be harmed. People are working hard to make sure our nuclear reactors are safe.

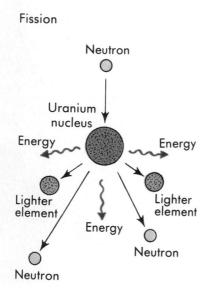

Fission

Neutron

Uranium nucleus

Energy

Energy

Lighter element

Lighter element

Energy

Neutron

Neutron

Uranium is the element used most often in nuclear fission. Finding enough good-quality uranium to use is a problem. It is found in an ore called **pitchblende.** The richest pitchblende deposits are found in Colorado, Wyoming, Utah, and New Mexico. Less than one percent of the uranium in pitchblende, however, is the type that can be used in a chain reaction. Complicated methods must be used to raise this percentage.

Engineers are designing a new type of reactor—the breeder reactor. It would change the unusable type of uranium into a fuel the reactor can use. Many people are concerned that breeder reactors might not be safe. Breeders make the element plutonium, which we have to guard carefully. Other people think breeder reactors are necessary and that we can make them safe.

Blue glow from a reactor

Fusion—Making Energy as the Stars Do

The sun and other stars produce energy by putting light nuclei together to make heavier ones. In this process, called fusion, a little mass is changed into a lot of energy. A form of hydrogen found in ocean water is suitable as a fuel for fusion reactions. As a result, the fuel supply for fusion is almost unlimited.

Fusion plants might be free of many of the problems that surround fission plants. Few radioactive materials would be used or created in fusion plants. But we do not yet know how to control fusion reactions. Fusion works only when temperatures are raised to and kept at millions of degrees Celsius. Such high temperatures are difficult to maintain in laboratories on earth. Also, scientists must find a way to hold such a hot reaction. Several methods are being tested and many scientists hope we will be able to build a fusion plant by the year 2000.

Have You Heard?

A fission power plant gives off fewer radioactive particles to the air than a coal plant does. The radioactive particles in coal are released into the air when coal burns. All substances—even the cells in your body—contain some radioactive particles.

Review It

1. How do we get energy from fission?
2. What are two problems to be solved before we can use fusion energy?

23–3
Renewable Energy Sources

If you live in San Francisco, you may not depend entirely on fossil fuels or nuclear power for your energy. San Francisco gets much of its heat and electricity from another kind of energy. As you read more about energy, keep in mind:

a. How can we use solar energy?
b. What are some other renewable energies?
c. How do we use geothermal energy?

Energy from the Sun

Energy from the sun falls on the earth every day. If we could capture it efficiently, we would not have to use so much fossil fuel or nuclear energy.

The easiest way to use solar energy is for heat. We can capture some of the sun's heat at no cost. For example, building a house with large windows facing the sun lets more light and heat into the house. More and more people are building **solar collectors** on the roofs of their homes. Solar collectors are usually made of glass panels over plates of metal that face south. The plates are usually black because black absorbs sunlight better than other colors. Water moves through the back of the collectors and absorbs the heat of the sun. The hot water can be used to heat both the house and the water that is used for cooking and washing.

It is hard and expensive to change sunlight into electricity. A **solar cell**—or **photovoltaic** (fō′tō vol tā′ik) **cell**—is made of material that gives off electricity when sunlight hits it. Solar cells are still too expensive for everyday use. But they already produce electricity for spacecraft and ocean buoys.

Some solar projects might one day generate enough electricity for many homes. The set of mirrors at the left, in Albuquerque, New Mexico, are used for testing ways of concentrating sunlight. The concentrated sunlight can boil water. The steam from the water turns the blades of a turbine. The turbine operates a generator that makes electricity.

Solar mirrors

Other Renewable Energies

Biomass   **Biomass** is plant or animal material. Energy from biomass is second-hand solar energy. Living organisms capture and store the sun's energy in their cells. Using biomass for energy releases the stored solar energy.

People use biomass for energy in many ways. Plants can be converted into alcohol that can be burned. Gasohol for cars and trucks is a mixture of alcohol made from grains and gasoline. Gasohol cuts down a little on the amount of gasoline used. In Hawaii, sugar cane wastes are burned to make electricity. More than half of the homes in Vermont use wood-burning stoves.

Using biomass for energy will not meet all the world's energy needs. It takes a great deal of energy to grow crops for biomass energy. For example, extra energy must be used to make fertilizers and to operate farm equipment. In addition, most of the world needs its plants for food more than for energy. Also, chopping down forests for wood to burn creates erosion problems.

Water   Water provides energy in many ways. The sun's energy sets the water cycle in motion. Hydroelectric energy is made at dams and waterfalls. The force of falling water turns the blades of a turbine, which, in turn, runs a generator and makes electricity.

Ocean Thermal Energy Conversion (OTEC) also uses water for energy. Floating OTEC energy plants would use the temperature differences found in ocean water to generate electricity. The process works because the water at the surface of the ocean in the tropics is warm enough to boil liquid ammonia. The steam produced from the boiling ammonia spins the blades of a turbine. The turbine runs a generator that makes electricity. Cold ocean water cools the steam, which condenses back into liquid ammonia. The liquid is then reused.

OTEC is still in an experimental stage. Thousands of floating OTEC plants would be needed to help meet world energy needs.

OTEC energy plant

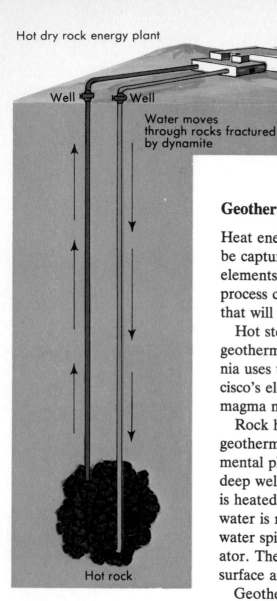

Hot dry rock energy plant

Well Well

Water moves through rocks fractured by dynamite

Hot rock

Geothermal Energy Taps the Earth's Heat

Heat energy from inside the earth—**geothermal energy**—can be captured to help meet our energy needs. Radioactive elements inside the earth release heat as they decay. This process creates a constant flow of heat through the earth that will not be used up for billions of years.

Hot steam escaping from the earth is one source of geothermal energy. The Geysers Plant in northern California uses the steam from geysers to make half of San Francisco's electricity. A test plant in Hawaii uses the heat from magma near a volcano to generate electric power.

Rock heated by volcanic activity is another source of geothermal energy called **hot dry rock energy.** At an experimental plant in Fenton Hill, New Mexico, engineers drilled deep wells into the hot rock. Water pumped into the wells is heated far above its boiling point. When the heated water is returned to the surface, steam from the boiling water spins the blades of a turbine, which operates a generator. The diagram shows how the water moves between the surface and the hot rocks.

Geothermal energy is useful only in places where it is especially hot underground. The use of geothermal energy in the United States is limited to regions in the West and Hawaii.

Have You Heard?

In 1960, a scientist named Robert Potter got an idea while he was reading *At the Earth's Core,* a science fiction book written by Edgar Rice Burroughs. Potter's idea developed into the hot dry rock energy process.

Review It

1. What is a solar cell?
2. What is an OTEC plant?
3. How can we get energy from hot dry rocks?

Activity

A Simple Generator

Purpose

To observe how electric energy is produced.

Materials
• bar magnet
• 2 meters of copper wire
• compass
• safety glasses

Procedure

1. *CAUTION: The ends of copper wire are sharp. Wear the safety glasses when you are bending the wire.* Wrap one end of the copper wire around the compass four times, as shown in *a*. Extend the remainder of the wire beyond the compass, and make 4, 5, or more coils that are large enough for the magnet to pass through. Run what is left of the wire back to and around the compass. Twist the two ends of the copper wire together.

2. When a magnet moves through coils of copper wire, it creates an electric current. Pass the magnet back and forth through the coils. Observe and record what happens when you do this. The compass is not used to find direction in this activity.

Analysis

1. What is the function of the compass in the procedure above?

2. Compare what you did in the procedure with *b*. Which of the items drawn in *b* corresponds to the activity performed by the magnet in the procedure?

3. List the kinds of renewable energy that are converted by turbines and generators into electrical energy.

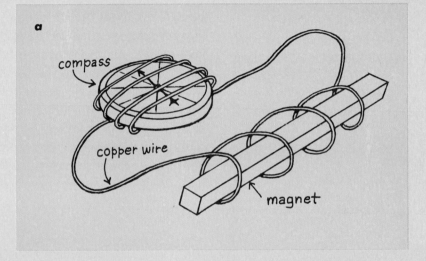

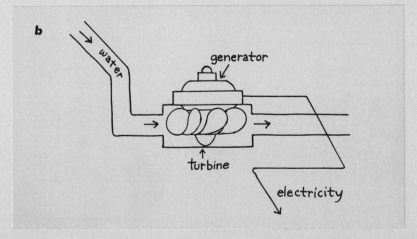

23—4
Saving Energy

During the last century, Americans have used and wasted energy as if there were no need to worry about the future. Today, scarce resources and high costs make us use our resources more wisely. Keep these questions in mind as you read about ways to save energy:

a. How have people been conserving energy recently?
b. What can you do to conserve energy?

We Are Saving Energy

Every bit of energy we do not use is energy we do not have to mine, produce, or buy. Conserving energy gives us more time to develop other energy sources. Conservation delays the day our fossil fuels run out.

In recent years, people have been using less energy. They have been installing more insulation in their homes, as shown in the picture to the right. Extra insulation allows them to use their air conditioners and heaters less. People have been keeping room temperatures much lower in winter and higher in summer. Motorists are driving less and joining car pools more often. Notice the sign in the photograph. They are also buying smaller cars that use less gas.

Industry is also conserving energy. This fact is important because industry uses a great amount of energy. Wasted heat represents a great energy loss for industry. Industry combats heat loss in buildings and factories partly with computers. For example, computers can adjust fans and vents in buildings to use heat more efficiently.

What You Can Do to Conserve Energy

You can contribute to saving energy. Turning the lights or television off when you are not in the room is a good way to save energy. If you do not leave doors and windows open more than necessary, the energy for heaters and air conditioners will not be wasted. You can dress warmly during cold weather and use fans rather than air conditioners in hot weather. During cold nights, you should close the curtains or pull the shades. This keeps the cold window from cooling the warm air in the room. During cold days, you should open the curtains or pull up the shades to let sunlight in.

Your family can make your home more energy efficient. Adding weatherstripping around doors and windows keeps out unwanted cold or hot air. It is useful to add insulation or storm windows to your house.

Most household appliances are now marked with an energy efficiency ratio. This ratio gives the consumer an idea of how much energy the appliance uses. Before you or your parents purchase an appliance, compare the energy efficiency ratios on several models.

Maintaining your appliances can save energy. For example, cracked rubber around a refrigerator door lets out cold air. Many ways of conserving energy require little effort.

Adding insulation

Review It

1. What are two reasons for conserving energy?
2. List four ways you can conserve energy.

Activity

Heat Storage

Purpose
To test three substances for heat absorption.

Materials
- three 189 mL foam cups
- three thermometers
- three 20 mL test tubes
- 400 mL beaker
- wire gauze screen
- tripod
- Bunsen burner
- table salt
- very fine gravel
- tongs
- heat mitt
- safety glasses

Procedure
1. *CAUTION: Wear safety glasses throughout this activity. Proceed carefully when working with fire and boiling water.* Set up the equipment, as shown in the diagram. Light the burner and bring the water to a boil.
2. Fill one test tube one-third full with water at about 25° to 30°C. Fill another test tube to the same height with gravel. Fill the third test tube to the same height with table salt.
3. With tongs, carefully lower the three test tubes into the boiling water for 5 minutes.
4. While the test tubes are heating, add water (about 30°C) to each of the three foam cups until each is 2/3 full. Carefully put one thermometer in each cup. Make certain that the water in all three cups is the same temperature.

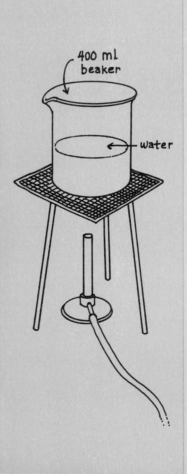

400 mL beaker

water

5. Use the tongs to remove the three test tubes from the boiling water. Place one test tube in each of the foam cups.
6. After 5 minutes, gently move each test tube around to stir the water. Read and record the temperature of the water in each cup. *NOTE: Read carefully, because the temperature differences will be small.*

Analysis
1. Which of the substances —water, gravel, or salt —absorbed the most heat from the boiling water?
2. What is the evidence for your answer to the first question?
3. Which of the substances absorbed the least heat?
4. How could the best heat-absorbing substance be used to store solar heat for your home?
5. In solar heating, why is it necessary to use substances that store heat?

Breakthrough

Unusual Sources of Energy

Some scientists are responding to the energy crunch by exploring unusual energy sources.

One source involves two kinds of bacteria that work together. One kind of bacteria uses photosynthesis to change carbon dioxide into different compounds. The other kind of bacteria feeds on these compounds and produces oil. The final substance made by this clever pair is not very different from the crude oil that comes out of a well.

Algae have also been put to work. One research team found that algae living in San Francisco make a gas from sewage. This gas, methane, is commonly used for fuel. These algae solve two of our problems at once. They get rid of garbage and make new fuel.

Algae that live in more attractive surroundings—the coral reefs—could also be used to make methane. They can be harvested, dried, and then converted to methane. The only things algae need for growth are water, dissolved minerals, carbon dioxide, and sunlight. These materials are abundant and free.

Kelp, a plant that grows in seawater, is another possible energy-producer. Kelp is one of the world's fastest growing plants. When it is harvested from seawater, it can be decomposed by bacteria. The product is methane gas.

A few land plants have provided surprises too. For example, members of the *Euphorbia* genus, shown below, are related to rubber trees. They produce a milky-white substance that resembles rubber. This material, however, contains compounds similar to those in petroleum and can be used as a substitute for oil.

These unusual energy sources are not likely to solve all our energy problems. But finding them is a tribute to people's imagination and resourcefulness.

For Discussion
1. What are some unusual energy sources?
2. What problems do you see in developing each of the sources described above?

Euphorbia plant

Chapter Summary

- We use energy to run machines and to keep warm. (23–1)

- Electricity is a convenient form of energy because it is available at the flip of a switch and it is easily transported. (23–1)

- A generator uses energy to turn large loops of wire in the presence of a magnet. This process causes electricity to flow. (23–1)

- Coal, oil, and natural gas are nonrenewable resources. When we use them up, no more will be available for millions of years. (23–1)

- Oil shale and tar sands can be processed to produce petroleum products. (23–1)

- Splitting the nucleus of an atom or joining the nuclei of two atoms provides energy. (23–2)

- Solar energy is used to heat water and homes and to make electricity. (23–3)

- Biomass, hydroelectric, and geothermal energy are renewable energies. (23–3)

- Conservation is important because it delays the day our fossil fuels run out. (23–4)

Interesting Reading

Cummings, Richard. *Make Your Own Alternative Energy*. David McKay, 1979. Shows how to make solar equipment and machines, including how to heat a dog house with solar energy.

Kiefer, Irene. *Energy for America*. R. R. Donnelley, 1979. Discusses energy sources and solutions to the energy problem.

Kiester, Edwin, Jr., and Burkard, Hans J. "Paydirt," *Geo*, December 1980, pages 67–86. Discusses the problems and potential of developing the tar sands of western Canada.

Questions/Problems

1. Explain why biomass is renewable, while coal and oil, which also come from plants and animals, are not.

2. How is the way that electricity is made by solar cells different from the way it is made with mirrors at the experimental solar tower in Albuquerque, New Mexico?

3. Explain how electricity is made from energy stored in hot dry rock.

4. Explain why fission energy is nonrenewable.

5. Describe two features that make one river more desirable for a hydroelectric plant than another.

6. List ways that fission and fusion are similar and different.

Extra Research

1. Using information given on page 49 of the book *Make Your Own Alternative Energy*, make a solar oven.

2. Write to your electric and gas companies. Find out what energy sources are used in your area now and what possibilities exist for the future. Write a one-page report on your findings.

3. Make an energy poster. Start by listing as many energy sources as you can find. Next, think of some way to divide the energies into groups. You may want to use groupings other than renewable and nonrenewable. Draw or find pictures of one example of each energy source to use on your poster.

4. Make a list of ten ways that you or your family waste energy. Next to each way, suggest how you could reduce each type of waste.

Chapter Test

A. Vocabulary Write the numbers 1–10 on a piece of paper.
Match the definition in Column I with the term it defines in Column II.

Column I

1. the splitting of an atomic nucleus

2. a device that uses energy to make electricity

3. uses the energy of falling water

4. a source of geothermal energy

5. substance often found with oil deposits

6. device that converts solar energy directly into electricity

7. uses hydrogen from the ocean as fuel

8. can be changed into gas or liquid fuel

9. an organic substance in oil shale

10. plant or animal material

Column II

a. biomass

b. coal

c. fission

d. fusion

e. generator

f. hot dry rock

g. hydroelectric power

h. kerogen

i. gas

j. photovoltaic cell

B. Multiple Choice Write the numbers 1–10 on your paper.
Choose the letter that best completes the statement or answers the question.

1. Most of our oil is used   a) to heat homes.
b) for transportation of people and goods.
c) to operate electric generating plants.   d) to run industrial plants.

2. The energy that is made from other energies is   a) oil.   b) coal.   c) gas.   d) electricity.

3. Anthracite is   a) soft coal.
b) clean-burning.   c) very plentiful in the United States.   d) always high in sulfur content.

4. Large tar sand deposits are located in
a) the Eastern States.   b) the Middle East.
c) the Gulf of Mexico.   d) Alberta.

5. Uranium occurs naturally in an ore called
a) hematite.   b) pitchblende.   c) galena.
d) fluorite.

6. Nuclear chain reactions are controlled in a
a) generator.   b) photovoltaic cell.
c) turbine.   d) reactor.

7. The raw material for fusion comes from
a) uranium.   b) the air.   c) the ocean.
d) none of the above.

8. All of the following are indirect forms of solar energy *except*   a) biomass.   b) OTEC power.   c) hot dry rock.   d) hydroelectric power.

9. Geothermal energy   a) is a nonrenewable energy.   b) is practical everywhere in the world.   c) comes from the decay of radioactive elements inside the earth.   d) a, b, and c.

10. On cold days, you can often save energy by   a) drawing the curtains on a sunny day.
b) opening the curtains on a sunny day.
c) closing the window shades at night.   d) b and c.

Chapter 24
The Environment

The Aswan High Dam on the Nile River in Egypt has taught us how sensitive our environment is. The dam provides electricity and water for irrigation, but it has also halted the growth of the Nile Delta. A few years after the dam was completed, sea life and farmlands around the delta were damaged. Also, changes in the flow of water destroyed a great number of bridges. Even with the best intentions, people can affect the environment in harmful ways.

This chapter explains how people can cause pollution of the water, air, and land. It also lists some steps people are taking to clean up our environment. The last section explains why we must be careful when changing natural systems to benefit people.

Chapter Objectives

1. Describe the major water pollutants and explain how groundwater is being polluted.
2. Describe the major air pollutants and how they affect life.
3. Explain how people can reduce erosion of the soil and pollution of the land.
4. Explain how a change in the environment can bring unexpected problems.

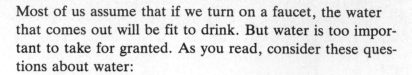

24–1
Protecting the Water

Most of us assume that if we turn on a faucet, the water that comes out will be fit to drink. But water is too important to take for granted. As you read, consider these questions about water:

a. What are some sources of water pollution?
b. How is groundwater being polluted and depleted?
c. How is water purified for drinking?

Sources of Water Pollution

Pollution is a change in water, air, or land that can be harmful or unpleasant for living things. The words "water pollution" may make you think of old tires, boots, or soda cans floating in a river. But some forms of water pollution are much harder to find and remove than tires, boots, or cans. Chemicals, sediments, disease-causing organisms, and heat are types of pollution that usually cannot be seen.

Chemicals Some of the chemical pollution comes from industrial wastes. Pollution also comes from detergents, bleaches, and fertilizers. The picture shows what can happen when too many nitrates and phosphates from these sources end up in a lake. The chemicals provide food for tiny plants—algae—that are necessary for organisms to grow well in a lake. But when nitrates and phosphates increase, too many algae develop. When the algae die they are decomposed by bacteria, which use up a lot of the lake's oxygen. Without oxygen, fish die.

Other poisonous chemicals such as lead, mercury, and pesticides are often found in rivers and lakes. A toxic compound called PCB is used in manufacturing and is also present in many of our water sources.

Sediments Erosion and runoff from agriculture and construction deposit trillions of kilograms of sediment in United States waters each year. These sediments fill in waterways, harbors, and reservoirs. They keep sunlight from reaching underwater plants and decrease plant growth. Fish that depend on these plants die.

Disease-causing organisms Sewage contains viruses and germs that cause diseases in humans and animals. If the sewage is not properly treated, diseases can spread. The wastes from farm animals, meat-packing plants, and leather-making industries also release harmful organisms into streams.

Heat Electric power plants give off a lot of heat. This heat is often released into a lake, river, or ocean. The heating of the water is called **thermal pollution.** The photograph of the river was taken with an infrared camera, which shows the warmer regions as red patches. The thermal pollution was caused by a nuclear power plant located along the river's banks.

Thermal pollution upsets the balance of life. Oxygen does not dissolve in warm water as well as it dissolves in cold water. In addition, the warmer the water is, the more oxygen the fish need. Thermal pollution can heat the water in winter, causing some fish to lay eggs early. When the eggs hatch, the young do not find the food they need to survive. Sometimes new species of fish adapt to the hotter water. But if the power plant shuts down, the water cools and these fish die.

Thermal pollution of a river

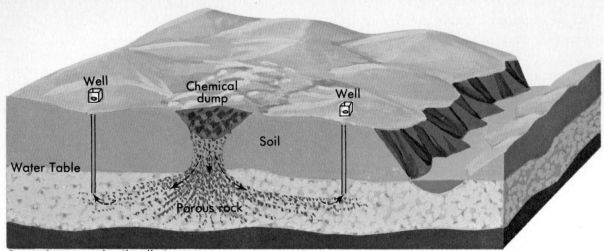

Groundwater and soil pollution

Labels in figure: Well · Chemical dump · Well · Soil · Water Table · Porous rock

Pollution and Loss of Groundwater

Many experts feel that the pollution of groundwater is the greatest danger that faces our environment. Groundwater provides about half the drinking water in the United States. Dangerous chemicals are now found in more and more groundwater reserves.

The 70,000 types of chemicals made each year in the United States help us in many ways. But some wastes from chemical manufacturing can be deadly poisons if they are not burned at high temperatures or changed to harmless products. However, chemical wastes are often merely packed in steel drums and buried. Unfortunately, the drums often rust and leak. The chemicals then drain into the soil and groundwater, as shown in the diagram.

Many chemicals were stored like this before people knew how dangerous the chemicals would be to the environment. Now, many companies are cleaning up their old disposal sites. One company in Michigan has built a huge vault to hold its chemical wastes. The company is pumping polluted water out of the ground, purifying it, and pumping it back into the ground. The company has also built a pipeline to carry fresh water to people whose wells were contaminated by chemicals.

Several problems arise when people pump groundwater out of the earth faster than rain and snow can replace it. One problem is that land sinks to a lower level—or subsides. Since 1925, large amounts of groundwater have been used to irrigate the crops in the San Joaquin Valley in California. Now, the land has sunk almost ten meters. The signs on the telephone poles in the picture show how much the land has sunk since 1925.

Using up the groundwater near an ocean creates a special problem. Under land next to the ocean, there is a boundary between fresh and salty groundwater. Usually, the fresh groundwater, which has little dissolved salt, exerts enough pressure to keep the salty groundwater out of water wells. If people use too much of the fresh groundwater, the water table drops. Then salt water creeps into the groundwater and into the wells. Sometimes people in ocean communities, such as those on Cape Cod and Long Island, notice a salty taste in their well water. The salt makes the wells unusable.

The signs on the post indicate past elevations

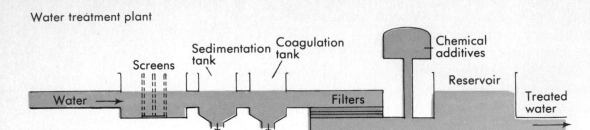

Water treatment plant

Water treatment plant

Water Treatment

Thousands of cities and towns in the United States have water treatment plants. The diagram shows how these treatment plants purify our water.

Water first passes through screens that keep out fish, plants, trash and other large items. Then, during **sedimentation** the water moves into a tank, where some of the solids settle out as sludge. In the next step —**coagulation**—chemicals are added to the water to remove more particles. The chemicals cause small, harmless globs to form in the water. Tiny solid particles stick to these globs and settle to the bottom of the water tank. Next, during **filtration,** the water passes through filters of sand and gravel. The filters remove any remaining particles. Finally, in **chlorination,** chlorine is added to the water to destroy disease-causing germs.

In some communities, it is necessary to **aerate** the water by bubbling air through it. This process improves the water's taste and smell. Some cities add fluorine to their water to help reduce tooth decay.

The largest water treatment plant in the world is shown in the photograph. It is located in Chicago, on Lake Michigan.

Have You Heard?

Aeration adds oxygen to the water to give it sparkle and make it taste better. You may have noticed air bubbles in your glass of water at dinner. Dissolved oxygen escapes and forms bubbles. When a glass of water is left standing in a warm room, the water loses most of its oxygen and tastes flat.

Review It

1. What are four water pollutants?
2. What are two problems related to groundwater?
3. Explain four major steps in water treatment.

Activity

The Sedimentation and Filtration of Water

Purpose

To clean dirty water using a filter.

Materials

- water containing soil and particles
- one large and three small glass jars
- cm ruler
- clear plastic bottle
- 5 ground charcoal briquets
- coarse sand
- pebbles
- cotton
- scissors
- masking tape
- funnel (optional)
- filter paper (optional)

Procedure

Part A

1. Put tape on the four jars. Label the largest jar #1. Label the remaining jars #2, #3, and #4, as in *a*.
2. Fill jar #1 with dirty water. Pour some of the water from #1 into #2 to a depth of four cm.

3. Observe and record the water's color and smell.
4. Set #2 aside and do not shake or move it. You will use it later.

Part B

1. You are going to make a water filter from the bottle. Cut off the bottom of the plastic bottle, as shown in *b*.
2. Close the narrow opening of the bottle with cotton.
3. Carefully arrange layers of charcoal, sand, and pebbles in the bottle, as shown in *b*.
4. Pour more of the dirty water from #1 into #3 to a depth of four cm.
5. Hold the filter (bottle) over #4, as shown in *b*. Then, pour dirty water from #3 into the filter (bottle). The water will take a couple of minutes to go through. *CAUTION: Do not drink the water that drips into #4; it is far from clean.*
6. Record how the water in jars #1, #2, and #4 looks and smells.
7. Remove a piece of the cotton from the filter and examine it.

Analysis

1. What is the process in Part A called? in Part B?
2. How do you know the cotton worked as part of the filter?
3. What could you do to get the filtered water cleaner?

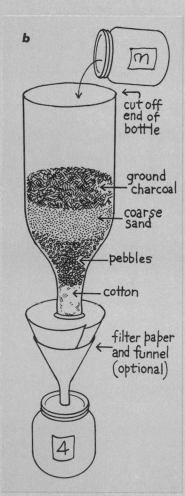

cut off end of bottle

ground charcoal

coarse sand

pebbles

cotton

filter paper and funnel (optional)

24–2
Protecting the Air

More likely than not, the air you are breathing is polluted in some way. Air pollution is present everywhere—in cities and on farms, outdoors and indoors. As you answer these questions, think about our need to protect our air:

a. What are the major causes of air pollution?
b. How can weather conditions make air pollution worse?
c. What can be done to reduce air pollution?

Causes of Air Pollution

Air pollutants are unwanted, harmful substances in the air we breathe. Burning fuel or solid waste releases both gases and particles into the air as pollutants. Most burning occurs in industrial plants, homes, and cars.

The pollutants released during burning can harm crops, trees, and even buildings. The picture shows the ruins of a 2,000-year-old building in Athens, Greece. Air pollution has damaged this building more in the last 40 years than in its first 2,000 years.

The Parthenon in Greece

Air pollutants also harm people, particularly babies, elderly people, and those who have heart or lung diseases. Five air pollutants are especially harmful to human health.

Sulfur oxides　Coal and oil contain small amounts of sulfur. When the fuel burns, the sulfur combines with oxygen. This reaction produces sulfur oxides, which irritate the eyes, nose, throat, and lungs.

One form of sulfur oxide reacts with water in the air to make sulfuric acid. This acid, mixed with raindrops, falls to earth as **acid rain.** Acid rain kills fish and damages crops and trees.

Particulates　Burning coal, oil, or wood also gives off **particulates** (pär tik′yə lāts)—or tiny particles of dust, soot, and oil. Diesel cars and trucks give off many particulates that can cause coughing and chest pains.

Nitrogen oxides　At normal temperatures, the nitrogen and oxygen gases that make up most of the atmosphere do not react with each other. At very high temperatures, however, nitrogen and oxygen form nitric oxide. This gas forms inside car engines and passes out of exhaust pipes into the air. Nitric oxide then reacts with oxygen in the air to form another compound, nitrogen dioxide. This gas has an unpleasant odor and causes the brown haze over many cities.

Hydrocarbons　Gasoline is a mixture of hydrocarbons (hi′drō kär′bənz), which are compounds of hydrogen and carbon. Hydrocarbon gases enter the atmosphere from spilled or partly burned gasoline. The diagram shows how sunlight causes nitrogen oxides to react with hydrocarbon gases. The reaction makes **smog,** which is similar to tear gas. Smog irritates the eyes, throat, and lungs.

Carbon monoxide　Most carbon monoxide in the air comes from automobile exhaust. Smokers also breathe in a lot of carbon monoxide from burning cigarettes. Carbon monoxide deprives the body of oxygen and can cause headaches and weariness. Concentrated carbon monoxide can kill.

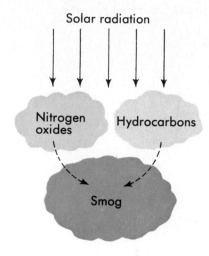

Solar radiation

Nitrogen oxides

Hydrocarbons

Smog

Have You Heard?

Natural processes, such as volcanoes, forest fires, and dust storms, also add pollutants to the air. These pollutants rarely build up to harmful levels.

Weather and Surface Features Affect Air Pollution

Both weather and topography (tə pog′rə fē)—the shape of the land—influence air pollution. Some of this influence is helpful. For example, the prevailing winds blow most of the pollutants in Boston and Honolulu out to sea. A steady flow of cool, clean air blows into San Francisco from the Pacific Ocean. As a result, San Francisco's air pollution is reduced. But the same wind that blows pollution away from one area carries the pollutants to another area.

Humidity also reduces air pollution. Moisture in the air dissolves many pollutants. When the moisture falls as rain or snow, the pollutants are removed from the air. However, this process may result in acid rain.

Topography often makes air pollution worse. For example, valleys often trap pollutants. Diagram A shows how hot air rises under normal conditions. Diagram B shows how cool air can be trapped under a layer of warmer air. During this situation, called a **temperature inversion,** air pollution can slowly build up to serious levels in the cool layer near the ground. Temperature inversions happen frequently in cities, such as Los Angeles, that lie in a valley surrounded by mountains. Temperature inversions occur about 160 days a year in Los Angeles. The mountains and temperature inversions combine to trap air pollution and cause smog alerts. People are cautioned to stay indoors and cut down on physical activity during smog alerts.

A

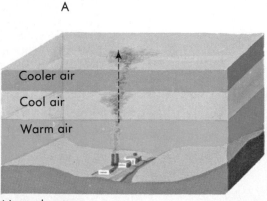

Normal pattern

B

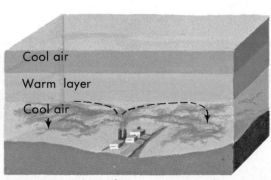

Temperature inversion

Air Pollution Can Be Reduced

We cannot take polluted air, purify it, and reuse it as we can with water. But we can control what we put into the air. Sulfur oxides and particulates can be reduced. Industries can use low-sulfur coal or shift from coal to other energy sources. Coal can also be converted to a gas or liquid fuel to remove most of its sulfur.

Particulates can be removed from the gases given off by smokestacks. The upper picture shows smoke and particulates pouring out of a smokestack. The smokestack's pollution control device is not on. The lower picture shows the stack with its device working.

Pollutants from cars can be reduced with catalytic (kat′l it′ik) converters. These devices convert polluting gases into carbon dioxide and water vapor.

Engineers may develop new kinds of car engines that produce less pollution. Engines that use hydrogen fuel, for example, would cause no pollution. But it is difficult to store and distribute hydrogen.

Electric cars do not give off harmful gases. Presently, however, their batteries have to be recharged and replaced too often to make them practical.

Recent studies show that pollutants also build up inside houses. Indoor air pollution can be worse than outdoor pollution. The pollutants can come from tobacco smoke, chemicals used for cleaning, gases from cooking stoves, and from building materials. This pollution can be reduced by letting outside air mix with the inside air.

Review It

1. Name five air pollutants and explain their sources.
2. How does a temperature inversion affect air pollution?
3. Explain three ways to reduce air pollution.

24–3
Protecting the Land

The topsoil that erodes in the United States each year would fill a freight train long enough to circle the world 18 times. On a holiday weekend, Americans throw away enough trash to fill a line of garbage trucks 69 kilometers long. But we can protect the land from some erosion and from solid waste pollution. As you read, consider these questions:

a. How do people affect erosion?
b. How does garbage create waste problems?
c. Why is recycling a useful process?

People Can Increase or Reduce Erosion

Erosion is a natural process that can damage the soil. Wind can blow away the topsoil and rain can wash it away. People's actions, however, can increase the rate of erosion.

Strip-mining is the stripping of the soil and rock at the earth's surface to remove coal or mineral deposits. The removal of vegetation and soil leaves the land scarred and open to erosion. All states now require mining companies to restore the land to its original condition. This involves refilling and replanting the area that was mined.

Unwise ranching and farming methods also increase erosion. For example, allowing livestock to overgraze speeds up erosion. The animals eat the plants that hold the soil in place.

Farmers can also reduce soil erosion by planting their fields in certain ways. For example, in hilly country, farmers often make flat steplike terraces on steep slopes to reduce water runoff. **Contour plowing** is plowing and planting along the land's natural contours, as shown in the picture. This type of plowing also slows the runoff of soil and water from the land. **Strip cropping** is another way to reduce erosion. Farmers plant their crops between strips of grass or clover. The grass or clover absorbs and holds the rainwater. When land is contour plowed and strip cropped soil erosion can be reduced by 75 percent.

Contour plowing

The roots of trees and other plants hold water and decrease erosion by rain and flooding. Planting rows of shrubs and trees as walls around fields cuts soil loss from wind. Protecting forests from being destroyed also cuts down on rapid wind and water erosion.

Garbage Has to Go Somewhere

Have you ever stopped to wonder what becomes of garbage after you throw it away? It does not disappear. We get rid of solid wastes by burning or by dumping them on land or into rivers, lakes, or oceans. But burning garbage leads to air pollution, and dumping causes water or land pollution.

Sanitary landfill park

Mining, industry, businesses, and homes all produce solid waste. But more than half of the solid waste in this country comes from agriculture. Animal and crop wastes make soil more productive, but when large amounts wash into the water, they become pollutants. Farmers can help limit this problem by spreading the wastes evenly over the land.

Cities and towns get rid of their solid wastes in three ways. The least desirable way is the **open dump.** Waste is collected, compacted, and taken to the dump. Open dumps are not only unsightly but also a source of disease. Rats and fleas breed in and near the exposed trash. The wastes seep into the ground and may contaminate groundwater.

Incineration (in sin ə rā′shən)—or controlled burning—is a second way of disposing of solid wastes. Incineration removes disease-carrying matter from trash, but it adds to air pollution.

Sanitary landfill is a third method of garbage disposal. Thin layers of compacted waste are covered with a fresh layer of soil each day. This method cuts down on disease and on water and air pollution. The park in the picture is the final layer of a "garbage" landfill. Some cities across the United States have covered hills of compacted garbage with soil to make parks. Many of these hills have been named Mount Trashmore! In northern cities, the Mount Trashmores can be used for toboggan slides or skiing hills in winter.

Recovery plant

Recycling

Perhaps the best way to handle our solid wastes is by **recycling,** or using a product more than once. Recycling conserves energy and other resources too.

Not all materials can be recycled. But paper, glass, iron, steel, and aluminum can all be recycled. Even tires are becoming more valuable. The rubber can be used in asphalt for paving roads.

The photograph shows a resource recovery plant in New Orleans, Louisiana. At plants like this, huge magnets remove iron and steel from the wastes. Workers are experimenting with ways to recover aluminum and glass. At other plants, organic materials, such as grass and leaves, are composted for use as a soil conditioner. Some recovery plants burn waste to produce steam, hot water, or electricity. Nearby buildings buy and use this energy. Unfortunately, high costs, frequent breakdowns, and air pollution have proved to be serious problems for resource recovery plants.

Wastes can be limited by using less material in the first place. Many products you buy have unnecessary packaging. This means that more material turns up as waste.

Young people around the country have become involved in recycling projects. You, too, can help conserve our resources by collecting the materials that recycling centers in your area use.

Review It

1. What are four ways that we can decrease soil erosion?
2. List three ways that cities and towns get rid of solid wastes.
3. What is a resource recovery plant?

Issues in Earth Science

Is Garbage a New Resource?

Garbage is beautiful! You may not believe that now, but the contents of your trash can are going to become more important in the future.

Until recently, people did not worry much about their garbage. Every community had a dump, such as the one in the picture, for everything that had to be thrown away. If the dump got too full, wastes were buried, set on fire, or pushed into a river or lake.

Now Americans are being buried in garbage. In 1978, we threw away 154 million tons of garbage—cans, bottles, paper, lawn and garden refuse, and food wastes. That is almost 2.5 kilograms of garbage *daily* for each man, woman, and child. In addition, farms, mines, and industry make billions of tons of garbage every year.

In New York City, most garbage is burned or dumped in landfills. But New York will soon run out of space for landfills.

Some cities are beginning to see that their trash problems may be blessings in disguise. People are finding creative ways to dispose of their garbage. In one project, for example, shredded garbage is combined with a sticky substance to form bricks for construction.

Some cities generate electricity by burning garbage. Garbage is also used to produce steam to sell to industry. The garbage is burned in giant incinerators lined with concrete tubes. The tubes are filled with water. Hot gases from the burning garbage boil the water in the tubes and produce steam.

The amount of garbage per person has doubled since 1960. Now we *must* find new ways to dispose of garbage. The old system of burning or dumping garbage into rivers is no longer acceptable. These methods add to water and air pollution.

For Discussion
1. Why is the amount of garbage a serious problem?
2. What happens to the garbage you throw away?

24–4
People and the Environment

Throughout the year you have learned about many slow, steady processes that occur naturally on earth. As you read how people have changed or controlled some of these processes to suit their own needs, consider these questions:

a. How do changes in the environment have unexpected results?
b. In what ways can people upset the delicate balance of nature?

People Affect the Environment

The Aswan High Dam, which was completed in 1971, is very useful. It reduces the flooding of the Nile River. The water stored behind the dam in Lake Nasser is used to irrigate the land. The irrigation has changed one million acres of desert into farmland. When the water of Lake Nasser is released, it flows under the dam, as shown in the diagram. The energy of the moving water generates electricity. The dam now produces half of Egypt's electricity.

Along with these benefits, however, have come some serious side effects. Sediments that moved along with the Nile's water built the fertile Nile Delta. But the dam has stopped much of the sediment from reaching the delta. Now, the delta is being eroded by the Mediterranean Sea faster than the river can build it up.

With less sediment, the Nile River flows much more quickly from the dam to the delta. The fast-flowing river has deeply eroded the riverbanks and destroyed at least 550 bridges.

The Aswan High Dam

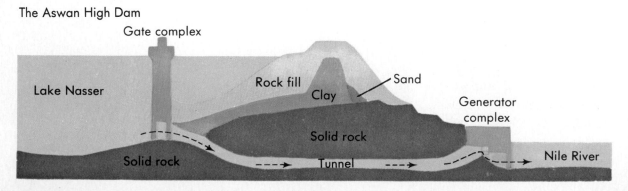

Gate complex

Lake Nasser

Rock fill

Clay

Sand

Generator complex

Solid rock

Solid rock

Tunnel

Nile River

The Temple of Abu Simbel

The sediment in the river once carried plankton and other sources of food for the sea life around the delta. The dam has cut these food sources by two-thirds. The lack of food sources has reduced the fish population around the delta. Many people who depended on the sardines from the delta have had to find other food sources. However, a new fishing industry has grown up in Lake Nasser.

Before the dam was built, floods of the Nile River deposited many sediments in the river valley. The sediments acted as a natural fertilizer for farmlands along the riverbanks. Now, farmers must buy fertilizers.

Problems have also occurred behind the dam. The reservoir does not fill up as fast as it should for two reasons. First, more water is lost by evaporation than was expected. Second, the sandstone under the reservoir absorbs millions of cubic meters of water per year.

Narrow valleys upstream from the dam were flooded to create Lake Nasser. This flooding destroyed dozens of ancient buildings and statues. The Temple of Abu Simbel, shown in the picture, was moved to higher ground at a cost of nearly $40,000,000. Now the Temple of Karnak and other ancient buildings are threatened by rising water.

The history of the Aswan High Dam provides us with a valuable lesson. When people change one part of the environment, serious side effects can develop in other parts of the environment. The message we learn is not that people should avoid change, but that we are limited by the laws of nature. People try to predict as many consequences as possible *before* disturbing a natural system. But additional unexpected consequences can occur.

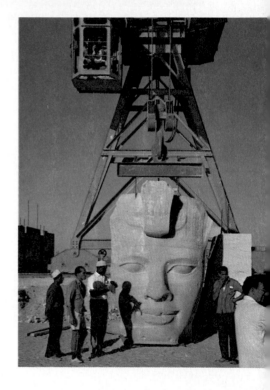

Have You Heard?

One problem with reservoirs is that they may fill with sediment. The Mono Reservoir in California had this problem. Two seasons of heavy rains washed enough sediment into the reservoir to fill it totally.

The city of Minneapolis, Minnesota

Nature in Balance

The astronauts' view of the earth has shown us that we live on a small island in space. Processes that occur on the earth's land and in its water and air exist in a delicate balance. When people's influence on the earth was less, natural processes usually had time to correct any problems.

The satellite picture shows how we have covered the land with farms and cities. We have dug up land and drilled under the water to look for minerals and energy sources. We have put pollutants into the air and water. The changes made by the four billion people on earth are sometimes drastic. Now, the earth cannot always heal itself quickly.

Changes can have wide-ranging effects. Particulates from smokestacks in the Midwest increase acid rain in New England. Dust storms that result from clearing out forests in Africa affect weather in the United States. A change in your community may wind up affecting people far away.

We must use our scientific knowledge and our common sense to protect the balance of nature on earth. It is our home in the universe.

Review It

1. What are three unexpected side effects of the Aswan High Dam?
2. Give an example of how a change in one part of the earth can affect another part.

Activity

Changing Environments

Purpose
To study the effects of changes in our environment.

Materials
• 2 sheets of paper
• pencil

Procedure
1. Study the map. It is a simple topographic map showing some features of an imaginary town. Because of their locations, the features may create a health hazard.
2. On a sheet of paper, draw the rivers shown on the map.
3. Relocate features A through F on your paper in places that will ensure a more healthful environment for the people who live in the area. You do not need to redraw the contour lines.
4. On a separate sheet of paper, give at least one reason for each change you made on the map.

Analysis
1. What method of plowing should be practiced on the farmer's field? Why?
2. The town owns land that contains one of the largest deposits of anthracite in the country. A mining company wants to buy the land and mine the coal. List the good and bad effects the mining might have on the town.
3. Suppose the river in the town is clear and fast-flowing. Twenty miles (32 km) upstream, another town wants to build a dam to provide a recreational lake and water for irrigation. List the good and bad effects the dam might have on the first town.

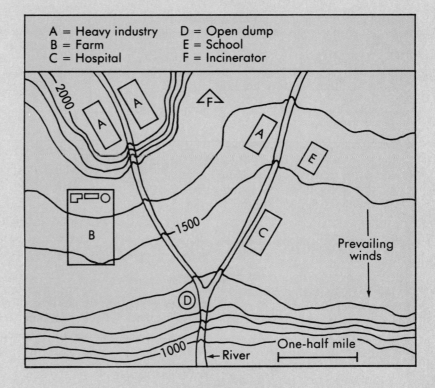

A = Heavy industry   D = Open dump
B = Farm   E = School
C = Hospital   F = Incinerator

Chapter Summary

- Four major sources of water pollution are chemicals, sediments, disease-causing organisms, and heat. (24–1)

- Improper disposal of chemical wastes has caused groundwater pollution. (24–1)

- The major steps taken to purify water are sedimentation, coagulation, filtration, and chlorination. (24–1)

- Five major air pollutants are sulfur oxides, particulates, nitrogen oxides, hydrocarbons, and carbon monoxide. (24–2)

- Farmers can decrease unnecessary soil erosion by contour plowing and strip cropping. (24–3)

- Cities dispose of garbage in open dumps, incinerators, and sanitary landfills. (24–3)

- Recycling and resource recovery decrease the amount of solid waste. (24–3)

- The Aswan High Dam teaches us that any change in one part of the environment can have many consequences. People must use scientific knowledge and common sense before changing the environment. (24–4)

Interesting Reading

Abercrombie, Thomas J. "Egypt: Change Comes to a Changeless Land." *National Geographic,* March 1977, pages 312–343. Explains the side effects of the Aswan High Dam.

Millard, Reed. *Clean Air—Clean Water for Tomorrow's World.* Messner, 1977. Describes methods of stopping pollution.

Muller, Jong. *The Changing Countryside.* Atheneum, 1977. Contains fold-out pictures of the same landscape as it changes over three-year intervals.

Questions/Problems

1. How is it possible that air pollution in St. Louis can affect a community 320 kilometers to the east?

2. If you had a farm on hilly land, what might you do to decrease soil erosion and water pollution?

3. Give two examples of how people and industry pollute groundwater.

4. How does the burning of gasoline help produce smog?

5. Explain how the Aswan Dam's blocking of sediments has affected the Nile Delta.

6. Why is a sanitary landfill more desirable than an open dump?

Extra Research

1. Find out what the source of drinking water is in your community. Write a one-page report on how the water is treated.

2. Make a list of all the ways you and your family contribute to air pollution in one day.

3. Find out how solid waste is collected and disposed of in your community. To do this, contact the Department of Sanitation. Report your findings to the class.

4. Investigate a controversial environmental issue, such as opening more western lands to mining. Prepare arguments supporting both sides of the issue. Use these arguments for a class debate.

Chapter Test

A. Vocabulary   Write the numbers 1–10 on a piece of paper.
Match the definition in Column I with the term it defines in Column II.

Column I

1. provides about half the drinking water in the United States

2. harmful increase in water temperature

3. planting alternate rows of regular crops and grass or clover

4. plowing along the contours of the land

5. disposal site that cuts down on pollution

6. uncovered disposal site

7. cool air trapped under warm air

8. an ingredient of smog

9. pollutant produced when coal is burned

10. stage of water treatment

Column II

a. coagulation

b. contour plowing

c. groundwater

d. hydrocarbons

e. open dump

f. sanitary landfill

g. strip cropping

h. sulfur oxides

i. temperature
   inversion

j. thermal pollution

B. Multiple Choice   Write the numbers 1–10 on your paper.
Choose the letter that best completes the statement or answers the question.

1. Too many algae in a lake   a) cause disease.
b) cause erosion.   c) use too much oxygen.
d) affect groundwater.

2. Groundwater supplies are affected by
a) chemical wastes.   b) saltwater.
c) overpumping.   d) a, b, and c.

3. Chlorine is added to water to   a) make it
taste better.   b) make it sparkle.   c) prevent
tooth decay.   d) destroy disease-causing
germs.

4. Most carbon monoxide comes from
a) leather industries.   b) automobile exhausts.
c) cigarettes.   d) incinerators.

5. Air pollution can be reduced by   a) using
low-sulfur coal.   b) using other forms of energy for automobiles.   c) collecting polluted air
and purifying it.   d) a and b.

6. Most of this country's solid waste comes
from   a) industry.   b) homes.   c) agriculture.
d) mining.

7. Trees decrease soil erosion by   a) absorbing
water.   b) blocking sunlight.   c) splitting
rocks.   d) a and c.

8. Rubber tires are recycled to   a) make
paper.   b) pave roads.   c) make medicines.
d) a and b.

9. Erosion has occurred downstream from the
Aswan High Dam because of   a) faster flowing water.   b) more sediment.   c) more
water.   d) warmer water.

10. The example of the Aswan High Dam
teaches us that   a) we should avoid change.
b) dams should not be built.   c) we are limited by laws of nature.   d) people can conquer
nature.

Careers

Crop duster

Dusting crops differs from dusting furniture. When you dust a table you remove the dirt. When you dust a field, you put chemicals on it. Agricultural pilots, called crop dusters, drop chemicals from the air onto a farmer's fields.

A crop duster's plane carries fertilizer or weed and insect killer. Flying low over fields, the duster tries to drop the chemicals evenly. Crop dusters must be able to operate airplanes and make flight plans, just as any airplane pilot does.

Crop dusters take pilot lessons and must spend at least 250 hours in flight time. Crop dusters may go to college to learn farming techniques.

Career Information:

Department of Transportation, Aviation Education Division, Federal Aviation Administration, 800 Independence Ave., SW, Washington, DC 20591

Waste-water plant operator

Did you ever wonder where water goes after you use it? It does not stay underground in sewers for long. In fact, waste water gets cleaned up and recycled. A waste-water treatment plant operator makes sure this happens.

At the plant, dirty water filters through special equipment. Plant operators run the machinery that removes harmful chemicals and unwanted particles. Operators also take samples, record data, and run laboratory tests on water coming through the plant. They must also know how to repair their equipment.

Operators have a high school education. They may take one or two years at a junior college or attend a trade school to get a technical degree.

Career Information:

Water Pollution Control Fed., 2626 Pennsylvania Ave., NW, Washington, DC 20037

Soil conservationist

When wind and rain carry away topsoil, farmers get low crop yields. As a result, food prices go up. Soil conservationists know how to increase crop yields.

Soil conservationists spend a lot of time outdoors. They examine field conditions and test the mineral content of soil. By doing this, they can determine the type of erosion acting on the soil. Then they advise farmers how to solve severe erosion problems. One solution a conservationist might suggest is to plant trees to cut erosion.

A soil conservationist may graduate from college with a degree in farm management or agriculture. They are often hired by a government agency or by an industry that makes farm products.

Career Information:

U.S. Dept. of Agriculture, Soil Conservation Service, Public Information, P.O. Box 2890, Washington, DC 20013

Air pollution inspector

Our lives depend on having clean air to breathe. The government sets clean air standards that must be followed to keep our air clear. Some scientists double as detectives and track down air pollutors.

Air pollution detectives work in teams that travel to various industries. These detectives test factory smoke for pollutants. They also collect samples of rain, smog, and air from the upper atmosphere in industrial areas. They test the samples in their laboratories to see if the samples meet the government's clean air standards. When pollution inspectors find a trouble spot, they suggest ways to clean it up.

Pollution inspectors spend four years in college. They may study chemistry, physics, or environmental law.

Career Information:
Environmental Protection Agency, Public Information Office, 401 M St., SW, Washington, DC 20460

Soil scientist

The ground itself tells soil scientists how a certain piece of land can best be used.

First, soil scientists map the land in question. High altitude photographs provide a good view of the ground. Then they collect samples of soil from different places in the mapped area. They run the samples through tests in the laboratory. After studying the test results, soil scientists can tell farmers what crops to grow on their land and what minerals are needed in the soil.

Soil examiners need four years of college where they learn soil-testing techniques and land use.

Career Information:
Environmental Protection Agency, Public Information Office, 401 M St., SW, Washington, DC 20460

Park ranger

How would you like to run the Grand Canyon, oversee Yellowstone Park, or regulate Niagara Falls? A park ranger takes care of areas like these National Parks.

Park rangers protect parks, people, and wildlife. Often, rangers map the trees, campgrounds, and landmarks at a park site. They may give nature tours or teach classes about their parks. In addition, a park ranger handles emergencies, such as forest fires and first aid for injured campers.

Rangers must have at least four years of college. They study forestry and science. Rangers usually have to take a written exam given by the government to get a park position.

Career Information:
National Park Service, Dept. of Interior, 18th and C Sts., NW, Washington, DC 20240

Acknowledgements

Positions of photographs are shown in abbreviated forms as follows: top (**t**), bottom (**b**), center (**c**), left (**l**), right (**r**). All photographs not credited are the property of Scott, Foresman and Company. **XVI,** Clifford B. Goodie; **2,** NASA/Grant Heilman; **4,** David Muench; **5,** NASA/Grant Heilman; **6,** Wayne Sorce/*Discover Magazine* © 1981 Time, Inc.; **7(l),** Geological Survey/U.S. Dept. of the Interior, **(r),** Woods Hole Oceanographic Institute; **8,** Lamont-Doherty Geologic Observatory; **9,** Jet Propulsion Laboratory/NASA; **11,** Culver Pictures; **22,** Jay M. Pasachoff; **24,** Hans Vehrenberg (Hansen Planetarium)/Jay M. Pasachoff; **25(l),** Karl Kernberger/The Solstice Project, **(r),** Mary E. Challinor; **26,** Bill Ross/West Light; **27(l,c,r),** Courtesy Science Graphics, Inc., Tucson, AZ; **29,** Hewlett Packard; **31(l),** California Institute of Technology, **(r)** Courtesy Harvey Tananbaum, Harvard-Smithsonian Center for Astrophysics; **32(l,r),** The National Radio Astronomy Observatory, operated by Associated Universities, Inc. under contract with the National Science Foundation; **34,** NASA; **35,** NASA; **38,** Tersch; **40,** © Association of Universities for Research in Astronomy, Inc., The Kitt Peak National Observatory; **41(l),** Courtesy Science Graphics, Inc., Tucson, AZ, **(r)** California Institute of Technology; **44,** California Institute of Technology; **45(l),** NASA, **(r),** California Institute of Technology; **46,** Tersch; **47,** Tersch; **52,** California Institute of Technology; **53,** California Institute of Technology and Carnegie Institution of Washington; **56,** Painting by Don Dixon; **60,** © 1980 Lucasfilm Ltd. All rights reserved; **62-63,** Akira Fujii; **65,** Eric E. Becklin, Institute for University of Hawaii and Gerry Neugebauer, California Institute of Technology; **66,(l),** U.S. Naval Observatory, **(r),** California Institute of Technology; **67(tl),** U.S. Naval Observatory, **(tr),** © Association of Universitites for Research in Astronomy, Inc., Cerro Tololo Inter-American Observatory, **(br),** © Association of Universities for Research in Astronomy, Inc.; **69(t),** Palomar Observatory photograph, **(b),** Carnegie Institution of Washington; **70,** Courtesy of Harvey Tananbaum, Harvard-Smithsonian Center for Astrophysics; **73,** California Institute of Technology; **76,** NASA; **79,** NASA; **80,** Painting by Don Dixon; **82,** NASA; **83,** Ames Research Center/NASA; **84,** NASA: **85,** NASA; **86,** NASA; **87,** NASA; **88,** NASA; **89(l),** NASA, **(tr),** Jet Propulsion Laboratory/NASA, **(br),** NASA; **90,** Jet Propulsion Laboratory/NASA; **91(l,tr,br),** NASA; **93,** NASA; **94,** (all) NASA; **95,** U.S. Navy; **96,** Lowell Observatories; **97(t),** Wide World, **(b),** Hale Observatories; **99,** NASA; **102(l),** FPG/Alpha; **103(l),** NASA, **(c),** Dan McCoy/Rainbow, **(r),** David Bartruff/FPG/Alpha; **104,** Georg Gerster/Photo Researchers; **106,** NASA; **113,** Ned Haines/Photo Researchers; **114,** NASA; **122,** By permission of the Controller of Her Britannic Majesty's Stationery Office. British Crown copyright; **128(t),** John Shelton, **(b),** Courtesy Gem Media Division of the Gemological Institute of America; **129(r),** Courtesy of Professor Martin J. Buerger, M.I.T.; **130(r),** E.R. Degginger; **131,** Henry Redl/Black Star; **132(t),** Courtesy Field Museum of Natural History, Chicago; **134(bl),** E.R. Degginger; **140,** Don Green/Kennecott Minerals Co.; **149(t),** Ed Cooper; **150,** John S. Shelton; **153(l),** J.K. Hillers/U.S. Geological Survey, **(r),** E.M. Shoemaker/U.S. Geological Survey; **156,** Grant Heilman; **157,** Leo Touchet; **161,** Painting by Don Dixon; **164,** Courtesy H.K. Barnett/Dinosaur National Monument; **166,** Courtesy Grand Canyon National Park; **168(l),** National Park Service, **(r),** Courtesy Field Museum of Natural History, Chicago; **169(tr),** Courtesy Dinosaur State Park, **(l,b,br),** Courtesy Field Museum of Natural History, Chicago; **172,** John S. Shelton; **174-5,** Painting by Charles R. Knight, Courtesy Field Museum of Natural History, Chicago; **177,** Painting by Don Dixon; **178,** G.J. Wasserburg, California Institute of Technology; **184(l),** Yoram Kahana/Peter Arnold, Inc., **(c),** Martha Simmons/Picture Group, **(r),** Courtesy Gemological Institute of America; **185(r),** FPG/Alpha; **186,** Franz Lazi; **190,** NASA; **193(l,r),** Jay M. Pasachoff; **206,** © 1980 Roger Werth, *Longview Daily News*/Woodfin Camp, Inc.; **210,** Photri; **211,** Stern/Black Star; **214,** University of California, Berkeley/NOAA; **217,** John S. Shelton; **218,** Solarfilma-Reykjavik; **219,** © Lon Stickney, *The Columbian*; **222(l),** Jet Propulsion Laboratory/NASA, **(r),** NASA; **223(l,r),** NASA; **224,** NASA; **228,** F. Gohier/Photo Researchers; **232,** Porterfield-Chickering/Photo Researchers; **234,** John S. Shelton; **235(l),** Josef Muench, **(r),** John S. Shelton; **237,** Larry Moon/Tom Stack & Assoc.; **239,** Jeremy Ross/Photo Researchers; **241,** Kenneth Garrett/Woodfin Camp, Inc.; **244,** David Muench; **246,** Ed Cooper; **247(t,b),** Grant Heilman; **248(l),** H. Armstrong Roberts, **(r),** Frank Press; **249(t),** Runk/Schoenberger/Grant Heilman, **(b),** Fred Mang, Jr./National Park Service; **250,** Courtesy Raymond Siever; **254(t,c,b),** Grant Heilman; **257,** Courtesy Mrs. Henry Rhoades; **260,** Rich Deuerling, Bureau of Geology/Florida Dept. of National Resources; **262,** John Colwell/Grant Heilman; **263(tr),** John S. Shelton, **(l,br),** Jerome Wyckoff; **265,** John S. Shelton; **266,** John S. Shelton; **267(t),** General Electric; **(b),** John S. Shelton; **269,** Illustration adapted from Ib Ohllson—*Newsweek*; **271,** Grant Heilman; **272(l),** Runk/Schoenberger/Grant Heilman, **(r),** John S. Shelton; **275(t,b),** John S. Shelton; **278,** Ken J. Uebel/Tom Stack & Assoc.; **279,** Grant Heilman: **282,** David Hiser; **288,** Charles J. Farmer/Tom Stack & Assoc.; **289,** Milton and Joan Mann; **290,** Dan McCoy/Balck Star; **292,** David Hiser; **293,** David Muench; **294,** David Muench; **295,** Breedlove/Photri; **296(t),** U.S. Forest Service, **(b),** U.S. Coast & Geodetic Survey/U.S. Geological Survey; **297,** Yoram Kahana/Peter Arnold, Inc.; **300(l),** S.J. Mirabello/FPG/Alpha, **(c),** Traver/Liaison Agency, **(r),** U.S. Geological Survey;

GLOSSARY

a hat	**i** it	**oi** oil	**ch** child	a in about
ā age	**ī** ice	**ou** out	**ng** long	e in taken
ä far	**o** hot	**u** cup	**sh** she	ə = i in pencil
e let	**ō** open	**u̇** put	**th** thin	o in lemon
ē equal	**ô** order	**ü** rule	**ͲH** then	u in circus
ėr term			**zh** measure	

absolute brightness: brightness a star would have if it were a standard distance away

abyssal (ə bis′əl) **hills:** low hills that cover parts of the ocean basin

abyssal (ə bis′əl) **plain:** large flat region on the ocean bottom

acid rain: precipitation that contains higher than normal amounts of sulfuric and nitric acids

active volcano: volcano that has erupted in the recent past

actual remains: fossilized hard parts of organisms, such as bones, shells, or teeth

aerate: add air to water to improve its flavor and to purify it

aftershock: small earthquake that follows a strong earthquake

air mass: giant body of air that has uniform temperature and moisture throughout

air pressure: the weight of air

alluvial (ə lü′vē əl) **fan:** fan-shaped feature deposited where a mountain stream moves onto flat land, especially in arid regions

***Alvin*:** a submersible, or underwater vessel, used to study the ocean bottom

amber (am′bər): hardened sap of an ancient tree

anemometer (an ə mom′ə tər): instrument that measures wind speed

aneroid (an′ə roid′) **barometer:** an instrument that measures air pressure; a can emptied of air which changes shape in response to changes in air pressure

anthracite (an′thrə sīt): hard coal that burns with a smokeless flame and produces a great amount of heat

anticline (an′ti klīn): upfold in rock layers

anticyclone (an′ti sī′klōn): any high pressure system; a high; winds move clockwise out of a high in the Northern Hemisphere

***Apollo* Program:** NASA program in which astronauts landed on the moon

apparent brightness: brightness a star has when you look at it

asteroid (as′tə roid): small rocky object that orbits the sun; minor planet

asteroid belt: region between the orbits of Mars and Jupiter where most asteroids are found

asthenosphere (as thēn′ə sfir): thin region in the upper mantle that is partly melted

astronomer: one who studies space and the objects in space

Aswan High Dam: dam across the Nile River in Egypt

atmosphere (at′mə sfir): the blanket of air around the earth

atom: building block of all substances; made of three kinds of particles—electrons, neutrons, and protons

auroras (ô rôr′əz): bands of colored light most often visible near the poles; northern and southern lights

axis (ak′sis): imaginary line that passes through the earth from the geographic North Pole to the geographic South Pole

A-zone: top layer of soil that contains sand and clay mixed with humus; topsoil

barometer (bə rom′ə tər): instrument used to measure air pressure

basalt (bə sôlt′): common extrusive igneous rock with small crystals or no visible crystals

batholith (bath′ə lith): massive intrusive structure of igneous rock

bedrock: solid rock under the loose material at the earth's surface

bench mark: an elevation marker

big bang theory: theory of how the universe began with a gigantic explosion

biomass: potential fuel that comes from living organisms

bituminous (bə tü′mə nəs): soft coal formed by heat and pressure acting on plant remains

black dwarf: an end stage of a star such as our sun

black hole: region in space in which so much mass is concentrated that nothing—not even light—can escape

black smokers: hot springs on the ocean bottom at spreading boundaries

breaker: collapsing ocean wave

breccia (brech′ē ə): sedimentary rock made of angular sediments cemented together

butte (byüt): very small flat-topped structure most commonly seen in the arid Southwest

B-zone: layer of soil that contains roots of large plants, clay, iron oxides, and other minerals leached from the A-zone above

calcite (kal′sīt): carbonate mineral made of calcium carbonate

Callisto (kə lis′tō): moon of Jupiter

calorie (kal′ər ē): unit used for measuring heat

carbon dioxide: a gas made of carbon and oxygen; present in small amounts in the atmosphere

carbon 14 (^{14}C): A type of carbon that is radioactive; used to find the age of organic materials

carbon imprint: fossil formed when a thin film of carbon remains, leaving an imprint of the life form

carbonate (kar′bə nāt): group of joined carbon and oxygen atoms

carbonic (kär bon′ik) **acid:** weak acid formed when water combines with carbon dioxide in the air or ground

cast: fossil that forms when minerals fill a cavity

Celsius (sel′sē əs): temperature scale in which water boils at 100° and freezes at 0°

Cenozoic (sen′ə zō′ik) **era:** division of geologic time that began about 65 million years ago

chain reaction: a reaction that, once started, continues on its own

chalk: type of limestone that can form when many small seashells are cemented together

chemical weathering: process that changes the minerals in rocks

chlorination: the addition of chlorine to water to destroy disease-causing germs

chlorine (klôr′ēn): poisonous greenish-yellow gas with a sharp odor

cinder cone: a steep-sided mountain that forms from volcanic eruptions of rock and ash

cirque (sėrk): bowl-shaped depression in mountains where a valley glacier starts

cirrus (sir′əs): thin, feathery clouds made of ice crystals

clay soil: soil that contains more than 30 percent clay-sized particles

cleavage (klē′vij): property of a mineral that causes it to break along one or more smooth, flat surfaces

climate: average weather over a period of years

cloud: water droplets that float in the air; condensed water vapor

cloud seeding: process in which chemicals are dropped into clouds in order to stimulate precipitation from the clouds

coagulation: in water purification, the addition of chemicals that cause many small particles to settle out of water

cold front: boundary along the leading edge of a cold air mass that is pushing out a warm air mass

colliding boundary: boundary between two plates that are bumping into each other

comet: ball of ice and gas that orbits the sun in a long, thin ellipse

compass: instrument used to find directions; a tool used to construct circles

composite (kəm poz′it) **volcano:** mountain formed by alternating eruptions of dust, ash, and rocks followed by quiet lava flows

compound: substance that forms when two or more elements join chemically

condensation (kon′den sā′shən): process in which a gas changes into a liquid; the moisture that appears during the process

conduction (kən duk′shən): movement of heat from one molecule to the next molecule

cone: mountain built by volcanic eruptions

conglomerate (kən glom′ə rit): a sedimentary rock made of round particles cemented together

constellation: a group of stars that is named for an object, person, or animal; the region in the sky where a particular star group is found

continental crust: outer layer of the earth that makes up the land portion of the surface; varies from 35 to 65 kilometers thick; primarily granite

continental glacier: lens-shaped sheet of ice that spreads over a large area

continental polar air mass (cP): cold, dry air mass

continental rise: gentle slope at the base of the steeper continental slope; borders the deep ocean basin

continental shelf: broad, gently sloping plain surrounding continents and covered by shallow ocean water

continental slope: steep slope on the ocean bottom that marks the end of the continental shelf

continental tropical air mass (cT): hot, dry air mass

contour (kon′tür) **interval:** vertical distance between two contour lines

contour line: line on a topographic map that connects points of equal elevation

contour plowing: plowing and planting that follow the land's natural contours

convection (kon vek′shən) **current (or convection cell):** circular movement of heat through liquids or gases

Copernicus, Nicolaus: Polish astronomer of the 1500s who studied the planets

coquina (kō kē′nə): large pieces of seashells cemented together; sedimentary rock

core: innermost layer of the earth, which is divided into the outer core (liquid) and inner core (solid); a cylindrical-shaped section of sediment removed from the crust

corer: device that brings up cylinders of sediment from the ocean bottom

Coriolis force: the effect of the earth's rotation that causes winds and ocean currents to shift to the right of their expected paths in the Northern Hemisphere

corona (kə rō′nə): faint layer of gas above the sun's surface

crater: bowl-like depression at the top of a volcanic cone

creep: very slow movement of topsoil down a slope

crescent (cres′sənt) **moon:** moon's phase when only a sliver of the moon is visible

crest: highest point of a wave

crude oil: petroleum

crust: the outer layer of the earth that varies from 8-65 kilometers in depth

crystal (kris′tl): outward sign of an orderly arrangement of atoms within a mineral

cubic centimeter: SI volume unit; a cube one centimeter on each side

cumulonimbus (kyü′myə lō nim′bəs): huge, black rain cloud that may produce an electrical storm

cumulus (kyü′myə ləs): fluffy or lumpy clouds

current meter: instrument that measures and records the speed and direction of currents

cyclone (sī′klōn): any low air pressure system; winds move counter-clockwise out of a low in the Northern Hemisphere; low

Cygnus: one region of the sky in which astronomers detect X rays that could be coming from a black hole

C-zone: lowest layer of soil; contains partly weathered bedrock

decay: the spontaneous breakdown of heavier nuclei into lighter nuclei

delta: fan-shaped feature deposited where a river slows down as it empties into a lake or ocean

density: term that describes how much mass is packed into a certain volume; mass/volume

density current: seawater that sinks and flows at deep levels because it is saltier, colder, or contains more sediments than the surrounding water

desalting: process of removing salts from seawater

dew: condensed water vapor that forms on cold surfaces

dew point: temperature at which water vapor in saturated air begins to condense into drops of water

diamond: mineral made of carbon atoms that are subjected to great pressures and temperatures in the mantle

dike (dīk): magma that cuts across existing rock layers at an angle

dinosaur: extinct reptile that lived during the Paleozoic and Mesozoic eras

Dione (dē ō′nē): moon of Saturn

distillation (dis′tl ā′shen): process in which water evaporates, leaving salts and minerals behind

dome mountain: geologic feature created when magma pushes up rock layers at the surface of the earth

dormant (dor′mənt) **volcano:** volcano that erupted in the past but has been quiet for many years

dredge (drej): device that ships drag along the ocean bottom to scoop up objects and soil samples

drift: any sediments deposited by a glacier

dune: hill of windblown sand

dwarf: star on the main sequence

earth science: the study of the land, air, and water of the earth and the space that surrounds it

earthquake: the shaking of the earth that accompanies the release of energy from rocks moving inside or at the earth's surface

echo sounder: device scientists use to find the depth of water with sound waves

eclipse: condition that occurs when one object in space passes between two other objects and blocks the passage of light from one to the other

Einstein, Albert: An American scientist famous for his work in the field of physics, especially gravity

Einstein Observatory: A spacecraft that observed X rays from space

El Niño: periodic warm current in the Pacific that flows down the west coast of South America

electricity: a type of energy which is transported through wires

electron: negatively charged particle outside the nucleus of an atom

element: one or more atoms that contain the same number of protons

ellipse (i lips′): oval-shaped figure that contains two special points called foci

elliptical (i lip′tə kəl) **galaxy:** large star group that is oval-shaped

energy: the ability to do work or move objects

epicenter (ep′ə sen′tər): point on the surface of the earth that is directly above the focus of an earthquake

era (ir′ə): geologic time division

erosion (i rō′zhən): movement of weathered rock and soil from one place to another

esker (es′kər): ridge made of layered sediments, which were deposited by a glacier

Euphorbia: plant that produces a substance that can be used as a substitute for oil

Europa (yů rō′pə): moon of Jupiter

evaporation: process in which a liquid changes into a gas

extinct (ek stingkt′) **volcano:** volcano that is not expected to erupt again

extrusive (ek strü′siv) **rock:** igneous rock that hardens on the earth's surface; usually has no visible crystals

eye: calm region in the center of a hurricane

eyepiece: telescope lens that magnifies an image

fault (fôlt): a break or crack in rocks along which the rocks can move

fault boundary: boundary between two plates rubbing past each other

fault-block mountain: mountain formed when rock layers along a fault are raised

feldspars (feld′sparz): a group of silicate minerals common on the earth's surface

field reversal: the change of polarity of the magnetic field in which the north pole becomes the south pole and the south pole becomes the north pole

filtration: step in water treatment process in which water passes through filters of sand and gravel

fiord (fyôrd): ocean-filled glacial valley along a coastline

fission: splitting of heavy nuclei into lighter ones

fissure (fish′ər): crack in the ground where lava can reach the surface

floodplain: flat land bordering a river where river water overflows during a flood

focal point: single point toward which the light passing through a lens is bent

focus (fō′kəs) **foci, plural:** point inside the earth where rock breaks or moves; one of two special points within an ellipse

fog: cloud at ground level

folded mountains: parallel mountains formed by two colliding plates

fracture (frak′chər): term used to describe the way some minerals break—curved surface, splintered, uneven, etc.

freezing rain: rain that freezes when it hits the ground

friction: a force that acts to slow winds

front: the boundary separating two unlike air masses

frost: substance formed when water vapor changes directly into ice on a cold surface

full moon: moon's phase in which the moon is completely lighted

fusion (fyü′zhən): light nuclei joined together to make a heavier nucleus

gabbro (gab′rō): intrusive igneous rock with large crystals

galaxy: a group of hundreds of billions of stars, gas, and dust that are relatively close together in space

galena (ga lē′nə): mineral made of lead and sulfur; exhibits good cleavage in three directions (cubic cleavage)

Galileo (gal′ə lā′o): Italian scientist who used a telescope to study the moons of Jupiter

gamma ray: a type of radiation found in the spectrum

Ganymede (gan′ə mēd): moon of Jupiter

generator: machine that changes mechanical energy into electrical energy

geologic time: period of time hundreds of thousands to millions of years long

geologist: one who studies the earth and the processes that act on the earth

geosyncline: sediment-filled trough that may be thousands of kilometers long and that surrounds continents

geothermal energy: heat from the earth

geyser: hot groundwater that erupts explosively

giant: star that is larger and brighter than other stars of the same temperature and color

gibbous (gib′bəs) **moon:** moon's phase when most but not all of the moon is visible

glacier: moving body of ice

glassy: term that describes volcanic material that cooled too quickly to allow minerals to form

Glomar Challenger: large research ship

gneiss (nīs): metamorphic rock, often banded

grab sampler: device used to gather samples of sediment from the ocean bottom

gram: SI mass unit

granite (gran′it): common intrusive igneous rock

graphite (graf′īt): black, soft, and slippery mineral made of carbon

gravitation: the attraction of one body for another

gravity: the attraction an object exerts on other objects

Great Lakes: five large lakes that formed from melting glaciers

Great Red Spot: huge, longlasting storm on Jupiter

greenhouse effect: process in which heat is trapped by carbon dioxide and water vapor in the atmosphere

groundwater: water in the ground near the earth's surface

Gulf Stream: a circular movement of warm water through the Atlantic Ocean

guyot (gē′ō): seamount with a flat top

gypsum (jip′səm): rock formed from minerals left behind when a large body of water evaporates

habitat: pressurized underwater dwelling

hachures (hash′ürz): marks on a contour line used to show depressions

hail: ball of ice that forms in clouds and falls as precipitation

hair hygrometer (hī grom′ə tər): tool that uses human hair for measuring humidity

half-life: length of time that it takes for half the atoms of a radioactive element to decay

halite (hā′līt): mineral made of sodium and chlorine; table salt

Halley's Comet: a bright comet that reappears every 75 years

hard water: water that contains minerals dissolved from rocks

hardness scale: scale of ten minerals—from talc (softest) to diamond (hardest)— used to determine how hard a mineral is

heat: energy in moving molecules

heft: weight of a mineral

helium (hē′lē əm): an element that is a gas at normal temperatures; each helium atom has two protons in its nucleus

hematite (hem′ə tīt): mineral containing iron and oxygen; leaves a red streak on a piece of unglazed porcelain

high: weather term that means high air pressure; anticyclone

high tide: condition that occurs about every 12 hours and 25 minutes, in which the ocean level is higher than normal

hornblende: dark-colored silicate mineral

hot dry rock energy: energy obtained by using buried hot rock to heat water

hot spot: area of great deal of volcanic activity

hot springs: hot groundwater and steam that flows out onto the surface

Hubble, Edwin: American astronomer who studies red shifts of galaxies

Hudson Bay: region in northern Canada where the magnetic north pole is located

humidity: water vapor in the air

humus (hyü′məs): decayed plant and animal matter in topsoil

hurricane: spiral-shaped low, or cyclone, that forms over tropical oceans

Hutton, James: a Scottish geologist who lived in the 1700s; often called the father of modern geology

hydrogen (hī′drə jən): an element that is a gas at normal temperatures; each hydrogen atom has one proton in its nucleus

Hyperion (hī pēr′ē ən): moon of Saturn

hypothesis (hī poth′ə sis): a reasonable guess about how or why an event happens

Iapetus (ē äp′ə təs): moon of Saturn

ice age: a period of time when ice sheets cover large parts of the world

iceberg: piece of ice that breaks away from an ice sheet

igneous (ig′nē əs) **rock:** fire-born rock formed from molten material

imprint: trace of a living thing that is preserved as a fossil

incineration (in sin ə rā′shən): controlled burning; one method of disposing of solid wastes

index contour: every fifth contour line, which is heavily colored and labeled with its elevation

index fossil: fossil found over large geographic areas and during a very short time span

infrared: a type of radiation found in the spectrum

inner core: center of the earth made of solid iron plus a lighter element

International Date Line: imaginary line at about 180° longitude that marks the place where a new day begins

intrusive (in trü′siv) **rock:** igneous rock that hardens inside the earth

Io (ē′ō): moon of Jupiter that has active volcanoes

ion (ī′ən): atom that has lost or gained electrons

ionosphere (ī on′ə sfir): layer of atmosphere in which the sun's energy strips electrons from atoms

irregular galaxy: large star group that has no regular shape

island arc: feature built by magma that rose from the molten edge of a sinking plate at a colliding boundary

isobar: line connecting points of equal air pressure

isostasy (ī sos′tə sē): state of balance that the earth's crust maintains as it floats on the mantle

isotherms (ī′sə thermz′): lines on weather maps connecting points that have the same temperature at the same time

Japan Current: movement of warm ocean water in the North Pacific

jet stream: fast moving currents of air in the upper troposphere

joint: a crack in a rock

Jupiter: the fifth planet from the sun

kelp: a type of plant that is attached to the ocean bottom

Kepler, Johannes: German astronomer of the 1600s who described the movements of the planets

kerogen: organic matter found in oil shale

kettle: depression left in the land by the melting of isolated blocks of glacial ice

kilogram: SI mass unit; 1,000 grams

kilometer: SI length unit; 1,000 meters

Krakatoa (krak′ə to ′ə): volcanic island in the South Pacific that was destroyed by a gigantic volcanic eruption in 1883

laccolith (lak′ə lith): mushroom-shaped intrusive igneous rock structure

Lake Agassiz (ag′ə sē): huge glacial lake that once existed in the Midwest and Canada

Lake Bonneville: huge glacial lake that once covered about one third of Utah

Lake Peigneur (pā nyùr′): a shallow lake in Louisianna that drained and refilled within a few days

land breeze: cool air from the land that moves off shore

landslide: fast movement of rocks and soil down a slope

lateral (lat′ər əl) **fault:** side-to-side movement of rocks along a fault line

laterite (lat′ə rīt): type of tropical soil that is rich in iron and aluminum

latitude lines: imaginary lines that run parallel to the equator

lava: magma that comes out on the surface of the earth through volcanoes or fissures

law: a widely accepted theory

layering: characteristic feature of sedimentary rocks caused by changes in type or size of sediments being deposited

leaching (lēch′ing): process in which water dissolves and carries away minerals in rocks

lead 206 (^{206}Pb): product of the decay of Uranium 238

legend: map feature that explains the symbols used on the map

lichen (lī′kən): small plantlike organism that can cause chemical weathering of rocks

light year: distance that light travels in one year

lightning: visible flash of light caused by the discharge of electricity in the air

lignite (lig′nīt): soft, woody coal

limestone: a common sedimentary rock made of calcium carbonate

liter: SI volume unit; 1,000 cm^3

lithosphere (lith′ə sfir): rigid outer shell of the earth containing the crust and upper mantle

load: sediment carried by rivers or the wind

loam soil: soil that contains a mixture of clay, sand, and silt particles

Local Group of galaxies: group of galaxies that includes the Milky Way.

loess (lō′is): sediment deposited by winds

longitude lines: imaginary lines that intersect the North and South Poles; meridians

longshore current: fast-moving water that runs parallel to the shore

low: weather term that means low air pressure; cyclone

low tide: condition that occurs about every 12 hours and 25 minutes, in which the ocean level is lower than normal

lunar eclipse: a darkening of the moon when it passes through the earth's shadow; occurs when the moon is on the opposite side of the earth from the sun

luster: property that tells how a substance (mineral) reflects light—greasy, pearly, glossy, silky, etc

L-wave: seismic wave that moves along the surface of the earth

Magellanic (maj′ə lan′ik) **Clouds, Large and Small:** galaxies closest to the Milky Way Galaxy

magma (mag′mə): molten rock inside the earth

magnetic field: region around a magnet in which its magnetism is felt

magnetite (mag′nə tīt): iron oxide mineral that can have magnetic properties; lodestone

magnetosphere (mag nē′tō sfir): region surrounding the earth in which the earth's magnetism is felt

main sequence: group into which most stars fall when stars are classified according to their temperature and brightness

mammoth (mam′məth): large mammal, now extinct, that lived during the Ice Age

mantle (man′tl): layer of the earth below the crust

map scale: map symbol that relates distance on the ground to distance on a map

marble: a type of metamorphic rock formed from limestone

maria (ma′rē ə): places on the moon where molten material flowed from the moon's interior billions of years ago, which we see as dark spots on the moon

maritime polar air mass (mP): cold, moist air mass

maritime tropical air mass (mT): warm, moist air mass

Mars: fourth planet out from the sun

mass: the amount of matter in a substance

mature river valley: erosional stage in which the U-shaped river valley is wider than the river's channel

meander (mē an′dər): looping curve in a river

Mercury: small planet closest to the sun

mercury barometer: an instrument that measures air pressure using an inverted tube of mercury

meridians (mə rid′ē ənz): imaginary lines that run from the North Pole to the South Pole; longitude lines

mesa (mā′se): small flat-topped plateau

mesosphere (mes′ə sfir): layer of the atmosphere that extends from about 30 to 80 kilometers above the earth

Mesozoic (mes′ə zō′ik) **era:** division of geologic time that began about 225 million years ago and ended about 65 million years ago; Age of Reptiles

metallic element: element that conducts heat and electricity, can be pounded into thin sheets, or can be drawn into a wire

metamorphic (met ə môr´fik) **rock:** rock altered by heat, pressure, or hot fluids

meteor: rock from space that burns as it passes through the earth's atmosphere; shooting star

meteorite (mē´tē ə rīt): remains of a meteor that are found on the earth's surface

meteoroid (mē´tē ə roid´): chunk of rock that orbits the sun between the planets

meteorologist (mē´tē ə rol´ə jist): scientist who studies the air conditions and weather

meter: SI unit of length

mica: a silicate mineral that breaks into thin sheets

Mid-Atlantic Ridge: spreading-boundary feature on the floor of the Atlantic Ocean

mid-ocean ridge: feature found at spreading boundaries in the ocean

Milky Way: broad band of light in the sky; part of the Milky Way Galaxy

Milky Way Galaxy: group of billions of stars, gas, and dust that are relatively close together; large star group to which our solar system belongs

millibar (mil´ə bar): unit of air pressure that indicates how much the air actually presses on the surface of the earth

milliliter: SI volume unit; 1/1000 of a liter

Mimas (mē´məs): moon of Saturn

mineral: naturally occurring inorganic substance with an orderly atomic arrangement

mineralogist (min´ə rol´ə jist): mineral expert

mixed layer: top layer of ocean water where the temperature is uniform throughout

mold: fossil; cavity that remains in a rock after an organism disappears

molecule (mol´ə kyul): smallest part of a substance that retains the properties of the substance

molten (mōl´tən): melted

monsoon (mon sün´): seasonal wind that can cause wet and dry seasons

Mont Pelèe (pə lā´): dome volcano on an island in the Caribbean Ocean

Montes Maxwell: huge mountain on Venus

moon: natural satellite that orbits a planet

moon phases (fā´zez): regular changes in the amount of the moon's surface that we see as the moon completes one period

moraine (mə rān): long, thin deposits that mark the sides and front of a glacier

mountain breeze: air that moves down a mountainside

mountain root: thickened part of a mountain that sinks deep into the mantle

mudflow: moving soil that flows like a liquid

National Aeronautics and Space Administration (NASA): a government group responsible for the space program

National Weather Service (NWS): United States government agency that collects weather data from satellites and all weather stations

natural gas: compounds of hydrogen and carbon formed by the action of heat and pressure on the remains of organisms

neap (nēp) **tide:** tide that occurs when sun and moon are at right angles to each other; tide that is a lower-than-average high tide and a higher-than-average low tide

nebula (neb´yə lə): cloud of gas and dust in space

Neptune: eighth planet out from the sun

neutron: particle with a neutral charge in the nucleus of an atom

neutron star: end stage of a star more massive than the sun

new moon: moon's phase in which the moon appears dark to us

Newton, Isaac: English scientist of the 1600s who developed three laws of motion

nimbostratus (nim´bō strā´təs): spread-out, dark rain clouds

nimbus (nim´bəs): term that means rain in a cloud name

nitrogen cycle: movement of nitrogen between the air and the ground

nodules (noj´ülez): lumps of minerals found on the ocean floor; also called manganese nodules

nonmetallic element: element that does not have metallic properties; usually a soft solid or gas

nonrenewable resources: materials that can never be replaced or cannot be replaced for millions of years

normal fault: type of fault in which rocks above the fault line move down compared to those below the fault line

nuclear energy: energy produced when the nuclei of atoms split or join

nucleus: part of the atom that contains most of the atom's mass; contains the protons and neutrons

obsidian (ob sid´ē ən): a glassy material that lacks crystals and is associated with volcanic rocks

occluded (o klüd´əd) **front:** front that forms when one front overtakes another front

ocean basin: ocean floor at a depth of more than 4,000 meters

ocean crust: outer layer of the earth that lies under the oceans and is up to eight kilometers thick; primarily basalt

Ocean Thermal Energy Conversion (OTEC): the process of generating electricity by using temperature differences in ocean water

oceanographer (ō´shə nog´rə fər): scientist who studies the oceans

oil: a useful compound of carbon and hydrogen that can form from plant and animal remains deposited in shallow seas

oil shale: sedimentary rocks that contain oil

oil trap: structural feature that causes oil and gas to accumulate in a small region

old river valley: erosional stage of a river valley characterized by a wide flood plain

olivine: dark-colored silicate mineral

Olympus Mons (ō lim´pəs monz): large volcano on Mars

open dump: location where solid wastes are dropped

optical telescope: scientific instrument used to study light from distant objects

ore: *metallic* mineral deposit

Orion (o rī′ən): a group of stars—constellation—named for a mythical giant-sized hunter.

outwash: layered sediment deposited by water that flowed out from a melting glacier

overfishing: removal of so many fish from an area that the fish population cannot reproduce itself

oxbow lake: lake that forms from a cut off meander

oxide (ok′sīd): substance that forms when oxygen combines chemically with another element

oxygen (ox′ə jen): gas in the atmosphere that is necessary for life on earth; has eight protons in the nucleus of each atom

ozone (ō′zōn): type of oxygen molecule present in small amounts in the atmosphere

Paleozoic (pā′lē ə zō′ik) **era:** division of geologic time that began about 600 million years ago and ended about 200 million years ago

Pangaea (pan jē′ə): supercontinent that broke up about 200 million years ago

parallax (par′ə laks): the apparent change in the position of an object as a result of your point of view

Paricutín (pa′ra kōō tēn′): a cinder-cone volcano that emerged and grew in a Mexican field in 1943

partial eclipse: when the sun (or moon) is only partly covered by the moon (or sun)

particulates (pär tik′yə lātz): tiny particles of dust, soot, etc.

peat (pēt): soft material formed from dead and decaying plant material; first stage in a series of changes that occur when plants turn into coal

peculiar galaxy: large star group that has a regular but unusual shape

period: length of time it takes a planet to orbit the sun

permafrost: soil that is frozen throughout most of the year

permeable (per′mē ə bel) **rock:** rock that has connected pores or cracks

petrified (pet′rə fīd): turned into stone

petroleum: compounds of hydrogen and carbon formed by the action of heat and pressure on the remains of organisms; crude oil

photosynthesis (fō′tō sin′thə sis): process in which plants use sunlight to manufacture food and release oxygen into the air

photovoltaic (fō′tō vol tā′ik) **cell:** solar cell; device that makes electricity directly from sunlight

physical weathering: process that causes rocks to break into smaller pieces

pipe: passage in a volcano in which diamonds are found

pitchblende: ore of uranium

planet: a body, such as the earth, that revolves around a star

plankton (plangk′tən): tiny organisms that drift with ocean currents

plate tectonic (tek ton′ik) **theory:** theory which states that the earth's surface is broken into about 20 large sections called plates

plateau (pla tō′): large area of flat, uplifted land

plates: pieces of lithosphere that move about on the earth's surface

plume: narrow, jetlike flow of hot material from a great depth in the mantle

Pluto: ninth planet out from the sun

polar creep: slow movement of cold, salty water away from the poles

polar easterlies: global wind that flows from the poles to about 60° north and south latitudes

polar front: moving boundary between the cold polar air and warmer air from the equator

Polaris: the North Star; used to find the direction *north*

pollution: change in water, air, or land that is harmful to or unpleasant for living things

Precambrian (prē′kăm′brē ən) **era:** longest and first division of geologic time that ended about 600 million years ago

precipitation (prē sip ə tā′shen): moisture that falls from the air to the ground; rain, snow, hail, sleet, freezing rain

pressure gradient force: force that causes air to move from a high pressure toward a lower pressure

Prime Meridian: imaginary line that runs from the North to the South Pole through Greenwich, England; 0° longitude

principle of superposition (sü′pər pə zish′ən): principle which states that the oldest rock layer is at the bottom of undisturbed rock column, and each higher layer is younger

principle of uniform processes: principle which states that the processes changing the earth's surface today are the same processes that have been acting since the earth formed

proton: positively charged particle in the nucleus of an atom

Proxima Centauri (prok′sə mə′ sen tor′ē): nearest star to our sun—four light years away

pulsar: neutron star that sends out pulses of radiation—usually radio waves

pumice (pum′əs): light-weight, holey rock from volcanoes

P-wave: fastest seismic wave that travels through any material in the earth

quadrangle (kwod′rang′gel): rectangular area with latitude and longitude lines for boundaries

quartz (kwôrtz): common mineral made of silicon and oxygen; silicate

quartzite (kwôrt′sīt): a type of metamorphic rock that can come from sandstone

quasars (kwā′särz): distant objects in space that have the largest known red shifts

radiation: energy that travels in waves even through empty space

radio telescope: instrument that collects and focuses radio waves from space

radio wave: a type of radiation found in the spectrum

radioactive: property indicating that elements decay into lighter elements

rain: a type of precipitation

rain gauge (gāj): device used to measure the depth of rain or snow

recycling: process that recovers a resource so that it can be reused

red shift: the change of each light wave from retreating objects to a redder color

reflecting telescope: instrument that uses a mirror to collect light from a distant object

refracting telescope: instrument that uses a lens to collect light from a distant object

relative humidity: a percentage that compares the amount of moisture in the air to the amount the air can hold at that temperature

renewable resource: resource that can be replaced right away or within a short time

rhyolite (rī′ə līt): igneous rock with predominately light-colored silicate minerals and very small crystals

Richter scale: open-ended scale describing the strength of earthquakes, based on the amount of energy released

rift: the center of a mid-ocean ridge

Ring of Fire: volcanically active region that surrounds the Pacific Ocean

ringlet: chunks of rock that orbit Saturn

rise: spreading boundary in the ocean with lower, less rugged mountains that the mid-ocean ridges

river system: all connected streams and rivers that drain one particular region

rock cycle: the set of processes that describes how rocks are created and destroyed

rock salt: compound of sodium and chlorine; halite

runoff: rainwater that drains off the land into streams

salinity (sə lin′ə tē): measure of how salty water is

sandbar (mudbar): sediment deposited in water

sandstone: a common sedimentary rock made of sand grains cemented together by quartz, calcite, or another mineral

sandy soil: soil that contains a large percentage of sand particles

sanitary landfill: type of solid waste removal in which each layer of garbage is covered with a layer of soil

Sargasso (sär gas′ō) **Sea:** calm region in the North Atlantic

satellite: object that revolves around another object

saturated (sach′ə rā′tid) **air:** air that contains all the water it can hold at a certain temperature; 100% relative humidity

Saturn: the sixth planet from the sun

scarp: cliff

schist (shist): metamorphic rock; can be platey, flakey, or have stretched crystals

sea breeze: air that moves from the sea toward land

sea cave: rock formation formed by waves that hollow out soft rock in a sea cliff

sea cliff: rock formation produced when waves wear away rock at the base of a rocky shoreline

sea stack: column of rock left when waves erode the shoreline

sea-floor spreading: formation of new crust on the ocean floor where plates move apart

sea-level air pressure: average weight of air at sea level; 29.92 inches (76.0 cm) of mercury; one atmosphere

seamount (sē′mount′): mountain that rises from the ocean floor

section: a subdivision of a township that is one square mile in area

sediment (sed′ə mənt): particles of various sizes that are the raw materials for sedimentary rocks

sedimentary (sed ə men′tər ē) **rock:** rock that forms at the earth's surface by processes that often involve the cementing or compressing of sediments or the precipitation of minerals from water

sedimentation: in the water treatment process, the settling out of solid wastes as a sludge at the bottom of a water tank

seismic (sīz′mik) **wave:** type of energy that moves through the earth or across the earth's surface in waves

seismograph: sensitive instrument that measures and records seismic waves

shale: a common sedimentary rock formed when sediments of mud and clay are compacted

shield (shēld): Precambrian rock that is the foundation of continents

shield (shēld) **cone:** mountain that develops from non-explosive volcanic eruptions of flowing lavas

SI: initials that stand for the International System, a system of weights and measures used throughout the world; basic units are the gram for mass and the meter for length

silicate (sil′ə kāt) **mineral:** mineral containing the elements silicon and oxygen

sill: intrusive igneous rock structure that lies parallel to surrounding rock layers

sinkhole: depression that forms in the ground when the roof of an underground cave sinks or collapses

Skylab: spacecraft that orbited the earth

slate: a common metamorphic rock usually formed from shale

sleet: ice pellets that form when rain freezes as it falls through the air

sling psychrometer (sī krom′ə tər): tool for measuring relative humidity; consists of two thermometers

slope: term used to describe the steepness of the land

slump: crescent-shaped sagging of sediment on a steep slope

snow: a type of precipitation; ice crystal

sodium: a metallic element that reacts readily with other elements

soft water: rainwater, or water with few dissolved minerals

solar cell: device that gives off electricity when sunlight hits it; photovoltaic cell

solar collector: device used to collect solar energy by means of a glass panel over plate of metal

solar flare: explosion of particles and radiation from the sun

soundings: measurements of the depth of water

space shuttle: vehicle used to launch satellites

space spinoff: a useful product that resulted from space research

Space Telescope: first large telescope to be launched into space

specific gravity: a comparison of the density of a mineral with the density of water

spectrometer (spek trom′ə ter):   one type of instrument that measures the decay rate of a radioactive element

spectrum: all radiation displayed in a particular order

spiral galaxy: large star group shaped like a pinwheel

spreading boundary: boundary between plates that are moving apart; region where new crust forms

spring tide: tide that occurs when the sun, moon, and earth line up; high tide is higher than average, and low tide is lower than average

stalactite (stə lak′tīt):   deposits that hang down from the ceiling of caves

stalagmite (stə lag′mit):   deposits that build up from the floor of caves

star: an object in space that shines because processes within it give off energy that escapes into space as radiation

stationary front: front that is not moving; static front

stock: intrusive igneous structure similar to but smaller than a batholith

stratosphere (strat′ə sfir):   second layer of the atmosphere that extends 30 kilometers above the earth characterized by horizontal air movements

stratus (strā′təs):   spread-out or layered clouds

streak: color of minerals when they are ground into fine powder

strip-cropping: planting alternating strips of cash crops and clover or alfalfa

strip-mining: process in which soil and rock at the earth's surface are removed to reach shallow coal deposits

submarine canyon: deep valley in the continental shelf

submersible (səb mer′sə bəl):   underwater research vessel

subpolar low: semi-permanent low pressure that develops over the oceans at about 60° north and south latitudes

subtropical highs: semi-permanent high pressure that develops over the oceans at about 30° north and south latitudes

sulfuric (sul fyür′ik) **acid:**   strong acid made of hydrogen, sulfur, and oxygen

Sun Dagger: a streak of sunlight that falls on a certain rock in New Mexico; Indians used it for calendar-making purposes

sunlight: energy from the sun that can be separated into the colors of the rainbow

sunspot: a region of very strong magnetic activity on the sun

sunspot cycle: regular pattern of changes in the number of sunspots on the sun; the maximum number of sunspots occur every 11 years

supergiant: a star that is much brighter and larger than other stars of the same temperature and color

supernova (sü′pər nō′və):   brilliant explosion of a supergiant

surface current: flow of ocean water near the surface that is influenced by the wind direction

Surtsey (sūRt′sē):   volcanic island that emerged at the spreading boundary near Iceland in the 1960s

syncline (sin′klīn):   downfold in rock layers

S-wave: seismic wave that moves about half as fast as the P-wave, and cannot travel through liquids

talus (tā′ləs):   sloping mass of broken rocks at the foot of a slope

tar sand: deposit of clay and sand that contains heavy oil

telescope: instrument used to study objects in space

temperature: the hotness or coldness of a body indicated in degrees Celsius or Fahrenheit; indicates how fast the molecules of an object are moving

temperature inversion: cool air trapped under a layer of warmer air

theory: a hypothesis that seems to be true in all cases

thermal pollution: unnatural heating of water in rivers or lakes

thermocline (thër′mō klīn):   layer of water that rapidly gets colder with increasing depth

thermosphere (ther′mə sfir):   layer of the atmosphere that begins 80 kilometers above the earth

thrust fault: a type of fault in which rocks above the fault line move up compared to rocks below the fault line

thunderstorm: gusty winds, lightning, and rain that occur along fronts where air is rising rapidly

till: glacial deposit that is unlayered and unsorted by size; drift

time zone: a region 15° of longitude wide and in which all locations have the same time

topographic (top′ə graf′ik) **map:**   map that shows the shape and elevation of the land surface

topography (tə pog′rə fē):   shape of the land

topsoil: surface soil that contains sand, clay, and humus; A-zone

tornado: small but violent cyclone

total eclipse: event that occurs when the moon passes in front of and completely covers the sun

township: area that is six miles on each side

trade winds: winds that move toward the equator from the subtropical highs

transform fault: type of fault found at plate boundaries

trench: deepest region on the ocean floor

trilobite (trī′lə bīt):   extinct marine organism that lived in the Paleozoic Era; index fossil

troposphere (trop′ə sfir):   bottom layer of the atmosphere that extends from 8 to 16 kilometers above the ground; layer in which weather occurs

trough: lowest point of a wave

tsunami (sü nä′mē):   series of waves caused by sudden movements of the ocean floor

turbidity (tër′bid′ə tē) **current:**   movement of dense seawater containing mud and sand

turbine (tur′bən):   machine with spinning blades that operates a generator

ultraviolet: type of radiation found in the spectrum

United States Geological Survey (USGS):   a government group responsible for map making and finding and conserving mineral resources

universe (yü′nə vers′):   everything that exists

upwelling: process in which deep ocean water rises to the surface

uranium 238 (^{238}U):   common type of uranium that is radioactive

Uranus (yür′ə nəs): the seventh planet out from the sun

urban sprawl: rapid and often unorganized growth of cities

valley breeze: air that moves from a valley up a mountainside

valley glacier: glacier that moves like a river of ice down a mountainside

vein: a band of rock that forms when quartz or other minerals dissolved in water enter cracks in rocks and harden

vent: passage in a volcanic cone through which lava, ash, and rock erupt

Venus: second planet out from the sun

Viking: spacecraft that orbited and landed on Mars

visible radiation: radiation that you can see—light

volcanic dome: mountain resulting from violent eruptions of thick lava

volcano: landform that develops at the surface of the earth where magma erupts

volume: amount of space that any object occupies

Voyager: spacecraft that flew by Jupiter and Saturn

warm front: boundary along a warm air mass that is pushing out a cold air mass

water: compound of hydrogen and oxygen that occurs as a liquid, solid, and gas at normal temperatures

water cycle: movement of water between the ground and the air by evaporation, condensation, and precipitation

waterspout: funnel of low air pressure over oceans

water table: the highest level of soil or rock saturated with groundwater

water vapor: the gaseous form of water in the air

wave cyclone: low that develops along the polar front and moves across continents in the middle latitudes creating the day-to-day weather and storms

wave height: distance from the crest to the trough of a wave

wavelength: distance from the crest of one wave to the crest of the following wave

weathering: geologic process that changes the minerals in rocks or causes them to break apart

weight: force that gravity exerts upon an object

westerlies: global winds that move from the subtropical highs toward the poles

white dwarf: star that is dimmer than other stars of the same color and temperature

wind vane: instrument that indicates wind direction; weather vane

X ray: type of radiation found in the spectrum

young river valley: an erosional stage in which a river has a V-shaped valley

INDEX